THE
JUMBO
BIBLE
CROSSWORD
COLLECTION
VOLUME 2

BARBOUR
PUBLISHING, INC.
Uhrichsville, Ohio

© MCMXCVII by Barbour Publishing, Inc.

ISBN 1-57748-206-9

Published by Barbour Publishing, Inc., P.O. Box 719, Uhrichsville, Ohio 44683
http://www.barbourbooks.com

Member of the
Evangelical Christian
Publishers Association

Printed in the United States of America.

THE
JUMBO
BIBLE
CROSSWORD
COLLECTION
VOLUME 2

PUZZLE 1

ACROSS

1. At the peak
5. "as for the stork, the _____ trees are her home" (Psalm 104:17)
8. "This is now_____of my bones" (Genesis 2:22)
12. Hawaiian herb
13. Mine product
14. "The sons of Mushi: Mahli, and ____" (1 Chronicles 23:23)
15. "...my flesh longeth for thee in a ____and thirsty land" (Psalm 63:1)
16. Long, narrow inlet
17. "son of Salathiel which was the son of _____" (Luke 3:27)
18. "Behold, the man is ____as one of us" (Genesis 3:22)
20. "So then they that are in the flesh cannot ___God" (Romans 8:8)
22. Leningrad's river
24. Preposition
25. What Malchus lost (John 18:10)
28. Bird's beak
29. "He lodgeth with one _____a tanner" (Acts 10:6)
33. Political group
35. NC capital
37. "we spend our years as a ____that is told" (Psalm 90:9)
38. Healthy glow
40. "Abner, the son of ___" (1 Samuel 14:50)
42. "And the first came out ___all over" (Genesis 25:25)
43. Continent (abbr.)
44. "___was a keeper of sheep" (Genesis 4:2)
46. Mount of _____
50. "his eye was not dim, nor his natural force____" (Deuteronomy 34:7)
54. Uncovered
55. Even (poet.)
57. Piece in a game
58. One who does (suffix)
59. WWII arena
60. "the same is Micaiah, the son of ____" (2 Chronicles 18:7)
61. "the elements shall ___with fervent heat" (2 Peter 3:12)
62. Went through a stop sign
63. "They that are whole have no ____of the physician" (Luke 2:17)

DOWN

1. "___rose up to go down to the vineyard of Naboth" (1 Kings 21:16)
2. Ripped
3. Chemical suffix
4. "The children of Sia, the children of ____" (Nehemiah 7:47)
5. "the kingdom, the power, and the glory ____" (Matthew 6:13)
6. "The sons of Bela:...Uzziel, Jerimoth and _____" (1 Chronicles 7:7)
7. "Whatsoever a man soweth, that shall he also ___" (Galatians 4:7)
8. "faithful and beloved partakers of the _____" (1 Timothy 6:2)
9. Ancient Greek auditoriums
10. Belonging to the father of Abner (1 Samuel 14:50)
11. Great Lake
19. Promise Keepers
21. ___Alamos
23. A river of Damascus (2 Kings 5:12)
25. Wane

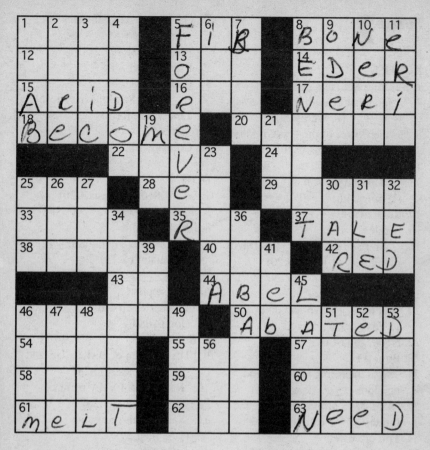

26. "As thou hast given him power over ___flesh" (John 17:2)
27. One of Winnie-the-Pooh's friends
30. Disfigure
31. Corrida cheer
32. Masculine name
34. "if any of you do err from the truth, and one ___him" (James 5:19)
36. "a well of living water and streams from_____"
(Song of Solomon 4:15)
39. Feminine name
41. Johnny ____
45. Language of ancient Rome

46. "And the children of Shobal...Shepho and ___" (Genesis 36:23)
47. Ancient stringed instrument
48. "Is this man Coniah a despised broken ___?" (Jeremiah 22:28)
49. "He that is now called a Prophet was...a ____" (1 Samuel 9:9)
51. "A ___to be born" (Ecclesiastes 3:2)
52. She (Fr.)
53. "Even God who quickeneth the ___" (Romans 4:17)
56. Greek letter

PUZZLE 2

ACROSS

1. Before (poet.)
4. "A man that beareth false witness is a ____" (Proverbs 25:18)
8. "as the flower of the grass, he shall ___ away" (James 1:10)
12. Doze
13. "Adoniram the son of ____" (1 Kings 4:6)
14. Russian sea
15. Single
16. "I am risen up in the ___ of David my father" (1 Kings 8:20)
17. Garden tool
18. Snooze (Sp.)
20. "Let him ____ evil and do good" (1 Peter 3:11)
22. Norse god of war
23. Born (Fr.)
24. "curse their king and their god and look ____" (Isaiah 8:21)
27. "And I was afraid, and went and hid thy ____" (Matthew 25:25)
31. Trio of vowels
32. "the prince of the power of the ___" (Ephesians 2:2)
33. "who gave Himself a ____ for all" (1 Timothy 2:6)
37. Chess piece (aka rook)
40. Anger
41. Mouth (pl.)
42. "a ____ unto honour, sanctified" (2 Timothy 2:21)
45. Interfere
49. "As he saith also in ____" (Romans 9:25)
50. Property claim
52. "He that loveth wine and ____ shall not be rich" (Proverbs 21:17)
53. Roman road
54. Cooking pot
55. ____ Hill (San Francisco locale)
56. Ten (comb. form)
57. Methods
58. Compass dir.

DOWN

1. Son of Seth (Genesis 4:26)
2. Indian princess
3. Fencing sword
4. "Antipas was my faithful ____" (Revelation 2:13)
5. All _____!
6. Chinese plant
7. "Ye shall weep and _____" (John 16:20)
8. Bundle
9. "The children of Dishan, Uz, and ____" (Genesis 36:28)
10. "Redeem us for thy mercies' ____" (Psalm 44:26)
11. "Saul ___ his thousands" (1 Samuel 29:5)
19. Train dep.
21. The Great ____
24. Formerly Egypt and Syria (abbr.)
25. Of the family of the Punites (Numbers 26:23)
26. "that I may ___ Christ" (Philippians 3:8)
28. Dine
29. Zilch
30. Three-point shot in basketball (var.)
34. Jael's victim (Judges 4)
35. Mine product

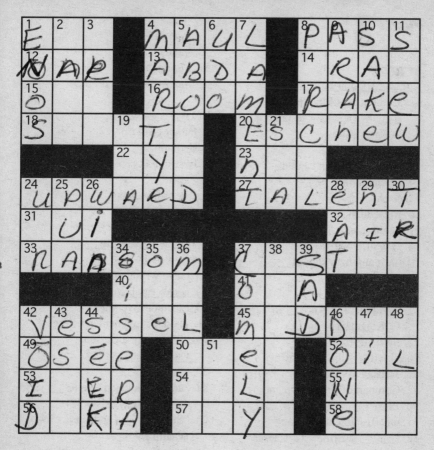

The crossword grid contains the following filled-in letters:

1 E	2	3		4 M	5 A	6 U	7 L		8 P	9 A	10 S	11 S
12 N	A	P		13 A	B	D	A		14	R	A	
15 O			16 R	O	O	M		17 R	A	K	E
18 S		19 T					20 E	21 S	C	H	E	W
		22 T	Y			23 N					
24 U	25 P	26 W	A	R	D		27 T	A	L	28 E	29 N	30 I
31	U	I								32 A	I	R
33 R	A	B	34 O	35 O	36 M		37 C	38	39 S	T		
		40 I					41 O		A	D		
42 V	43 E	44 S	S	E	L		45 M		D	46 O	47	48
49 O	S	E	E		50	51		E		52 O	I	L
53 I		E	R		54			L		55 N		
56 D		K	A		57			Y		58 E		

36. Soft and sweet
37. "Thy cheeks are _____"
    (Song of Solomon 1:1)
38. Sports venues
39. "be not as the hypocrites, of a
    ___ countenance"
    (Matthew 6:16)
42. "And the earth was without form,
    and ____" (Genesis 1:2)
43. This (Sp.)
44. Search for
46. "and having ___ all, to stand"
    (Ephesians 6:13)
47. Maned beast

48. German river
51. Longshoreman's org.

7

PUZZLE 3

ACROSS
1. Rhine tributary
4. "all the trees of the field shall _____ their hands" (Isaiah 55:12)
8. Man in a kilt
12. Swimsuit top
13. South American capital
14. Declaration
15. Sack
16. Masculine name
17. More (comb. form, var.)
18. One of David's wives
20. "lest any man should _____" (Ephesians 2:9)
21. Omega
22. "And there was no ___ in the pot" (2 Kings 4:41)
23. So be it! (pl.)
26. "I will ___ the pride of Jerusalem" (Jeremiah 13:9)
27. Comparative adjective ending
30. Ebb
31. Old Testament offering
32. "___ ___, Brute!" (J. Caesar reproach)
33. Beseech
35. Synthetic fabric
36. Proportion
37. Ever (poet.)
38. "Have the gates of ___ been opened" (Job 38:17)
40. "And _____ hearing these words fell down" (Acts 5:5)
44. Indian princess
45. Auto pioneer
46. Presidential nickname
47. Gasoline brand
48. Melville character
49. "shew yourselves ___" (Isaiah 46:8)
50. Valley
51. Mountain lake
52. Sandwich order (abbr.)

DOWN
1. Father (Aram.)
2. Bedouin
3. East Indian cereal grass
4. Tidies
5. Pale from anger
6. A son of Helem (1 Chronicles 7:35)
7. Temple vessel: fire ___
8. Sleep (Lat.)
9. "I also will laugh at your _____" (Proverbs 1:26)
10. Elevator inventor
11. Thought (phonetic spelling)
19. "But ye are a chosen _____" (1 Peter 2:9)
20. Sand ___
22. "and Noah begat Shem, ___, and Japheth" (Genesis 5:32)
23. "Stand in ___, and sin not" (Psalm 4:4)
24. Isle of ____
25. Admission
26. Pad
28. WWII arena
29. Flow
31. Feminine name
32. Deserve
34. Biblical verb ending
35. "Come, let us _____ together" (Isaiah 1:18)
37. "a woman that hath a familiar spirit at _____" (1 Samuel 28:7)
38. Pull behind
39. Nobleman

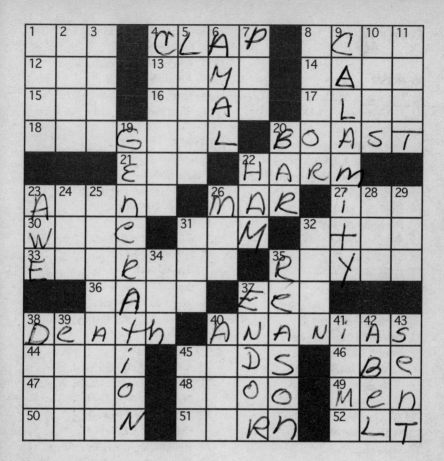

40. Egyptian dancing girl
41. Poetic foot
42. "____offered unto God a more
   excellent sacrifice"
   (Hebrews 11:4)
43. "the Father which hath ____him"
   (John 5:23)
45. Out (Scot.)

ACROSS

1. The son of Michael
   (1 Chronicles 27:18)
5. Vigor
8. "our righteousness are as filthy
   ___" (Isaiah 64:6)
12. Masculine name meaning "red"
13. Hockey great
14. Husband of Judith
    (Genesis 26:34)
15. Sloping passage
16. Small
17. Lean-to
18. Employ
20. "taking the ____of faith"
    (Ephesians 6:16)
22. Patrick Henry was one
25. Printer's measure (pl.)
26. Lustrous black shade
27. "exhort one____daily"
    (Hebrews 3:13)
31. Tropical bird
32. Within (comb. form)
33. Eggs (Lat.)
34. Remote
37. Biblical outcast
39. Ashland, VA, college
40. "I will ____them as silver"
    (Zechariah 13:9)
41. Beloved son of Israel
44. WWI group
45. Info. agency
46. New Zealand clan
48. Son of Seth
52. Group of Indo-European lan-
    guages spoken in Afghanistan
    and Pakistan
53. Of an Egyptian king
    (Jeremiah 47:25)
54. Where water became wine
55. Observes
56. Three (colloq.)
57. What the duffer did

DOWN

1. To row
2. Beneficiary of telethon (abbr.)
3. "And Hezron begat ___"
   (Ruth 4:19)
4. Ascribe
5. "the Son of man hath ___on earth"
   (Matthew 9:6)
6. Linking verb
7. "that ye ____your bodies a living
   sacrifice" (Romans 12:1)
8. "Whom ____stedfast in the faith"
   (1 Peter 5:9)
9. Tennis great
10. A Celt of Scotland
11. Masses of weeds on the White
    Nile
19. "This is my beloved ___"
    (Matthew 3:17)
21. Health-care provider (abbr.)
22. Toward the mouth
23. Indian princess
24. Bird (Lat.)
27. "Go to the ___, thou sluggard"
    (Proverbs 6:6)
28. Native American
29. Tied
30. "it is a ___thing that the king
    requireth" (Daniel 2:11)
32. Delight
35. "He ___the winepress of
    the...wrath of God Almighty"
    (Revelation 19:11, NIV)

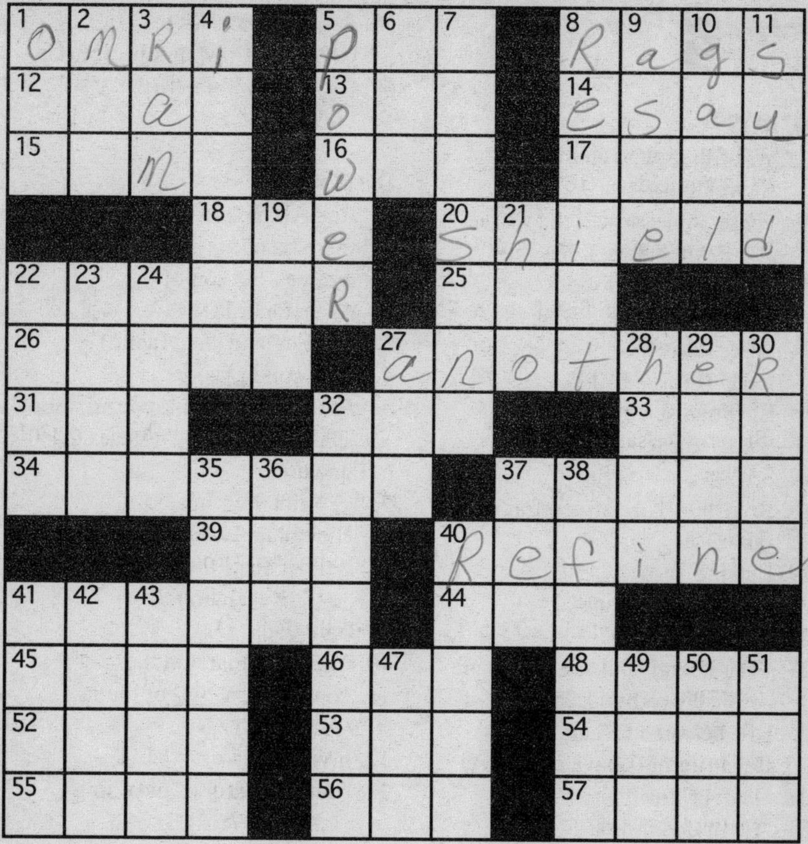

36. Electrical meas.
37. Southern officer and gentleman
38. "and the ____of righteousness quietness" (Isaiah 32:17)
40. "Destroy this temple, and...I will ___it up" (John 2:19)
41. New Testament book
42. Anthem beginning
43. Father
47. Craggy hill
48. No (Scot.)
50. Uno (Eng.)
51. Blue

PUZZLE 5

ACROSS

1. One of the seven churches (Revelation)
7. "These...have turned the world ___down" (Acts 17:6)
13. "and now shall I die for ____" (Judges 15:18)
14. "Blessed is the _____whose God" (Psalm 33:12)
15. Egyptian sun god
16. Satisfied exclamation
17. Spy soc.
18. Branch of U.S. armed forces (abbr.)
19. Linking verb
20. Tropical Asian ape
22. British farewell
23. "The liberal soul shall be made ___" (Proverbs 11:25)
25. Riv. between GA and SC
26. Celebrity of Calaveras County
28. Duck or down
31. "I will do all thou ____" (Ruth 3:11)
33. Spat
35. Pierre _____ Renoir
38. Secular
42. Cold (Sp.)
43. Belonging to Einstein, informally
45. Japanese outcast
46. "And great was the ___" (Matthew 7:27)
47. Biblical pronoun
49. Swamp
50. Windy City trans.
51. Look! See!
52. Norma ___(Sally Field role)
54. Stagger
56. Put in writing
59. Goddess of law and justice (Gr.)
60. City of the Philistines (1 Samuel 5)

DOWN

1. "And Abram said unto Lot, Let there be no ____" (Genesis 13:8)
2. "Azareel, the son of ____" (Nehemiah 11:13)
3. New England state (abbr.)
4. Bore (colloq.)
5. "At that day, saith the Lord, thou shall call me ___" (Hosea 2:16)
6. Punctures
7. "____not your heads" (Leviticus 10:6)
8. "Neither shall there be any more ___" (Revelation 21:4)
9. Train dep.
10. Age of Roman toddler
11. "Gamaliel, a ____of the law" (Acts 5:34)
12. Involve
21. "but a handful of meal in a ____" (1 Kings 17:12)
24. Mission accomplished in the end zone (abbr.)
26. "when the day of Pentecost was ___come" (Acts 2:1)
27. King and Emperor (abbr.)
29. "they are ___unto the angels; and are the children of God" (Luke 20:36)
30. Nickname of Cyrus
32. Which is (Lat.)
34. Kettledrums used by Moors
35. Influence
36. Russian mountain range
37. Actor Girard
39. Expeditionary force (abbr.)

12

40. Resident of (suffix)
41. Gave a sloping edge to
44. Middle Eastern country
48. Belonging to (suffix, pl.)
51. What to wear with a muumuu
53. Anglo-Saxon letter
54. Second note of a scale
55. Printer's measure
57. Part of the psyche
58. Preposition

ACROSS

1. ___haw
4. "the children of ___, six hundred fifty and five" (Nehemiah 7:20)
8. "the spirit of God descending like a ___" (Matthew 3:16)
12. "of his government shall be no ___" (Isaiah 9:7)
13. But (Sp.)
14. Collar
15. WWII arena
16. ____ tea
17. "I will pay my ___before them that fear him" (Job 22:25)
18. Saddle part
20. Australian native
22. Fiddler crab genus
23. "He leadeth me ___still waters" (Psalm 23:2)
27. Supplications
31. Outcast
32. To feel ill
33. Shoe width
34. Droop
36. ___potato
39. Tumors (KJV)
42. "Enter in at the ___ gate" (Matthew 7:13)
44. Chemical suffix
45. Education org.
46. Amateur
50. "If any of you ___ wisdom" (James 1:5)
53. Cheese
55. Actor Aldo
56. Hurt
57. "I ___to see you" (Romans 1:11)

58. "These three are ___" (1 John 5:7)
59. Anjou is one
60. O.T. book
61. Masculine name

DOWN

1. Uriah ____
2. Inner (comb. form)
3. Land of Esau
4. Each
5. "I will ___ thy name" (Psalm 22:2)
6. Anger
7. "And they made war with the Hagarites,...and ____" (1 Chronicles 5:19)
8. "Woe to them that ___ iniquity" (Micah 2:1)
9. Ear (comb. form)
10. Say "I do"
11. Printer's measures
19. Very (Sp.)
21. ___ Aviv
24. Itself (Lat.)
25. "And I saw the ___, small and great stand before God" (Revelation 20:12)
26. Unit of work (pl.)
27. High moccasins
28. Vivid display
29. Lake Albert tribe
30. "But we ___ Jesus" (Hebrews 2:9)
34. Distinguished
37. "And their word will eat as doth a ____" (2 Timothy 2:17)
38. Hurry
40. "It is____; Joseph ...is alive" (Genesis 45:28)
41. N.T. book

43. "Can God furnish a ___in the
    wilderness?" (Psalm 78:19)
47. "a conscience seared with a hot
    ___" (1 Timothy 4:2)
48. Split rattan
49. Espied
50. "Separate those who ___the
    water" (Judges 7:5, NIV)
51. Pro
52. Half a dance
54. ___Alamos

PUZZLE 7

ACROSS

1. "And when I looked, behold a ___in the wall" (Ezekiel 8:7)
5. Small, pointed tool
8. Naomi's self-appointed name
12. Sixth month of Jewish calendar
13. Fabricate
14. "tomorrow is cast into the ___" (Matthew 6:30)
15. "_____shall my heavenly father do also unto you" (Matthew 18:35)
17. Hollow
18. Compass dir.
19. Grandmother of Enos
20. That is (Lat.)
21. "ye are all ___in Christ Jesus" (Galatians 3:28)
22. "If ye ____ chastening" (Hebrews 12:7)
26. "And Jesse ___David the king" (Matthew 1:6)
29. Graduate degree
30. "Then arose Peter and ___unto the sepulchre" (Luke 24:12)
31. Once popular magazine
32. Brother of Shem
33. Josip Broz
34. Faerie Queene heroine
35. By means of
36. "____are in the book of life" (Philippians 4:3)
37. She is also called Hadassah
39. Entreat
40. Right eye (abbr.)
41. Bird's beak
42. "The lot is cast into the ___" (Proverbs 16:33)
45. "The young lions ___" (Psalm 104:21)
48. "in one hour she is made ____" (Revelation 18:19)
50. "tell in the ___of thy son...what things I have wrought" (Exodus 10:2)
51. Gold (Sp.)
52. River of SW England
53. Kilmer subject
54. Edge
55. Sew a sock

DOWN

1. Revolutionary War spy
2. Norse mythological figure
3. ____of fire (Revelation 20:14)
4. "come down ___my child die" (John 4:49)
5. "I am ___for evermore" (Revelation 1:18)
6. "they that be ___shall shine as the brightness of the firmament" (Daniel 12:3)
7. Away from the wind (naut.)
8. Transported
9. Clark's costar in Mogambo
10. Kin (abbr.)
11. One (Scot.)
16. "many of his disciples ___back" (John 6:66)
20. Elected officials
21. "an angel...sat under an___ which was in Ophrah" (Judges 6:11)
22. Common street name
23. "___and the Thummin" (Exodus 28:30)
24. Proportion
25. Grandson of Adam
26. Indigo
27. Ages

28. Old Testament offering
29. "lest I __my own inheritance" (Ruth 4:6)
32. Pronoun
33. ___ sale
35. Foot (comb. form)
36. Mountain visited by Moses
38. Equestrian's need
39. Broom (arch.)
41. Greek form of Neriah
42. Kilauea's evidence
43. One who acts (suffix)
44. Noted Quaker
45. Prepare flax

46. Row
47. Linking verb
48. Land whose name means "dwelling" (Joshua 11)
49. Youth

PUZZLE 8

ACROSS

1. Chop down (as a tree)
4. Prong
8. "without him was not any thing ___" (John 1:3)
12. Gershwin
13. Golf club
14. "We ought to ___ God rather than men" (Acts 5:29)
15. Captain of the Canaanites (Judges 4:2)
17. Member of an ancient Jewish sect
19. "the wicked ___ their bow" (Psalm 11:2)
21. Wales from a whip
22. Traveled with Paul to Syria and Cilicia
25. Cain was his uncle
27. Blue (Sp.)
28. Large pitcher
29. In this manner
32. "I am like a broken _____" (Psalm 31:12)
34. Begat by Mizraim (Genesis 10:13)
36. Time zone (abbr.)
37. To tilt to one side, as a ship
39. Machete
40. Splendor
41. He led 10,000 men down Mt. Tabor
42. "There went up ___ ___ from the earth" (Genesis 2:6)
45. Chinese monetary unit
47. Word repeated in the Psalms (pl.)
49. "Sing ___ to the Lord God" (Judges 5:3)
53. Navigate
54. Shortly
56. Street___
57. Ancient kingdom at the head of the Persian Gulf
58. Writes
59. "But the poor man had nothing, save one little ___" (2 Samuel 12:3)

DOWN

1. Pronoun
2. Of the family of the Erites (Numbers 26:16)
3. Linking verb
4. Turbans (KJV usage)
5. Middle Eastern country
6. What you should just say
7. Compass dir.
8. When he died at 120 his vision was most likely 20/20
9. He offered a "more excellent sacrifice" (Hebrews 11:5)
10. Impression
11. Notices
16. Belonging to a child of Shobal (Genesis 36:23)
18. Promised
20. ___ point
22. "He will...hear their cry and will ___ them" (Psalm 145:19)
23. Causes to become (suffix)
24. "not fulfill the ___ of the flesh" (Galatians 5:16)
26. Tidy
29. Love (Lat.)
30. Feminine name
31. In a rage
33. City on the Red Sea, in the land of Edom (2 Chronicles 8:17)
35. River of Damascus (2 Kings 5:12)

38. Caleb was one
40. Song of praise
41. "so shall thy ___ be filled" (Proverbs 3:10)
42. South African fox
43. "the barrel of ___ shall not abate" (1 Kings 17:14)
44. Hip bones
46. Preposition
48. Weaken
50. "He casteth forth his __ like morsels" (Psalm 147:17)
51. Proverb
52. Before (poet.)

55. Dir. from Beersheba to Jericho

ACROSS
1. Attic
5. Wanders
9. Boys' org.
12. Love (Lat.)
13. Biblical wild ox
14. With "out," to get by
15. "are choked with ___and riches" (Luke 8:14)
17. "if they drink any ___thing, it shall not hurt them" (Mark 16:18)
19. "their conscience ____with a hot iron" (1 Timothy 4:2)
21. Vowel trio
22. Bucolic setting
24. Female roe
25. Dined
26. Signs (colloq.)
28. City inherited by children of Asher (Joshua 19:30)
30. Eleventh month of Jewish calendar
32. "Let the sea roar...let the ____rejoice" (1 Chronicles 16:32)
34. "as if a man had inquired at the ____of God" (2 Samuel 16:23)
36. Football stat.
37. Model
39. Widow of ____ (Luke 7)
40. "his eyes were set by reason of his ___" (1 Kings 14:4)
41. "It will be fair weather: for the sky is ___" (Matthew 16:2)
43. Hwy.
44. Shade tree of olive family
45. "He is ____himself" (Mark 3:21)

47. "____, O Lord, unto the many thousands of Israel" (Numbers 10:36)
49. "For my name's sake will I ____ mine anger" (Isaiah 48:9)
52. Great Sea city of the Promised Land
53. Creeks
55. Halo
56. Eye drs.
57. "Bring forth the ___robe and put it on him" (Luke 15:22)
58. Vanish

DOWN
1. Resin
2. Medical suffix
3. "Cease from anger and ____wrath" (Psalm 37:8)
4. "Jesus, whom ye slew and hanged on a ___" (Acts 5:30)
5. Judah's firstborn (Genesis 38)
6. "In famine he shall ____thee from death" (Job 5:20)
7. "a measuring ___of six cubits long" (Ezekiel 40:5)
8. Little (Scot.)
9. Misrepresent
10. Terrier
11. Diphthong
16. Down
18. Hilly city of kingdom of Israel, not far from Mt. Gilboa
20. Awaken
22. "___up your heads, O ye gates" (Psalm 24:7)
23. Ms. Bagnold
25. Swiss river
27. Slender

29. "In that day a man shall cast his idols of silver...to the ___ " (Isaiah 2:20)
30. Dismounted
31. Nota ____
33. Pres. inits.
35. "Martha, thou art ____and troubled about many things" (Luke 10:41)
38. Spheres of action
40. Belonging to Zilpah's second son (Genesis 30)
42. "Many times ___he deliver them" (Psalm 106:43)

44. Of the family of the Arodites (Numbers 26)
45. Cheese
46. "But I, as a ___man, heard not" (Psalm 38:13)
48. Opp. of rur.
50. Ever (poet.)
51. Feminine name
52. Ditto (abbr.)
54. Poem pt.

ACROSS

1. Biblical ointment
5. Stadium cheer
8. Not out
12. Fever, chills
13. Nancy Hanks's son
14. Roman road
15. Particulars (abbr.)
16. Prof. sports org.
17. "the ___ that is in thy brother's eye" (Matthew 7:3)
18. Tribe of Israel
20. Disciple who was sent by Paul to Crete
22. Whom Peleg begat (Genesis 11)
24. Uncle (Sp.)
25. "Lord, wilt thou...___again the kingdom to Israel?" (Acts 1:6)
29. "And ___walked with God" (Genesis 5:22)
33. Corrida cheer
34. "__ __ Alpha and Omega" (Revelation 1:8)
36. Indo-Chinese native (var.)
37. "___the Lord, o my soul" (Psalm 103:1)
40. "Thou shalt be a father of many ____" (Genesis 17:4)
43. "they opened their mouth wide against me, and said, ___ " (Psalm 35:21)
45. Enclosure
46. Component
50. "____foolish questions, and genealogies" (Titus 3:9)
54. Eye____
55. Jehovah
57. Son of Shammua (Nehemiah 11)
58. ___-European
59. Son of Benjamin (Genesis 46)
60. Prepared food shop
61. Average
62. Operate
63. "The ___of your understanding being enlightened" (Ephesians 1:18)

DOWN

1. Nothing (Sp.)
2. Matures
3. Wife of Mahlon
4. "make straight in the ___ a highway for our God" (Isaiah 40:3)
5. Hied
6. Father (Aram.)
7. "Let not your ___be troubled" (John 14:1)
8. "Of the tribe of____were sealed twelve thousand" (Revelation 7:7)
9. Tiny particle
10. Cheese
11. To be (Sp., var.)
19. Vintage auto
21. "and ___the kine to the cart" (1 Samuel 6:7)
23. Eastern state univ.
25. "Will a man ___ God?" (Malachi 3:8)
26. Building addition
27. Understand
28. Belonging to (suffix)
30. Siouan
31. Tin
32. Pronoun
35. Chart
38. The thirteenth judge of Israel
39. Pronoun
41. Beverage

1	2	3	4		5	6	7		8	9	10	11
12					13				14			
15					16				17			
18				19		20		21				
			22		23		24					
25	26	27				28		29		30	31	32
33					34		35			36		
37			38	39		40		41	42			
			43		44		45					
46	47	48				49		50		51	52	53
54					55		56		57			
58					59				60			
61					62				63			

42. "whom thou would not let
___Israel" (2 Chronicles 20:10)

44. "The discretion of a man defer-
reth his ___" (Proverbs 19:11)

46. Place of twelve wells of water
(Exodus 15)

47. "Their ___is gone out through all
the earth" (Psalm 19:4)

48. Norse saga

49. Great-grandfather of Elkanah
(1 Samuel 1)

51. Confidence

52. Lazy

53. Raised platform

56. Noise

ACROSS

1. "and if a son, then an___of God " (Galatians 4:7)
4. Energy
7. Printer's measures
10. Eastern U.S. state
11. "For there is hope of a ___, if it be cut down" (Job 14:7)
12. Churchill gesture
13. High school ____
15. Nard
17. Twelve lions stood around his throne (1 Kings 10)
19. Vowels in chorus of children's song
20. Carter cabinet member
22. North Atlantic food fish
26. Deborah accompanied him
29. They travel through the Loop
31. Year (Sp.)
32. "And the king of the south shall be moved with ____" (Daniel 11:11)
34. "The ____ pot is for silver" (Proverbs 17:3)
36. Small bit
37. "Eat not of it ____...but roast it with fire" (Exodus 12:9)
39. To tend
40. Father of Peleg and Joktan (Genesis 10:25)
42. Sister of Absalom
44. Preposition
46. "___shall any plague come nigh thy dwelling" (Psalm 91:10)
50. After dusk (poet.)
54. Congolese river that forms Ubangi
55. Light touch
56. Sanction
57. Egyptian sun deity
58. Tropical bird
59. Son of (Heb.)
60. Fencing implement

DOWN

1. Rose seedcases
2. "an___is nothing in the world...there is none other God" (1 Corinthians 8:4)
3. Dismissal
4. "the ___of the power of the air" (Ephesians 2:2)
5. Even (poet.)
6. St.___ (FL cty.)
7. Palindromic name
8. "Quit you like ___" (1 Corinthians 16:13)
9. Arrange
11. Sat. TV fare (colloq.)
14. Recto (abbr.)
16. Wrong (prefix)
18. "Woe unto him that striveth with his ___" (Isaiah 45:9)
21. Mischievous one
23. Absalom's defining feature
24. Yearbooks (abbr.)
25. Venetian magistrate
26. Alphabet sequence
27. Jezebel's "better" half
28. The ____, Douglas novel
30. "the Lord spake unto Moses in the wilderness of ___" (Numbers 3:14)
33. Rodent
35. "Bring them up in the ____and admonition of the Lord" (Ephesians 6:4)

38. "your children shall ___in the wilderness" (Numbers 14:33)
41. Tore
43. "And if it be___that I go also" (1 Corinthians 16:4)
45. Puncture
47. Amass
48. Building extension
49. To advise; counsel
50. Greek letter
51. Actor Johnson
52. Spire ornament
53. Philippine tree

ACROSS

1. Teen's task?
4. "Into your ___ are they delivered" (Genesis 9:2)
8. King of the Amalekites (1 Samuel 15)
12. Govt. agency
13. Hatred (Ital.)
14. At any ___
15. The sound of this sent a fiery mountain into the sea (Revelation 8, 2 words)
18. Three ___ years (Isaac's age at fatherhood; Genesis 25)
19. Year (Sp.)
20. Funeral ___
23. Desire
27. Thought
30. Cooking pot
32. Encore! (Fr.)
33. "For John came to you in the way of _____" (Matthew 21:32)
36. Used to form feminine name (suffix)
37. Bramble (Heb., var. pl.)
38. Auditoriums
39. Melchizedek, king of ___ (Genesis 14)
41. Dines
43. Vehicle
45. Springs where John baptized (John 3)
49. "a good ___ have all they that do his commandments" (Psalm 111:10)
54. River of France and Germany
55. Great Lake
56. Meadow
57. Entertainment award
58. "there were ___ between Rehoboam and Jeroboam" (2 Chronicles 12:15)
59. Of the family of the Erites (Numbers 26)

DOWN

1. ___ kit
2. Oil org.
3. Texas town
4. Nectar
5. "I will ___ unto thy days fifteen years" (2 Kings 20:6)
6. Young louse
7. Feminine name
8. "Put on the full ___ of God" (Ephesians 6:11, NIV)
9. Mountain ravine
10. Dined
11. ___ real! (colloq.)
16. Wife of Chilion
17. Character in The Last of the Mohicans
21. "as swift as the ___ upon the mountains" (1 Chronicles 12:8)
22. Oak (Heb., pl.)
24. Resting
25. Clamp
26. U.S. agency which incorporates the Weather Bureau
27. Eye part
28. Actress Merrill
29. Evenly proportioned (Fr.)
31. Hawaiian feast
34. Wife of Judah's son Er (Genesis 38)
35. Snooped
40. "___ knee shall bow" (Isaiah 45:23)
42. Flat, rectangular pieces

44. All dirs.
46. White____
47. Extraordinary person
48. East African folklore character
49. Employ
50. One-time war zone (colloq.)
51. Hoover___
52. ___-la
53. "the fowls of the ___" (Job 12:7)

27

ACROSS

1. "Thy word is a ___unto my feet" (Psalm 119:105)
5. Actor Alan
9. "___iniquity unto their iniquity" (Psalm 69:27)
12. Egg shaped
13. Oust
14. Feminine name
15. Rectangular sections
17. "The heavens ____the glory of God" (Psalm 19:1)
19. Object of adoration
21. Believed
22. Asian country (abbr.)
23. In the same place (Lat.)
25. So-so (abbr.)
26. "perfumed my bed with myrrh, ___, and cinnamon" (Proverbs 7:17)
27. Pioneer in steel
32. Kin (abbr.)
33. "from the tower of ___shall they fall" (Ezekiel 30:6)
34. Inhabitant of (suffix)
35. "in his law doth he____day and night" (Psalm 1:2)
37. "they love to ___standing" (Matthew 6:5)
38. Either___
39. Continent (abbr.)
40. Munch
41. Of a Damascus river (2 Kings 5)
45. The man behind McDonald's
47. Feels contrite
49. Sound of a dropped melon
52. ___-de-France

53. "if he shall ___the whole world" (Matthew 16:26)
55. Apollo's mother in myth
56. Careless
57. He was (Lat.)
58. Anglo-Saxon slave

DOWN

1. "the Lord of hosts shall __the bough with terror" (Isaiah 10:33)
2. Star of The Barefoot Contessa
3. "Yet thou in thy____mercies forsook them not" (Nehemiah 9:19)
4. "What___shall I give thee?" (Genesis 38:18)
5. Direction for printer (abbr.)
6. First___
7. Slave Scott
8. To die
9. Son of Kemuel (Genesis 22)
10. "for a good man some would even ___to die" (Romans 5:7)
11. Act
16. King of Egypt (2 Kings 17)
18. Lift (Fr.)
20. Tripoli is its capital
22. Toward the wind
24. Red root vegetables
26. Branch
28. Move stealthily
29. "for no man can do these____" (John 3:2)
30. State (Fr.)
31. King (Sp.)
33. Alien
36. Bulwer-Lytton heroine
37. "sin is a reproach to any ____" (Proverbs 14:34)
41. Seed covering after fertilization
42. Lugosi

43. Peak
44. "the bright and morning ___"
(Revelation 22:16)
46. Currency of India (abbr.)
48. A Nethinim family, the children
of ___ (Nehemiah 7)
50. Chewed
51. Anderson's High
54. Bib. div.

PUZZLE 14

ACROSS

1. Spending limit
4. Drilled
9. Scottish topper
12. Eskimo knife
13. Speak pompously
14. Stream
15. Cyrus, king of ____ (2 Chronicles 36)
17. "we are of the truth, and shall ___our hearts before him" (1 John 3:19)
19. Becomes boring
21. Small (suffix, pl.)
22. Passageways
24. Stolen
28. Dill herb
29. C. Bronte heroine
30. Steamer (abbr.)
31. British 'bye
32. "and he said in the sight of Israel, ___,stand thou still" (Joshua 10:12)
34. Of vegetable origin (suffix)
36. Pronoun
37. Alphonso's queen
39. No coins are needed to operate its meter
41. Grad. degrees
43. "their laws are___from all people; neither keep they the king's laws" (Esther 3:8)
45. "And though...____destroy this body" (Job 19:26)
46. Some vowels
47. To be stationary with the head of the wind, as a ship
49. Carries

52. Explorer
55. Assist
56. "Thou shall not oppress an ____servant" (Deuteronomy 24:14)
58. Historical period
59. Affirmative answer
60. "the enemy...sowed ___among the wheat" (Matthew 13:25)
61. "he is a ___creature" (2 Corinthians 5:17)

DOWN

1. "Let this ___pass" (Luke 22:42)
2. Ginger ___
3. Lydia's color
4. "Job was covered with ___" (Job 2:7)
5. Spoken
6. Egyptian sun god
7. Greek letter
8. "he shall give thee the ___of thine heart" (Psalm 37:4)
9. Has faith
10. ___mail
11. First name of life preserver vest
16. Seasons
18. "Siddim, which is the salt ___" (Genesis 14:3)
20. Case out, clandestinely
22. "the Lord saw that Leah was ___" (Genesis 29:31)
23. Seventh son of Elioenai (1 Chronicles 3:24)
25. One of the dukes of Edom (Genesis 36:43)
26. City just across the Red Sea (Exodus 13)
27. Attire
29. Son of Seth

33. "Stand ___ on thy feet" (Acts 14:10)
35. Describe dramatically
38. Eludes
40. Slippery one
42. "I have ___ the bands of your yoke" (Leviticus 26:13)
44. Poetic p.m.
45. "the ___ were wrapped about my head" (Jonah 2:5)
48. Words of understanding
49. ___ of Fundy
50. Primitive species of wheat (KJV)
51. Assembly (Heb.)

53. Before (poet.)
54. Harsh
57. Union Pac. was one

PUZZLE 15

ACROSS

1. "the ___above the liver, with the kidneys" (stomach part mentioned in Leviticus 3:15 for an offering)
5. Gasp
9. Mordecai the ___
12. A king of Israel (1 Kings 16)
13. West African tribe
14. Japanese apricot
15. Disfigure
16. "We spend our years as a ___that is told" (Psalm 90:9)
17. Uproar
18. Make possible
20. Aka Araunah the Jebusite
22. "Do not __because ye know not the scriptures" (Mark 12:24)
24. Makes less difficult
26. Summer drink
28. Actor Robert
30. Ancient Thebes (Jeremiah 46)
31. Mid. East. country
32. ___Grande
33. Witty remark
35. I ___ (God)
36. "shall they heap to themselves teachers, having itching ___" (2 Timothy 4:3)
39. Judah's daughter-in-law (Genesis 38)
41. Compass dir.
43. Hosea's wife
45. Area of Judea that included Beersheba
50. "all they are brass, and ___, and iron" (Ezekiel 22:18)
51. Appear indistinctly

53. Kaiser___
54. Chemical suffix
55. "God __ __ respecter of persons" (Acts 10:34)
56. Duke___(Genesis 46)
57. Cruise the ___ (pastime for the 90s)
58. "justified in the Spirit, ___of angels" (1 Timothy 3:16)
59. ____room

DOWN

1. "___unto me" (Matthew 11:28)
2. "Will __ ___ rob God?" (Malachi 3:8)
3. Auk genus
4. Arm, for example
5. Cephas
6. Alias (abbr.)
7. ___contendere
8. Layered
9. ____tree
10. "thou buildest thine___place in the head of every way" (Ezekiel 16:31)
11. Benign skin tumor
19. Actress Grant
21. Son of Caleb (1 Chronicles 4)
23. "I will ___me up a faithful priest" (1 Samuel 2:35)
25. Egyptian king (2 Kings 17)
26. Preposition
27. "Your old men shall ___" (Acts 2:17)
29. Biblical interjection
31. "the people ___a vain thing" (Psalm 2:1)
32. B & O, e.g.
34. ___ a roll
35. Preposition

37. Belonging to the son of Gad (Numbers 26)
38. "Take up thy ___,and go unto thine house" (Matthew 9:6)
40. French impressionist
42. "___, called Peter" (Matthew 4:18)
44. ___of Sharon (Song of Solomon 2)
46. "the breastplate of judgment the ___" (Exodus 28:30)
47. Less is ___ (fashion dictum)
48. Zeal

49. "that thine ___may be in secret" (Matthew 6:4)
50. Mus. part
52. Chemical (suffix)

PUZZLE 16

ACROSS

1. "There is a way which seemeth right unto ___" (Proverbs 14:12)
4. "whereby we cry ___, Father" (Romans 8:15)
8. Harness part
11. "Why make ye this __and weep?" (Mark 5:39)
12. "___down all thy strong holds" (Micah 5:11)
13. Alphonso's queen
14. Still
15. Trav. org.
16. Mother of Ishmael
18. The month of April (Exodus 13)
20. Telegram
21. Grad. degree
22. "___ cumi" (Mark 5:41)
25. "Thou shalt lay up ___as dust" (Job 22:24)
26. "a great gulf ___between us" (Luke 16:26)
27. Printer's measure
28. One (Scot.)
29. Before (poet.)
30. "will do all that thou shall___us" (2 Kings 10:5)
31. Pronoun
32. Planted
34. Complete
35. "For by him were all things created,...whether they be___" (Colossians 1:16)
37. Office holders
38. Camel's ___
39. "in___will I call them my people" (Romans 9:25)
41. Fire (Sp.)
43. Egg (comb. form)
44. "thou shalt put __away iniquity" (Job 22:23)
47. Reply (syn.)
48. Not in your wildest dreams
50. A son of Caleb (1 Chronicles 4)
51. Earl Grey, for example
52. Wither
53. Number of Joseph's brothers who went to buy corn in Egypt (Genesis 45)

DOWN

1. Cape ___, NJ
2. Fruit drink
3. "a ___ prisoner named Barabbas" (Matthew 27:16)
4. An evil king of Israel
5. S.A. country
6. "First" name of nursery rhyme character
7. Short time
8. "Take ye wives, ___sons and daughters" (Jeremiah 29:6)
9. Actress Claire
10. ___ paper
12. A group of Asian languages (var.)
17. Parched
19. Good (colloq.)
20. "For this people's heart is ___gross" (Matthew 13:15)
21. Sivan, the third ___(Esther 8)
22. Bores
23. "And if children, then ___ of God" (Romans 8:17)
24. Aunt Bea's nephew
25. Manner of walking
26. "to the ___, ye shall give the less inheritance" (Numbers 33:54)
30. "that ye might have a second ___" (2 Corinthians 1:15)

32. Rise above
33. "melons, leeks, and the _____"
    (Numbers 11:5)
34. Compete
36. Son of Zorobabel (Luke 3:27)
39. Preposition
40. Term of address
41. Physical trait of Mrs. Sprat
42. Chemical suffix
43. Female cell (pl.)
45. Linking verb
46. "rejoiceth as a strong man to
    ___a race" (Psalm 19:5)
49. Shoe width

ACROSS

1. QEII milieu
4. Noun case (abbr.)
7. Hot ____
11. Pull behind
13. Gold (Sp.)
14. Feminine pronoun (Fr.)
15. Emanation
16. Comparative suffix
17. "he burned the bones of the king of Edom into ___" (Amos 2:1)
18. "Go, ___an altar unto the Lord" (2 Samuel 24:18)
19. Another name for Jesus
21. "we receive the ___ reward of our deeds" (Luke 23:41)
23. Preposition
24. "ye that labour and are heavy ___" (Matthew 11:28)
27. Registered
32. ___-a-dale (var.)
33. Scold
34. Raised (Fr., masc.)
35. The sun
37. "Then the ___taketh him up into the holy city" (Matthew 4:5)
38. Pronoun
39. "a ___for a burnt offering" (Leviticus 9:2)
40. "his understanding is _____" (Psalm 147:5)
45. Son of Seth
49. Inescapable ruin
50. Pray (prefix)
51. Captain of the Nautilus
52. ___ of students
53. "Cain...dwelt in the land of ___" (Genesis 4:16)
54. Edible root
55. Cooking pot
56. Caleb was one
57. ___-Tin-Tin

DOWN

1. Sixth month of Jewish calendar
2. "we know that thou art ___" (Matthew 22:16)
3. Heroine of Dr. Zhivago
4. "Let us make a joyful ___" (Psalm 95:1)
5. Classic cookie
6. "Joy cometh in the ____" (Psalm 30:5)
7. "I can of mine own ___ do nothing" (John 5:30)
8. "And they came to ___,where were twelve wells" (Exodus 15:27)
9. Feminine name
10. High school student
12. "I made me ____and orchards" (Ecclesiastes 2:5)
20. Can. prov.
22. Not (prefix)
24. Boy
25. In the manner of
26. "so that __come upon you unawares" (Luke 21:34)
27. "incline thine ___unto me" (Psalm 17:6)
28. Constituent
29. The apocalypse (abbr.)
30. A prince of Midian (Joshua 13)
31. "The First State" (abbr.)
33. "by these were the ___ divided in the earth after the flood" (Genesis 10:32)
36. Jack Haley portrayed this man
37. Lawyer for the state (abbr.)

39. "be ___always to give an
    answer" (1 Peter 3:15)
40. The seer against Jeroboam
    (2 Chronicles 9)
41. Christmas (Fr.)
42. Young horse
43. A son of Helem (1 Chronicles 7)
44. Cancer is one (abbr.)
46. "my salvation is ___to come"
    (Isaiah 56:1)
47. He defeated Zimri (1 Kings 16)
48. Not later

ACROSS

1. Linking verb
4. About half a pint in the Old Testament
7. Son of Seth
11. "____fast that which is good" (1 Thessalonians 5:21)
13. Lyric poem
14. Hawaiian goose
15. Father of Asa (Matthew 1)
16. Belonging to the city that was the destination of Joshua's spies (Joshua 7)
17. Ten (prefix)
18. "And seeing the ____, he went up into a mountain" (Matthew 5:1)
21. Brother of Miriam
23. Night before
24. "And the beginning of his [Nimrod's] kingdom was ____" (Genesis 10:10)
25. Turkish title of respect
26. Arabic robe
29. Saltwater lake east of Caspian Sea
30. 66 is one (abbr.)
31. "forbidden of the Holy Ghost to preach the word in ____" (Acts 16:6)
32. Father
33. "____your affection on things above" (Colossians 3:2)
34. The son of Nun (Numbers 13)
35. Goal
36. "Well done,...____thou into the joy of thy lord" (Matthew 25:21)

37. "For unto ____much is given,...shall be much required" (Luke 12:48)
41. Spanish greeting
42. Seven, in Rome
43. Egyptian dancing girl
47. Minor prophet
48. Circle segment
49. "I will not drive them out from before thee in one ____" (Exodus 24:29)
50. One trillion (comb. form)
51. Tennis call
52. "Go to the ____, thou sluggard" (Proverbs 6:6)

DOWN

1. Exclamation of discovery
2. Embezzle
3. "Now the sons of ____were sons of Belial" (1 Samuel 2:12)
4. "thou shalt heap ____of fire on his head" (Romans 12:20)
5. Mine entrance
6. "And Saul called the people to ____David" (1 Samuel 23:8)
7. To provide with
8. "to abound and to suffer ____" (Philippians 4:12)
9. "or shall a nation be born at ____?" (Isaiah 66:8)
10. "For he hath founded it upon the ____" (Psalm 24:2)
12. "the ____is not dead but sleepeth" (Mark 5:39)
19. A son of Bani (Ezra 10)
20. Federal corp. org. in 1933
21. "Call me not Naomi, call me ____" (Ruth 1:20)
22. O.T. bk.
24. Word to describe Miss Muffet

25. Comm. conglom.
26. Tennis great from Richmond, VA
27. Coffin and frame
28. Club for a jump or a tow (abbr.)
30. Dismissal
31. "in the greatness of his folly, he shall go ___" (Proverbs 5:23)
33. Family mem.
34. United
35. The son of Jether, captain of the host of Judah (1 Kings 2)
36. Oust
37. So ___?

38. ___ Office (British government dept.)
39. Swan genus
40. Ireland
44. Cows congregate here
45. Isle of ___
46. Jackie's TV sidekick

PUZZLE 19

ACROSS

1. Pronoun
4. Essential
9. Genetic inits.
12. Wrath
13. ____the Netophathite (Jeremiah 40)
14. "having Bethel on the west, and ___on the east" (Genesis 12:8)
15. "let thy cattle gender with a ___kind" (Leviticus 19:19)
17. "Let us ___before the Lord our maker" (Psalm 95:6)
19. "take thine ___, eat, drink, and be merry" (Luke 12:19)
20. Component of teen's "uniform" (pl.)
21. "The street" on the Left Bank
23. Evangelist's family
26. Prophet who interceded for Judah (2 Chronicles 28)
27. "Claudius commanded all Jews to depart from ___" (Acts 18:2)
28. Saturate in liquid
29. Brit. isl. off Normandy
30. Tumors (KJV)
33. Cathode (abbr.)
34. Santa___
36. Slave
37. Layer
39. "his meat was ___and wild honey" (Matthew 3:4)
41. Belonging to Shakespeare (with "the")
42. Actress Peggy
43. "Jubal, father of all such as handle the ___and organ" (Genesis 4:21)

44. "Otello" is one
46. Those who bring about
49. "the Lord shall ___the bough" (Isaiah 10:33)
50. "O ___, where is thy victory?" (1 Corinthians 15:55)
52. Sup
53. Fine point (abbr.)
54. "___into his gates" (Psalm 100:4)
55. Former Ford model

DOWN

1. "Your life is __with Christ in God" (Colossians 3:3)
2. A son of Bela (1 Chronicles 7)
3. Extreme
4. Usually a sentence from a Bible chapter
5. ____ dixit
6. Article
7. Twelve-step group (abbr.)
8. "who...can be ____unto the Lord?" (Psalm 89:6)
9. Belonging to the son of Zorobabel (Luke 3)
10. Negative vote (var.)
11. Bother
16. Escape
18. Masculine name
20. Bodily swelling
21. Of a limited area
22. Chief of David's captains (2 Samuel 23)
23. "Lazarus, which was laid at his gate full of ___" (Luke 16:20)
24. "Be ye not unequally ____" (2 Corinthians 6:14)
25. Boxes
27. Retires
31. Sermon

40

32. "I will exalt my throne above the
    ___" (Isaiah 14:13)
35. "my servant Job shall pray for
    you: for him will I ___"
    (Job 42:8)
38. A city of Benjamin (Joshua 18)
40. Middle East. rep.
41. Brand well known to hockey
    players
43. "___mercy upon me, O Lord"
    (Psalm 6:2)
44. "For if God...spared not the
    ___world" (2 Peter 2:4-5)
45. American author
46. Siamese
47. Tattle, with "on"
48. Reg.
51. TLC giver

ACROSS
1. A king of Judah (1 Kings 15)
4. Shoshonean
7. __ Aviv
10. Equal to absorption of 100 ergs of energy per gram of material
11. Tribe of prophetess Anna (Luke 2)
12. Contributed
13. "they laid her in an upper ____" (Acts 9:37)
15. "___came I out of my mother's womb" (Job 1:21)
16. Unruly crowds
17. Signal
18. One of the sons of Hothan (1 Chronicles 11)
20. One who prophesies
23. First name in fairy tales
24. "so he bringeth them into their desired ___" (Psalm 107:30)
25. CA metro.
26. Sierra Club concern (abbr., var.)
27. "Let us solace ourselves with ___" (Proverbs 7:18)
28. N.T. bk.
29. Artificial language
30. Belonging to an Indonesian island
31. Descartes
32. Eli's grandson and Phinehas's son (1 Samuel 4)
34. ____ Heights
35. Israeli statesman
36. What to say to a horse
37. "slay me, that men say not...A ___slew him" (Judges 9:54)
39. To walk in a clumsy way

42. "neither ___ you up a standing image" (Leviticus 26:1)
43. "____ Girl," once-popular sitcom
44. Ever (poet.)
45. At a distance (arch.)
46. Grain
47. To be situated

DOWN
1. Circle part
2. Czech distance measure
3. "they made their hearts as an ___ stone" (Zechariah 7:12)
4. "learn to maintain good works for necessary___" (Titus 3:14)
5. Area adjacent to a house (abbr.)
6. Eldest son of Judah (Genesis 38)
7. "She shall be called woman..she was ___out of man" (Genesis 2:23)
8. She played opposite Gale in "Our Miss Brooks"
9. "To him which ___his people through the wilderness" (Psalm 136:16)
11. Father (as God)
12. Actor Macleod
14. Parents
15. Parts of churches
17. "Ye ___of Lamech, hearken unto my speech" (Genesis 4:23)
18. Feminine name
19. Destruction
20. Grandson of Obed
21. Feminine Hispanic name, perhaps
22. "Who provideth for the ___for his food?" (Job 38:41)
24. City of the tribe of Judah (Joshua 15:51)
27. Rebekah's brother (Genesis 24)
28. Give a new name

30. Fictional elephant
31. "I have prepared the house and
    ___for the camels"
    (Genesis 24:3)
33. Son of Joel (1 Chronicles 6)
34. Coastal range of India
36. Journalist's query
37. Dryly humorous
38. Economic org.
39. ___-Na-Na (singing group)
40. Given on May Day in Maui
41. Before (poet.)
43. Preposition

ACROSS

1. Father of Naum (Luke 3:25)
5. Female animal parent
8. "Hath God ___away his people?" (Romans 11:1)
12. "he armed him with a ___of mail" (1 Samuel 17:38)
13. Historic period
14. Author of Proverbs 30
15. Hair groomer
16. Home (abbr.)
17. Son of Melchi (Luke 3:27)
18. Father of Hophni and Phineas (1 Samuel 2)
20. What Peter's friend Simon would do (Acts 10)
22. "For the words are ___up till the end of time" (Daniel 12:9)
25. Book of the Pentateuch
29. "But I will ___far off from the northern army" (Joel 2:20)
30. Eye membrane
31. Popular contraction
32. Muscle spasm
33. Scat!
37. "I have not hastened from being a ___to follow you" (Jeremiah 17:16)
40. "I cry in the daytime,...and in the night___" (Psalm 22:2)
41. A son of Rizpah and Saul (2 Samuel 21, var.)
42. Salaried player (abbr.)
43. Roman 901
44. "the promise is to...all that are ___off" (Acts 2:39)

47. "the Lord hath called by name Bezeleel the son of ___" (Exodus 35:30)
49. Pronoun
53. "I gave Egypt for thy ranson, Ethiopia and ___" (Isaiah 43:3)
54. Arabic letter
55. "Lord, ___mercy on my son" (Matthew 17:15)
56. "ye shall carry up my bones ___with you" (Exodus 13:19)
57. Casual greeting
58. Hied

DOWN

1. O.T. book subtitled "The Preacher" (KJV)
2. Late actor Jack
3. O.T. book
4. "If __ __ __, why am I thus?" (Genesis 25:22)
5. "they shall ___every strong hold" (Habakkuk 1:10)
6. Linking verb
7. "If I be a ___, where is my fear?" (Malachi 1:6)
8. "the heaven of heavens ___contain thee" (1 Kings 8:27)
9. Era
10. Big ___
11. ___glyceride
19. Bk. of the Pentateuch
21. Tool not heard at the site of Solomon's temple (1 Kings 6)
22. Mangers
23. Quay
24. "I am Alpha and ___" (Revelation 1:8)
26. Duplicate
27. Lincoln's lads
28. Holy (Fr.)

34. Fowl not to be eaten
(Leviticus 11)
35. Conjunction
36. Sufficient
37. "The wrath of a king is as...death:
but a wise man will ___ it"
(Proverbs 16:14)
38. "And to whom is the ___of the
Lord revealed?" (Isaiah 53:1)
39. "And he carried away all
Jerusalem...all the...___"
(2 Kings 24:14)
44. Third king of Judah
45. Handful

46. Judicial junta (abbr.)
48. Woman's name
50. "her ___was to light on a...field
belonging to Boaz" (Ruth 2:3)
51. Blvd.
52. "Nightline" nickname

ACROSS

1. Butter unit
4. "with lies ye made the heart of the righteous ___" (Ezekiel 13:22)
7. "Doth he thank that servant...? I ___ not" (Luke 17:9)
11. Naboth couldn't stand in his way
13. Mary Todd's fiance, to friends
14. Luzon native
15. Worry
16. O.T. bk.
17. ___ Hill, "pulpit" of Paul
18. A wife of Esau (Genesis 36)
21. Fabled bear
23. "offer the tenth of a bath out of the___" (Ezekiel 45:14)
24. "he overturneth the mountains by the ___" (Job 28:9)
25. Actor Ayres
26. FDR program
29. Part of cosmetics brand name
30. Two (Sp.)
31. "Jesus went not with his disciples into the ___" (John 6:22)
32. "Arise, take up thy ___" (Matthew 9:6)
33. Period
34. "___ ___ would see Jesus" (John 12:21)
35. Feel poorly
36. "I have graven thee upon the ___of my hands" (Isaiah 49:16)
37. He intercedes with King Zedekiah for Jeremiah (Jeremiah 38, 39)
41. Where coed "crashes"
42. ___de siecle

43. One of Lamech's wives (Genesis 4)
47. Operatic solo
48. Footed vase
49. An unclean "beast" (Leviticus 11)
50. Hebrew letter
51. "The Son of man hath not where to ___his head" (Luke 9:58)
52. Hoover ___

DOWN

1. Type of moccasin
2. Exclamation
3. ___adiddle (Brit., a fib)
4. Reception hall
5. By his action, "he being dead yet speaketh" (Hebrews 11:4)
6. "He disappointeth the ___of the crafty" (Job 5:12)
7. Absalom's sister (2 Samuel 13)
8. 500 sheets of paper
9. Other (Sp.)
10. "___me thoroughly from mine iniquity" (Psalm 51:2)
12. "array thyself with glory and ___" (Job 40:10)
19. Pronoun
20. Early movie star
21. Tree trunk
22. "Whither have ye made a ___today?" (1 Samuel 27:10)
24. "___not the poor" (Proverbs 22:22)
25. Abraham's nephew
26. "Neither was there any ___there-in" (Exodus 16:24)
27. Handles clumsily
28. Chewed
30. "lament with a ___lamentation" (Micah 2:4)

31. Handmaid of Rachel (Genesis 30)
33. Poorly lit
34. Pouch
35. One of the fenced cities of Naphtali (Joshua 19)
36. Woman's nickname
37. "Israel...spread his tend beyond the town of ___" (Genesis 35:21)
38. "His master shall ___his ear through" (Exodus 21:6)
39. Belonging to the head of the Erites
40. What to fork over in Firenze

44. Father
45. A son of Jether (1 Chronicles 7)
46. Search for right word

PUZZLE 23

ACROSS

1. Where to find a franc
5. Fabulous bird of prey
8. An early inhabitant of Moab (Deuteronomy 2)
12. Bread spread
13. I love (Lat.)
14. Mount ___ (ancient peak)
15. "Is the seed yet in the ___?" (Haggai 2:19)
16. Isl. off east coast of Afr.
17. City in Oklahoma
18. "It is of the Lord's mercies that we are __ __" (Lamentations 3:22)
21. ___ache
22. Climbing vine
23. "a time to ___" (Ecclesiastes 3:2)
26. King of Judah
27. Eur. country
30. "Thou shalt not approach to his wife: she is thine___" (Leviticus 18:14)
31. ___ hill
32. "And the ___was upon the earth forty days and forty nights" (Genesis 7:12)
33. To cause to become (suffix)
34. Wt. meas.
35. Weird
36. Swiss river
37. Ref. book
38. "because his ___fail not" (Lamentations 3:22)
43. Extinct creature
44. Cut with an ax
45. Promises
47. Danish measure
48. Excerpts may have been (abbr.)
49. Bibliog.
50. Male deer
51. Can
52. "yet he abideth faithful: he cannot ___himself" (2 Timothy 2:13)

DOWN

1. Haircut style
2. Actor Hale
3. Roman emperor who reigned from 54-68 A.D.
4. "be ___with your wages" (Luke 3:14)
5. "there shall no ___come upon his head" (1 Samuel 1:11)
6. Gulf of ___
7. "he is before all things, and by him all things ___" (Colossians 1:17)
8. "Haman the Jews' ___" (Esther 8:1)
9. Word written on the wall (Daniel 5)
10. In the same place (Lat.)
11. Quant's clothes
19. Pet
20. Southern univ.
23. Hadad's city (1 Chronicles 1)
24. Later became Bethel (Genesis 28)
25. One (Scot.)
26. Years (Fr.)
27. ___ East
28. Roman tot's age
29. Direction
31. "___believed God" (James 2:23)
32. "But the high places were not ___" (1 Kings 15:14)
34. "The lot is cast into the ___" (Proverbs 16:13)

35. "as she continued praying...
    ___marked her mouth"
    (1 Samuel 1:12)
36. Preposition
37. Equally clever
38. "ye shall find a ___whereon
    never man sat" (Mark 11:2)
39. Auditoriums
40. "The kings of Sheba and ___shall
    offer gifts" (Psalm 72:10)
41. Observe
42. Fowl not to be eaten
    (Deuteronomy 14)
43. German article

46. Roguish

ACROSS

1. Fowl that is unclean (Deuteronomy 14)
4. Baby food
7. "faith, ____, and charity" (1 Corinthians 13:13)
11. College grad
13. Patriotic inits.
14. Zest
15. "casting all your __upon him" (1 Peter 5:7)
16. Kin (abbr.)
17. Dodecanese island
18. "Fear God. Honour the ___" (1 Peter 2:17)
19. "The Lord make his face shine upon thee, and be____unto thee" (Numbers 6:25)
21. Wrath
23. West. state
24. "let thy servant ___instead of the lad" (Genesis 44:33)
27. Abraham's second wife (Genesis 25)
32. Kept from falling
33. ___-a-vis
34. Blue ___
35. "we were ___of God to be put in trust with the gospel" (1 Thessalonians 2:4)
37. "and ___the anger of the Lord was kindled against Israel" (Proverbs 17:1)
38. Article
39. Aunt's mate in Matanzas
40. "they will not endure sound___" (2 Timothy 4:3)
45. Dew ____

49. "next to them builded Zaccur, the son of ___" (Nehemiah 3:2)
50. Weep
51. Feminine name
52. "The earth shall ___to and fro" (Isaiah 24:20)
53. __ __ limb
54. Tale
55. "be like a ___planted by the rivers ofwaters" (Psalm 1:3)
56. He follows Ezra (abbr.)
57. King____, Clavell work

DOWN

1. ___ court
2. Turkish regiment
3. "And Naomi said, ___ again my daughters" (Ruth 1:11)
4. "___me with hyssop" (Psalm 51:7)
5. Tribe of Israel (var., Luke 2)
6. "Peace...within thy walls, and prosperity within thy ___" (Psalm 122:7)
7. Radiant (comb. form)
8. Tastes like butter
9. Butterfly fish
10. Son of Seth (Genesis 5)
12. Where Ahaziah and Josiah were slain (2 Kings 9, 23)
20. Tractor
22. Back (prefix)
24. Exclamation of surprise
25. ____ canto
26. "Love worketh no ___" (Romans 13:10)
27. Leather
28. "the floods of____men made me afraid" (2 Samuel 22:5)
29. Stream
30. Feminine nickname

31. "as a ___gathereth her chicks
under her wings"
(Matthew 23:37)
33. Prepared by Esau (Genesis 25)
36. "And there was ___in heaven"
(Revelation 12:7)
37. Achan's sin caused defeat at this
city (Joshua 7)
39. Son of Nahor and Reumah
(Genesis 22)
40. Bane of Mr. Clean
41. "according to his eating, an
___for every man"
(Exodus 16:16)

42. Canadian Indian tribe
43. Playing piece
44. "___other name under heaven"
(Acts 4:12)
46. "the young lions ___after their
prey" (Psalm 104:21)
47. Extra (Scot.)
48. "that ___after the dust of the
earth" (Amos 2:7)

ACROSS

1. "Whomsoever I shall ___, that...is he" (Matthew 26:48)
5. Paging device
7. "Let me go and __my vow" (2 Samuel 15:7)
8. Property claim
10. Fire
11. "one____destroyeth much good" (Ecclesiastes 9:18)
13. Admirer
14. Window part
15. Part of Chaldea (Ezekiel 23)
17. "And she coming in that ___gave thanks" (Luke 2:38)
19. "But as many as received him, gave he ___ " (John 1:12)
21. Artificial language
22. Pronoun
23. City of Judah built by Benjamin's descendants (1 Chronicles 8)
24. East. state
25. "it is better for thee to ___into life maimed" (Mark 9:43)
27. Insane
29. Below normal
30. "___up the mighty men" (Joel 3:9)
31. Stadium sound
32. "___of false prophets" (Matthew 7:15)
34. Banking (abbr.)
35. ___of Solomon
36. Disciple of Paul (abbr.)
37. Idyllic
39. Theatre notices (abbr.)

DOWN

1. "to him was given the ___to the bottomless pit" (Revelation 9:1)
2. Common (Lat., abbr.)
3. To hold in place
4. River of northern France
5. Prohibit
6. New birth (abbr.)
7. "thou shalt make his __to receive his ashes" (Exodus 27:3)
9. Among the remnant of returning Levites (Ezra 2:48)
10. Basic principles
11. Without (Fr.)
12. Tiff
13. "gold tried in the ___ " (Revelation 3:18)
14. "they sold...the poor for a ___of shoes" (Amos 2:6)
16. Antenna
18. Another name for the city of No
19. Corn____
20. Far from destitute
23. Gospel writer
26. Large basin
27. More grand
28. London transporation
30. Shoots of a tree
33. "___unto us! Who shall deliver us?" (1 Samuel 4:8)
34. Found in a pencil case
36. It is (poet.)
38. Japanese drama (var.)

ACROSS

1. Chicago time, perhaps (abbr.)
4. Jeanne et al.
8. Chinese seal
12. "Eat not of it ___, nor sodden" (Exodus 12:9)
13. Kilmer subject
14. ___ worship
15. Daughter of Cadmus (myth.)
16. Mrs. Chaplin
17. Encourage
18. "grown fat as the heifer at grass, and ___as bulls" (Jeremiah 50:11)
20. "We do not ___ after the flesh" (2 Corinthians 10:3)
22. Slippery one
23. "the calf, the young lion, and the ___together" (Isaiah 11:6)
27. City in Judah (Joshua 15:52)
29. Jobs education act (abbr.)
30. New (prefix)
31. Cleveland player (abbr.)
32. Sounded like a cow
33. "an hollow place...in the ___, and there came water" (Judges 15:19)
34. Knot
35. Preposition
36. "all ___to dust again" (Ecclesiastes 3:20)
37. "The Lord shall reign for ever ___ ___" (Exodus 15:18)
39. "cast off their clothes and threw dust into the ___" (Acts 22:23)
40. Son of (Heb.)
41. "under his tongue is mischief and ___" (Psalm 10:7)

44. "Moab shall howl over ___" (Isaiah 15:2)
47. Winglike
49. Surprise!
50. Of the family of the Eranites (Numbers 26:36)
51. Infamous emperor
52. Grecian ___
53. "But whosoever shall ___ me before men" (Matthew 10:33
54. Between 12 and 20
55. Turf

DOWN

1. "Where no oxen are, the ___is clean" (Proverbs 14:4)
2. Hamlet was one
3. "to open before him the ___ ___ gates" (Isaiah 45:1)
4. "let us set for him there a bed, a table and a ___" (2 Kings 4:10)
5. Believe (arch.)
6. Evening (poet.)
7. Found in the Caspian (2 words)
8. Peasant
9. Pronoun
10. Assn.
11. "The Raven" writer
19. Mideast country (abbr.)
21. "And they came to the threshing-floor of ___, which is beyond Jordan" (Genesis 50:10)
23. Less than
24. "Who was before a blasphemer, and a persecutor, and ___" (1 Timothy 1:13)
25. "for my salvation is ___to come" (Isaiah 56:1)
26. Ball ___
27. Collection of writings (scient.)
28. Pour

29. "he is the mediator of a better ___" (Hebrews 8:6)
32. "___worketh no ill to his neighbor" (Romans 13:10)
36. ___ ear
38. "they brought thee for a present horns of ivory and ___" (Ezekiel 27:15)
39. Brother of Moses
41. Weasel
42. Straight ahead (var., poet.)
43. Farther (arch.)
44. Masculine name
45. Sooner than (poet.)
46. Outlaw
48. Light-horse Harry ___

PUZZLE 27

ACROSS

1. Word for Scrooge
4. Toothed wheel
8. "Ye shall not ___ of it" (Genesis 3:5)
11. Son of Hur, father of Bezaleel (Exodus 38)
12. "the scapegoat, shall be presented ___before the Lord" (Leviticus 16:10)
13. Ginger ___
14. Grandson of Lois, son of Eunice (abbr.)
15. Belonging to (suffix)
16. Israeli leader
18. "a measure of fine flour be ___for a shekel" (2 Kings 7:1)
20. "planted in a good ___by great waters" (Ezekiel 17:8)
21. ___ culpa
22. "Who hath...given us the ___of the Spirit" (2 Corinthians 1:22)
25. Ego
26. Dress style
27. Pronoun
28. Something Sandy says
29. Bridle part
30. Brother of Japheth (Genesis 6)
31. Editor's (abbr.)
32. Bathsheba's husband
34. "In ___was there a voice heard" (Matthew 2:18)
35. "on my ___is the shadow of death" (Job 16:16)
37. Shoshonean
38. Demolish (Brit.)
39. Sup
41. "that no man should ___us in this abundance" (2 Corinthians 8:20)
43. Author Harper
44. "The beams...are cedar, and our rafters are ___" (Song of Solomon 1:17)
47. Like dialing 911
48. Turn over
50. Indian shell currency
51. "Stand in __and sin not" (Psalm 4:4)
52. "To him that is afflicted ___should be showed" (Job 6:14)
53. "For God hath heard the voice of the __where he is" (Genesis 21:17)

DOWN

1. Except
2. Uris protagonist
3. "A man that hath friends must show ___friendly" (Proverbs 18:24)
4. "Let us be ___and rejoice" (Revelation 19:7)
5. Chemical suffix
6. Certain school equipment (abbr.)
7. One who's been saved by Jesus Christ
8. "As an ___stirreth up her nest" (Deuteronomy 32:11)
9. Famed pugilist
10. "And Joseph's ___ brethren went down to...Egypt" (Genesis 42:3)
12. Feel much less than 100 percent
17. One (Ger.)
19. Clumsy one
20. Spoke (KJV)
21. "for his ___endureth forever" (Psalm 136:1)
22. "Others said, That it is ___" (Mark 6:15)
23. "they were counted worthy to suffer ___for his name" (Acts 5:41)

24. "inhabitants of the land of
    ___brought water to him"
    (Isaiah 21:14)
25. White ___
26. "let every man...___with God"
    (1 Corinthians 7:24)
30. "a cage of every unclean and
    ___bird" (Revelation 18:2)
32. A son of Peresh (1 Chronicles 7)
33. "___ ___ and get you from among
    my people" (Exodus 12:31)
34. "For the eyes of the Lord ___to
    and fro" (2 Chronicles 16:8)
36. Expunge

39. "Lest I be full and ___thee"
    (Proverbs 30:9)
40. Past tense (suffix)
41. Org. for young men
42. American founder of Girl Scouts
43. Tennis call
45. Longshoreman's org.
46. "Thy ___and thy staff"
    (Psalm 23:4)
49. Greek letter

ACROSS

1. "That as ___hath reigned unto death" (Romans 5:21)
4. "a ___of dove's dung" (2 Kings 6:25)
7. Poses
11. Formerly Mesopotamia
13. Swedish coin
14. Verve
15. Forbidden
16. Feminine name
17. Abnormal breathing sound
18. "Not with ____, as menpleasers" (Ephesians 6:6)
21. "It shall be in thy mouth sweet as ___" (Revelation 10:9)
23. Opponent
24. Houses of finance in LeHavre
25. To extend
26. Athlete Thorpe
29. Valley of ___ (in Judea)
30. Becoming slower, in music (abbr.)
31. Italian seaport on the Adriatic
32. Around 2000 pounds
33. "When I remember thee upon my ___" (Psalm 63:6)
34. "The ___of Ethiopia shall not equal it" (Job 28:19)
35. Owns
36. Pulled behind
37. "Now I had not been ____sad in his presence" (Nehemiah 2:1)
41. A son of Eliphaz (Genesis 36)
42. Spoil
43. ___ duck
47. "burned the bones of the king of Edom into ___" (Amos 2:1)
48. Not paid (abbr.)
49. "garment was white as ___" (Daniel 7:9)
50. Prince of the Midianites (Judges 7)
51. Summer on the Seine
52. Ascot is one

DOWN

1. "___ still, my daughter" (Ruth 3:18)
2. "And ___also the Jairite was a chief ruler about David" (2 Samuel 20:26)
3. Catch
4. ___ Island
5. Belonging to a son of Jether (1 Chronicles 7)
6. "they are faithful...partakers of the ___" (1 Timothy 6:2)
7. "Henceforth we should not ___ sin" (Romans 6:6)
8. ___the Ahoite (1 Chronicles 11:29)
9. Powder
10. Large knife
12. "that thou ___not the light of Israel" (2 Samuel 21:17)
19. "our message to you is not '___'" (2 Corinthians 1:18)
20. Fish eggs
21. Angel adjunct
22. Brother of Er (Genesis 38)
24. Hunch
25. Cover
26. To joke
27. Grandson of Cain, son of Enoch
28. Feminine form of address (southern dial.)
30. "Will he ___his anger forever?" (Jeremiah 3:5)

31. Inner parts
33. "Shut the doors and ___ them" (Nehemiah 7:3)
34. Male cat
35. Mount where children of Israel removed their ornaments (Exodus 33)
36. "And Pilate wrote a ___, and put it on the cross" (John 19:19)
37. Machete
38. Arab ruler
39. "they spread abroad his ___" (Matthew 9:31)
40. Horn honk

44. "Go to the ___, thou sluggard" (Proverbs 6:6)
45. Pronoun (Fr.)
46. "what mean these seven ___lambs which thou hast set by themselves?" (Genesis 21:29)

ACROSS:
1. I'm all ___
5. "Ahasuerus sat on the throne...in Shushan the ___" (Esther 1:2)
7. "the name of the wicked shall ___" (Proverbs 10:7)
8. "And Judas begat Phares and ___of Thamar" (Matthew 1:3)
10. "And the first came out ___all over" (Genesis 25:25)
11. Hermits
13. The Great ___
14. Of a city of David, near Mt. Carmel
15. Festival (comb. form)
17. "___the horses; and get up" (Jeremiah 46:4)
19. "If ye fulfil the ___law according to the scripture" (James 2:8)
21. A bone (abbr.)
22. Of a town that encountered Joshua's men, slaying 36 (Joshua 7)
23. Actor Chaney
24. Cause to become (suffix)
25. "a ___shall compass a man" (Jeremiah 31:22)
27. "To ___such an one unto Satan" (1 Corinthians 5:5)
29. U.S. troops were here (colloq.)
30. "thou shalt bruise his ___" (Genesis 3:15)
31. ___de la Cite (Paris site)
32. The healing ___of Bethesda
34. "they ___ away as an eagle toward heaven" (Proverbs 23:5)
35. Purple seaweed
36. Vowel trio
37. Take baby steps

39. New ___

DOWN:
1. Greasy spoon sign, maybe
2. Southern state (abbr.)
3. Straight and safety are two
4. Looks over quickly
5. Seed vessel
6. Before (poet.)
7. "Go up, ___an altar unto the Lord" (2 Samuel 24:18)
9. Son of Saul and Rizpah (2 Samuel 21)
10. "Come now, let us ___together" (Isaiah 1:18)
11. "for now there shall be no ___of any man's life" (Acts 27:21)
12. Allege
13. "With the pure thou wilt ___thyself pure" (2 Samuel 2:27)
14. Your (Ger.)
16. "Then shalt thou walk in thy way ___" (Proverbs 3:23)
18. "none of them [lepers] was cleansed, saving ___the Syrian" (Luke 4:27)
19. "And Joshua said, ___great stones upon ...the cave" (Joshua 10:18)
20. Ancient instrument
23. Sheltered places
26. One stomach of a cow, e.g.
27. "they shall ___every strong hold" (Habakkuk 1:10)
28. "For the ___person will speak villany" (Isaiah 32:6)
30. ___the Great, king of Judea
33. Small child
34. Enemy
36. Under the weather
38. Yes (Russ.)

ACROSS
1. Not a gentleman
4. Title
7. A luxury hotel may have one
10. Mature
11. Anger
12. "He maketh them also to___like a calf" (Psalm 29:6)
13. "his ___ ___ ___ as the sun" (Matthew 17:2)
16. "of Eri, the family of the ___" (Numbers 26:16)
17. Brother of Shem (Genesis 5)
18. Sounds at a library (var.)
19. "And ye shall ___the city" (Joshua 6:3)
23. Asa's father (Matthew 1)
25. "The ___of the mighty men are broken" (1 Samuel 2:4)
26. Environmental gp.
27. "the ___shall not give her light" (Matthew 24:29)
28. Dined
29. "Which in other ___was not made known" (Ephesians 3:5)
30. Sea eagle
31. ___ Rabbit
32. To counsel
33. Farmers of the Old West
35. Droves of docs belong (abbr.)
36. Summer cooler
37. Belonging to Miss Dunne
40. "This is ___ ___ ___ in whom I am well pleased" (Matthew 17:5)
43. Pigeon peeps
44. Worth (abbr.)
45. Direction
46. Coward
47. A head of the family of Gad (1 Chronicles 5)
48. Chemical (suffix)

DOWN
1. ___ au lait
2. Product made from seaweed
3. Judgments
4. Take ___
5. Spring flower
6. "Feed me...with that same ___pottage" (Genesis 25:30)
7. Be sparing
8. "And she [Delilah] fastened it with the ___" (Judges 16:14)
9. Mimic
12. Pillow covers
14. "For he was wiser than all the men; than ___the Ezrahite" (1 Kings 4:31)
15. "there shall be an overflowing ___" (Ezekiel 13:11)
19. Sheds for fowl
20. Arm of the Mediterranean between Greece and Turkey
21. Tore
22. Publisher's request (abbr.)
23. So be it
24. Drilled
25. "but a handful of meal in a ___" (1 Kings 17:12)
29. Prepared for a struggle
31. Belonging to an English theologian
34. Barak's destination: Mt._____ (Judges 4)
35. One of the seven sons of Gad (Genesis 46)
37. "Where are the gods of Sepharvaim, Hena, and ___?" (2 Kings 18:34)

38. Ages and ages
39. Large knife
40. 1200 in Rome
41. Pronoun
42. Egg (pl.)

PUZZLE 31

ACROSS

1. "In those days there was no ___ in Israel" (Judges 17:6)
5. Greek letter
8. A child of Dishan (Genesis 36)
12. Construction item
13. Evening (poet.)
14. "see, O Lord, for I am become ___" (Lamentations 1:11)
15. ___ -tasse
16. Prepare flax
17. Son of Eliphaz (Genesis 36)
18. "mercy and truth unto such as keep his ___" (Psalm 25:10)
21. Dinky in Dogpatch
22. Where Cain dwelt (Genesis 4)
23. "Your remembrances are like unto ___" (Job 13:12)
26. "they hunt every man his brother with a ___" (Micah 7:2)
27. Beverage
30. Pay attention
31. Certain engineers (abbr.)
32. "thy ___ and thy she goats have not cast their young" (Genesis 31:38)
33. Swiss river
34. "these things must first come... but the ___ is not by and by (Luke 21:9)
35. "___ was translated that he should not see death" (Hebrews 11:5)
36. Mouths
37. Mil. rank
38. "And David perceived that the Lord had ___ him king over Israel" (2 Samuel 5:12)
43. City in SW England
44. "which god that cannot ___ promised" (Titus 1:2)
45. City in southern Judah (Joshua 15)
47. "It's ___ ___ to tell a lie"
48. Sup
49. Intense star
50. Father of Salathiel (Luke 3)
51. "my flesh longeth for thee in a ___ and thirsty land" (Psalm 63:1)
52. Ivan was one

DOWN

1. "One ___ of the goats for a sin offering" (Numbers 7:34)
2. Composer Stravinsky
3. City in W. Alaska
4. "the cattle were ringstreaked, speckled, and ___" (Genesis 31:10)
5. "Who shall separate us from the love of Christ? shall... ___" (Romans 8:35)
6. Appear
7. Chants
8. "unlearned questions ___" (2 Timothy 2:23)
9. Hoarfrost
10. Exclamation of regret
11. The father of Abner (1 Samuel 14)
19. Famous Dickens line: "___ a far, far better thing I do"
20. Slangy negative
23. "they opened their mouth against me and said ___" (Psalm 35:21)
24. Red or Dead is one
25. Pronoun
26. Masculine name
27. Number of Naomi's daughters-in-law

28. European financial concern (abbr.)
29. "he planteth an ___and the rain doth nourish it" (Isaiah 44:14)
31. "I thank Christ Jesus the Lord who hath ___me" (1 Timothy 1:2)
32. Delight
34. Historical period
35. From (prefix, pl.)
36. First son of Shemaiah (1 Chronicles 26)
37. "learn first to show ___at home" (1 Timothy 5:4)

38. "And among these nations thou shalt find no ___" (Deuteronomy 28:65)
39. Awake
40. "for he is a ___and the father of it" (John 8:44)
41. Son of Seth (Genesis 5)
42. Opera star
43. Outlaw
46. Spoil

PUZZLE 32

ACROSS

1. Hook on a pole
5. "___of the leaven of the Pharisees" (Mark 8:15)
7. Marsh
8. Hawaiian isle (abbr.)
10. Swiss river
11. "The ___pot is for silver" (Proverbs 17:3)
13. Father of Bezaleel (Exodus 35:30)
14. Common contraction
15. "___I will bring one plague more" (Exodus 11:1)
17. "he that sat was to look upon like a jasper and a ___ stone" (Revelation 4:3)
19. "they laughed them to ___and mocked them" (2 Chronicles 30:10)
21. Judah's firstborn (Genesis 38)
22. Superlative ending
23. Japanese drama
24. One (Scot.)
25. Mother of Isaac
27. Country between Israel and Judah
29. Not yet a state (abbr.)
30. Final outcome
31. Banking (abbr.)
32. "And Solomon had forty thousand ___of horses" (1 Kings 4:26)
34. ___ Alamos
36. Opera company, informally
37. "And they shall ___him in an hundred shekels of silver" (Deuteronomy 22:19)
39. Another name for Esau (Genesis 25)

DOWN

1. Bible bk. with 50 chapters
2. Word of disgust
3. "not a ___of bread...but of hearing the word of the Lord" (Amos 8:11)
4. Where the battle rages
5. Atlantic isle (abbr.)
6. He took Samuel under his wing
7. "she was a woman of ___counte-nance" (2 Samuel 14:27)
9. A sweet spice mentioned in Exodus 30
10. Mountain in E. Turkey
11. Baptismal basin
12. Earth (comb. form)
13. "learn to maintain good works for necessary ___" (Titus 3:14)
14. "Bring a ___to share" (church supper request?)
16. Rears
18. "there should be great ___through-out all the world" (Acts 11:28)
19. A few
20. Tidy
23. Acrobats from India
26. Grad student's task
27. "For every one shall be ___with fire" (Mark 9:49)
28. "faithful children not accused of ___or unruly" (Titus 1:6)
30. "the angel of the Lord ascended in the ___of the altar" (Judges 13:20)
33. Candlenut tree fiber
34. Actress Merriwether
36. 1900, to Tiberias
38. Artificial language

ACROSS

1. Of an enzyme (suffix)
4. Huge bird of prey
7. "But I beseech you, that I may not be ___" (2 Corinthians 10:2)
11. Used to make powder
13. "Why make ye this __ and weep?" (Mark 5:39)
14. "all they which dwelt in ___heard the word" (Acts 16:6)
15. Old-fashioned feminine name
16. Torah tome (abbr.)
17. Malicious look
18. "for he that is now called a Prophet was...called a ___" (1 Samuel 9:9)
19. "as for the beauty of his ___he set it in majesty" (Ezekiel 7:20)
21. A very long time (abbr.)
23. Yr. in school
24. "The ungodly are...like the ___which the wind driveth away" (Psalm 1:4)
27. "I shall not die, but live, and ___the works of the Lord" (Psalm 118:17)
32. Hawaiian island
33. U.S. currency (abbr.)
34. Shortly (arch.)
35. You may meet one outside a stadium
37. ____ the course (pl.)
38. A necessity in Aug.?
39. Body of water (Fr.)
40. "And he dwelleth in ___ cities" (Job 15:18)
45. "My Old Kentucky ___"
49. Scent
50. "___though I walk through the valley" (Psalm 23:4)
51. An early inhabitant of Moab (Deuteronomy 2)
52. Former senator from Kansas
53. If human, one does
54. Feminine nickname
55. Sign
56. Son of Jacob
57. Prepare flax

DOWN

1. To become (suffix, pl.)
2. White ___
3. French pronoun
4. Gaseous element
5. Central European river
6. "And Saul asked ___ of God" (1 Samuel 14:37)
7. "Is there no ___ in Gilead?" (Jeremiah 8:22)
8. "in ___, I will call them my people" (Romans 9:25)
9. Right to ownership
10. "Till a __ strike through his liver" (Proverbs 7:23)
12. "Be ___ for nothing" (Philippians 4:6)
20. Circle part
22. Preposition
24. Aka Romaine (lettuce)
25. Horse for hire (var.)
26. Exclamation of surprise
27. Manasseh's children dwelt here (1 Chronicles 7:29)
28. "whose shoe's ____I am not worthy to unloose" (John 1:27)
29. Collection of anecdotes
30. Rogers
31. Printer's measures

33. "I will raise up the ___ places thereof" (Isaiah 44:26)
36. Chum
37. Continent (abbr.)
39. "That thou mayest ___to fear the Lord" (Deuteronomy 14:23)
40. "after him was Eleazar the son of ___" (2 Samuel 23:9)
41. The land of Esau
42. Only
43. A son of Jerameel (1 Chronicles 2:25)
44. One trillion (comb. form)
46. Ancient Hebrew dry measure

47. "I sink deep in ___" (Psalm 69:2)
48. Discharge

ACROSS

1. "Arise, lift up the ___, and hold him in thine hand" (Genesis 21:18)
4. Downcast
7. Editor's mark
11. King who was punished for sparing Ben-hadad (1 Kings 20)
13. Color
14. And others (Lat.)
15. Ease off
16. Jeanne d'___
17. "Be of good cheer: __ __ I" (Mark 6:50)
18. "Lest ye corrupt yourselves, and make you...the ___of any figure" (Deuteronomy 4:16)
21. "let every man, wherein he is called, therein ___with God" (1 Corinthians 7:24)
23. Without limit
24. "the people did ___with Moses" (Exodus 17:2)
25. ___-la-la
26. "___and eat of my venison" (Genesis 27:19)
29. "with what measure ye ___, it shall be measured unto you" (Mark 4:24)
30. "Who changed the truth of God into a ___" (Romans 1:25)
31. "there shall the vultures be gathered, every one with its ___" (Isaiah 34:15)
32. German currency (abbr., pl.)
33. Bog
34. Jesus encounters "a woman ___ in adultery" (John 8)
35. Small amount
36. "Ye are my brethren...my ___" (2 Samuel 19:12)
37. "O faithless and perverse ___" (Matthew 17:17)
41. Region comprising Spain and Portugal (abbr.)
42. Feminine name
43. Among Bo-peep's flock
47. Kingdom near Sheba
48. "when I am ___and greyheaded" (Psalm 71:18)
49. "the ___is not to the swift" (Ecclesiastes 9:11)
50. Ancient city in Asia Minor
51. Bible translation (abbr.)
52. Part of stringed instrument

DOWN

1. "On these two commandments hang all the ___" (Matthew 22:40)
2. Expression of discovery
3. Son of Bilhah and Jacob (Genesis 30)
4. "they were counted worthy to suffer ___for his name" (Acts 5:41)
5. Ear (comb. form)
6. "that which I have seen I will ___" (Job 15:17)
7. Divinity
8. "__ __, Brute!"
9. "we know not where they have ___ him" (John 20:2)
10. Ultimatum word
12. "the Lord he is God; there is none else ___ him" (Deuteronomy 4:35)
19. Chemical suffix
20. Actress Claire
21. Attention, please!

22. Scraps
24. Military post (abbr.)
25. "purge away thy dross, and take away thy ___" (Isaiah 1:25)
26. Purpose
27. Residents (suffix)
28. "Peradventure ___ shall be found there...I will not destroy it" (Genesis 18:32)
30. "let fire...devour the cedars of ___" (Judges 9:15)
31. Behavior
33. "___ be it from me!"
34. Also

35. Disorder (arch.)
36. Bandages
37. Essence
38. Father of Peleg and Joktan (Genesis 10)
39. "Woe unto ___! for it is spoiled" (Jeremiah 48:1)
40. Currency of Western Samoa
44. Pale
45. Five-franc piece
46. Game, ___, match

ACROSS

1. "ye that ___God give audience" (Acts 14:1)
5. What God took from Adam
8. "God saw ___ it was good" (Genesis 1:26)
12. This (Sp.)
13. Before (poet.)
14. "lest he ___ thee to the judge" (Luke 12:58)
15. "the Lord hath ___ of him" (Luke 19:31)
16. Oolong is one
17. Mature
18. Naval agency (abbr.)
20. Place of rejuvenation
22. "A soft ___ turneth away wrath" (Proverbs 15:1)
25. "And the desolate land shall be ___" (Ezekiel 36:34)
29. "He went to ___and begged the body of Jesus" (Matthew 27:58)
30. "Samuel came; and Saul went out...that he might ___ him" (1 Samuel 13:10)
31. Title of respect in Turkey
32. Guevara
33. "To ___his son in me" (Galatians 1:16)
37. "And he ___ up the pillars before the temple" (2 Chronicles 3:17)
40. Clef
41. "Be not among...riotous ___ of flesh" (Proverbs 23:20)
42. To arrange, with "up"
43. Union is one (abbr.)

44. "Bel boweth down, ___ stoopeth, their were upon the beasts" (Isaiah 46:1)
47. Roman toddler's age
49. "it is a ___ thing that the king requireth" (Daniel 2:11)
53. Norse mythological figure
54. Belonging to Peleg's son, who revoltedagainst Moses (Numbers 16:1)
55. Word in title of Christmas carol
56. Civil War soldiers, familiarly
57. "Elias is come already, and they knew him ___" (Matthew 17:12)
58. Iron-containing pigment of hemo-globin

DOWN

1. Swamp
2. Direction
3. Enjoyed a repast
4. Bohemian dance
5. "___ye from him, that he may be smitten and die" (2 Samuel 11:15)
6. Wrath
7. "That which was torn of ___I brought not" (Genesis 31:39)
8. To enslave
9. "And he went...where his tent had been at the beginning, between Bethel and ___" (Genesis 13:3)
10. Swiss mountain
11. Summer shirt
19. Hair ___
21. Swedish feminine name
22. "And the land shall mourn, every family ___" (Zechariah 12:12)
23. "Simeon that was called ___" (Acts 13:1)
24. ___ driver

26. "not greedy of filthy ___"
(1 Timothy 3:3)
27. City in Judah allotted to the tribe
of Simeon (Joshua 15)
28. "I will recompense them according to their ___"
(Jeremiah 25:14)
34. Belonging to a city near
Jerusalem (var.)
35. ___ Baba
36. "My name is ___: for we are
many" (Mark 5:9)
37. "___the devil and he will flee"
(James 4:7)

38. "thou shalt not __ of it"
(Genesis 2:17)
39. Mother of Onam (1 Chronicles 2)
44. Conjunction
45. Netherlands city
46. Lettuce variety
48. Daughter of Cadmus
50. "Stand in __, and sin not"
(Psalm 4:4)
51. Drive into
52. "when thine __is single, the
whole body is full of light"
(Luke 11:34)

ACROSS

1. Secular
5. Minor prophet (abbr.)
8. Feminine name
12. Chorus part
13. Historical period
14. Ancient Hebrew dry measure
15. British gun
16. N.T. bk.
17. "He lieth in ___ secretly" (Psalm 10:9)
18. "Let now the_____, the stargaz-ers...save thee from these things" (Isaiah 47:13)
21. "whose ___is destruction" (Philippians 3:19)
22. Former Middle East nation (abbr.)
23. "the ___ of hell gat hold upon me" (Psalm 116:3)
26. War ___
27. Washington bigwig (abbr.)
30. To sanction
31. How a coquette acts
32. "A sword is upon liars, and they shall ___" (Jeremiah 50:36)
33. ___ paper
34. Pol ___, Cambodian dictator
35. Country girl (arch.)
36. Years and years
37. Buddy
38. "let us wait on our ___: or he that teacheth, on teaching" (Romans 12:7)
43. "it was ordained by angels in the __ of a mediator" (Galatians 3:19)
44. Member of NATO
45. Ultra
47. Preposition
48. Family of Jewish patriots (abbr.)
49. Father of Peleg and Joktan (Genesis 10)
50. "And Balak brought Balaam unto the top of ___" (Numbers 23:28)
51. Before (poet.)
52. Belonging to Dale's "pard"

DOWN

1. ___ Cruces, NM
2. Canadian province (abbr.)
3. Inhabitants (suffix)
4. "be ___ with such things as ye have" (Hebrews 13:5)
5. "for ___ will seek the young child to destroy him" (Matthew 2:13)
6. First name of pitching great
7. "And make me ___ meat such as I love" (Genesis 27:4)
8. Farther down
9. Second son of Eliphaz (Genesis 36)
10. Made in the Aloha State
11. Linkletter
19. Hospital employees (abbr.)
20. Enola ___
23. Butter serving
24. Lots of lawyers belong (abbr.)
25. Comparative suffix
26. Fold-up bed
27. ___ of man
28. Relative of et al.
29. O.T. bk.
31. "I will utterly ___ all things off the land" (Zephaniah 1:2)
32. "___us from evil" (Matthew 6:13)
34. Hawaiian luau dish

35. "And there was ___ in heaven" (Revelation 12:7)

36. "there is a woman that hath a familiar spirit at ___" (1 Samuel 28:7)

37. "If thou hadst known...the things which belong unto thy ___!" (Luke 19:42)

38. Horse hair

39. Preposition

40. Nicholas was one

41. Mount not too far from Moab

42. "The beauty of old men is the ___ head" (Proverbs 20:29)

43. "And he smote them ___ and thigh" (Judges 15:8)

46. Time periods (abbr.)

ACROSS

1. Stylish
5. Patriotic women (abbr.)
8. Island group of Indonesia
12. Signature
13. Mother of all living (Genesis 3)
14. Third son of Leah and Jacob
15. Shortly
16. Brand-name item for student
17. "For now should I have ___ still and been quiet" (Job 3:13)
18. "To know wisdom and instruction; to ____ the _____ of understanding" (Proverbs 1:2)
21. "So Manasseh made...the inhabitants of Jerusalem to___" (2 Chronicles 33:9)
22. Charged atom
23. Home of the Louvre
26. Res.
27. Fam. member
30. Descended
31. "To him that overcometh will I grant to ___ with me in my throne" (Revelation 3:21)
32. Promote
33. ____ Sea
34. Seasoning in Strasbourg
35. "Master, the multitude throng...and ___ thee" (Luke 8:45)
36. Day (Sp.)
37. Greek letter
38. Intelligence
45. Appear
46. Hockey great
47. At all
48. Grapevine disease

49. Saul's uncle (1 Samuel 14)
50. Church area
51. Depots (abbr.)
52. "____ King," children's TV show of years past
53. A spell of warm weather

DOWN

1. "the trees of the field shall ___ theirhands" (Isaiah 55:12)
2. Sharpen
3. Stravinsky
4. "The rich man's wealth is...an high wall in his own ___" (Proverbs 18:11)
5. "And the border went up toward ___" (Joshua 15:7) N. border of Judah
6. Tel ___
7. "Matthew sitting at the ___ of custom" (Matthew 9:9)
8. "And their coast was from Heleph from___" (Joshua 19:33) Naphtali's land
9. "neither ___ you up a standing image" (Leviticus 26:1)
10. Roman poet
11. German article (pl.)
19. Belonging to Judah's first son
20. "as for Moses...we ___ not what has become of him" (Acts 7:40)
23. Standard
24. Ginger ___
25. Free
26. Feel under the weather
27. "for ye tithe mint and ___" (Luke 11:42)
28. Curve
29. Indicating one hand (abbr., pl.)
31. "He appointed the moon for ____" (Psalm 104:19)

32. "A ___ man concealeth knowledge" (Proverbs 13:16)
34. Title
35. Camera shot
36. "Luke...and ___ greet you" (Colossians 4:14)
37. "turn...into your servant's house and ___ all night" (Genesis 19:2)
38. Needs
39. Aerie
40. Ten (comb. form)
41. Arduous journey
42. "Where is the king of Hamath...of Hena, and ___?" (2 Kings 19:13)
43. Leningrad's river
44. "the child Samuel ___ before the Lord" (1 Samuel 2:21)

PUZZLE 38

ACROSS
1. With it
4. "I suffer trouble, even as an evil ___" (2 Timothy 2:9)
8. Mentioned
12. Mouths
13. This (Sp.)
14. "the people did ___ themselves in caves" (1 Samuel 13:6)
15. Russian space station
16. Thatch for Malayan huts
17. Tribe of Anna (Luke 2)
18. "For he hath regarded the low ___ of his handmaiden" (Luke 1:48)
20. Tear
22. "he planteth an ___ and the rain doth nourish it" (Isaiah 44:14)
23. "As the word went out...they ___ Haman's face" (Esther 7:8)
27. "he was manifested to ___ away our sins" (1 John 4:7)
29. "let us __ one another" (1 John 4:7)
30. Employ
31. "He casteth forth his ___ like morsels" (Psalm 147:17)
32. "able to stand against the ___ of the devil" (Ephesians 6:11)
33. Son of Bilhah and Jacob
34. Botch
35. Just made it, with "out"
36. Several Popes
37. "he shall give thee the ___ of thine heart" (Psalm 95:10)
39. "behind him a ___ caught in a thicket" (Genesis 22:13)

40. "the mountains shall drop down ___ wine" (Joel 3:18)
41. "like Israel, when God went to ___ for a people to himself" (2 Samuel 7:23)
44. Municipality
47. ___ the Ahohite (1 Chronicles 11:29)
49. Never (Ger.)
50. Soothing plant
51. "what shall be the ___ of thy coming?" (Matthew 24:3)
52. Three (comb. form)
53. European river
54. Belonging to Seth's mother
55. Gel

DOWN
1. "we are at ___ in the body" (2 Corinthians 5:6)
2. Perennial flower
3. "for we are all ___ of that one bread" (1 Corinthians 9:13)
4. "neither ___...shall be able to separate us from the love of God" (Romans 8:38,39)
5. Bone (Ger.)
6. Greek letter
7. "He, that being often ___ hardeneth his neck" (Proverbs 29:1)
8. "And the Holy Ghost descended in a bodily ___" (Luke 3:22)
9. Of the town beside Bethaven (Joshua 7)
10. Chemical (suffix)
11. German article
19. Of an enzyme (suffix)
21. American composer
23. Belonging to Mr. Porter
24. "after the ___ of the world, and not after Christ" (Colossians 2:8)

78

25. He was not his mother's favorite
26. Retreats
27. "ye shall find a colt ___"
(Mark 11:2)
28. Land measure
29. "Go, and do thou ___"
(Luke 10:37)
32. Used to be
36. Walk softly
38. "go into an ___ chamber to hide
thyself" (1 Kings 22:35)
39. "the righteous God trieth the
hearts and ___" (Psalm 7:9)
41. Storm

42. Ireland
43. Encounter
44. Philippine peasant
45. "We have a father, an __ man"
(Genesis 44:20)
46. "___unto them that call evil
good" (Isaiah 5:20)
48. Actress Ullman

ACROSS

1. Bishop's jurisdiction
4. Doctoral degree (abbr.)
7. "Behold, we are thy ___ and thy flesh" (1 Chronicles 11:1)
11. Own
13. Expression of delight
14. Epic poetry
15. Summers in Nice
16. Feminine name
17. Glucoside root
18. "Behold, the ___of God is with men" (Revelation 21:3)
21. KJV verb
23. Purchased
24. Scarlett's third husband
25. ___-oni, Rachel's son
26. ___ blond
29. Christmas
30. Where King Ahaziah was attacked (2 Kings 9:27)
31. "Whosoever hath sinned against me, him will I ___ out of my book" (Exodus 32:33)
32. "of making many books there is no ___" (Ecclesiastes 12:12)
33. Grain
34. Bridle part
35. Father of Phineas and Hophni (1 Samuel 1)
36. "called...___...because I drew him out of the water" (Exodus 2:10)
37. "when I have a ___season, I will call for thee" (Acts 24:25)
41. Medicinal plant
42. Precarious gov't. agency
43. "Half...followed Tibni, and half followed ___" (2 Kings 16:21)

47. Balak brought Balaam atop here (Numbers 23)
48. "For ___ have sinned" (Romans 3:23)
49. "Therefore I will ___ and howl" (Micah 1:8)
50. Entertainment award
51. Affirmative
52. No (Scot.)

DOWN

1. Pronoun
2. "Come, ___ of my bread" (Proverbs 9:5)
3. Day before holiday
4. "O thou of little faith, wherefore didst thou ___?" (Matthew 14:31)
5. Tending to be (suffix)
6. "Give me...John Baptist's head on a ___" (Matthew 14:8)
7. Sired (arch.)
8. Oil org.
9. Knot fiber
10. Slave
12. "the angels which kept not their first ___" (Jude 6)
19. Ht.
20. Son of Elishama (1 Chronicles 7:26)
21. "But ___profane and vain babblings" (2 Timothy 2:16)
22. "When Moses ___ up his hand" (Exodus 17:11)
24. Deli dough
25. Conjunction
26. "thou makest this people to trust in ___ ___" (Jeremiah 28:15)
27. "a day when the ___of God came to present themselves" (Job 1:6)
28. Peaks (abbr.)

30. "which all your adversaries shall not be able to ____" (Luke 21:15)
31. "And though I ____ all my goods to feed the poor" (1 Corinthians 13:3)
33. Corrida cheer
34. Masculine name
35. "And God created...____...living creature" (Genesis 1:21)
36. Repasts
37. Mil. rank
38. Bread spread
39. "Evening, morning and at __ I will pray" (Psalm 55:17)

40. Emerald ____
44. "What is ____ that thou art mindful" (Psalm 8:4)
45. Narrow inlet
46. __ du Diable, French penal colony

ACROSS

1. What you get when you sit
4. Hair quality
8. "any that is nigh of __unto him...may redeem him" (Leviticus 25:49)
11. Be human
12. "____, behold thy son!" (John 19:26)
13. Mouths
14. River in Scotland
15. Mischievous one
16. "neither be ye ___, for the joy of the Lord is your strength" (Nehemiah 8:10)
18. "The Son of man shall____...his angels" (Matthew 13:41)
20. River in England
21. Write
22. Implant
25. "he that receiveth me receiveth him that ___ me" (Matthew 10:40)
26. ___cum laude
27. Eastern U.S. state
28. "for as often as ye ___this bread" (1 Corinthians 11:26)
29. Mine product
30. A vote against
31. Overhead train
32. Ward off
34. "the governor was ___ to release...a prisoner" (Matthew 27:15)
35. "But the queen Vashti ___ to come" (Esther 1:12)
37. "Go to the ___, thou sluggard" (Proverbs 6:6)

38. Lacking (suffix)
39. Girl
41. "behold every one that is proud, and ___ him" (Job 40:11)
43. "they fled from the swords...and...the grievousness of ___" (Isaiah 21:15)
44. ___the son of Hur (Exodus 35:30)
47. Old Testament offering
48. "Call me not ___" (Ruth 1:19)
50. Frantic
51. One (Scot.)
52. Sea eagle
53. Self

DOWN

1. "thou hast___captivity captive" (Psalm 68:18)
2. Linking verb
3. "There is not a ___ to bring to the man of God" (1 Samuel 9:7)
4. "the flock shall be cut off from the ___" (Habakkuk 3:17)
5. World banking org.
6. Continent (abbr.)
7. "And he will lift up an ___ to the nations from far" (Isaiah 5:26)
8. Asian country
9. Subpar merchandise (abbr.)
10. Old Testament negative
12. Sebaceous cyst
17. Extra (Scot.)
19. Within (comb. form)
20. "And the ___ of the Lord appeared unto him in a flame" (Exodus 3:2)
21. Noted American minister and writer

22. "a rough valley which is neither ___ nor sown" (Deuteronomy 21:4)
23. ___-runner
24. Color
25. "And Samuel answered Saul...I am the ___" (1 Samuel 9:19)
26. Is gloomy
30. "a fire not blown shall ___ him" (Job 20:26)
32. Regrets
33. Member of ancient Jewish sect
34. Used to be

36. "as the ___ setteth the mountain on fire" (Isaiah 35:6)
39. "[Mephibosheth] was ___ on both his feet" (2 Samuel 9:13)
40. Onassis
41. A son of Jether (1 Chronicles 7)
42. Prohibit
43. "A brother offended is harder to be ___ than a strong city" (Proverbs 18:19)
45. ___time
46. Wedding words (2 words)
49. Chemical element that is an inert gas (abbr.)

ACROSS

1. "And be ye ___ one to another" (Ephesians 4:32)
5. Midwest state (abbr.)
8. The ___ Jabbok, passed over by Jacob and family (Genesis 32)
12. Dies ___
13. Car club (abbr.)
14. Third son of Asher (Genesis 46)
15. Hoover et al.
16. Car agency (abbr.)
17. Any tribe or clan
18. He eats at the king's table, because of David's friendship with his father
21. "___ a boy!"
22. The farthest (abbr.)
23. "her princes are become like ___that find no pasture" (Lamentations 1:6)
26. Dryly humorous
27. Grammatical org.
30. Great Lake
31. First word in many conversations
32. "for he [the devil] is a ___ and the father of it" (John 8:44)
33. Fair weather p.m. sky
34. ___ poodle
35. "I will sweep it with the ___ of destruction" (Isaiah 14:33)
36. ___ canto, singing style
37. Possesses
38. "This is __ ___ ___ in whom I am well pleased" (Matthew 17:5)
44. British nobleman
45. Russian space station

46. "Where are the gods of Sepharvaim, Hena, and ___?" (2 Kings 18:34)
48. Three (Ger.)
49. The ear (comb. form)
50. Promontory
51. Wave (Fr.)
52. Where Cain dwelled (Genesis 4)
53. "Ye blind guides, which strain at a ___" (Matthew 23:24)

DOWN

1. "Goatie"?
2. A duke of Edom (1 Chronicles 1)
3. "thou shalt call his ___ Jesus" (Matthew 1:21)
4. Notwithstanding
5. Arab valleys that are mostly dry (except when it rains!)
6. Poetic foot
7. "And make me ___ meat" (Genesis 27:4)
8. "The Lord shall ___for you, and ye shall hold your peace" (Exodus 14:14)
9. "As he saith in ___, I will call them my people" (Romans 9:25)
10. Smallest one
11. "I will wipe Jerusalem as a man wipeth a ___" (2 Kings 21:13)
19. Alts.
20. Clever
23. Pronoun
24. Linking verb
25. "I will ___ evil beasts out of the land" (Leviticus 26:6)
26. "I am the ___" (John 14:6)
27. Wrong (prefix)
28. Laotian (abbr.)
29. "And to whom is the ___ of the Lord revealed?" (Isaiah 53:1)

31. Son of David
32. German dramatist
34. __ Aviv
35. ___ blood
36. Prove false
37. ___ Antipas, N.T. ruler
38. ___-Persian Empire
39. Raconteurs can spin one
40. Sired
41. Masculine Italian name
42. Kiln
43. U.S. agcy.
47. Pres. inits.

PUZZLE 42

ACROSS

1. High, rocky hill
4. Owns
7. "Thy neck is an iron sinew, thy ___ brass" (Isaiah 48:4)
11. Mr. Guinness
13. How to answer the phone in Arles
14. City in Italia
15. Son of Zechariah (1 Chronicles 27)
16. Mr. Cole
17. To use (Lat.)
18. "Lord, consider my ____" (Psalm 5:1)
21. "And Adam gave ___ to all the cattle" (Genesis 2:20)
23. Island (Fr.)
24. "David...came to the brook ___" (1 Samuel 30:9)
25. Boys' club (abbr.)
26. "The poor man had nothing save one little ___ lamb" (1 Samuel 12:3)
29. Shortly
30. Scrooge syntax
31. Way to get out of jail
32. Agt.
33. Tennis call
34. "there shall be some...which shall not ___of death" (Luke 9:27)
35. ___ de deux
36. "the heart of the wicked is little ___" (Proverbs 10:20)
37. "A ____ revealeth secrets" (Proverbs 11:13)
41. "For he is cast into __ __ by his own feet" (Job 18:8)
42. Before (poet.)
43. "___ not the oppressor" (Proverbs 3:31)
47. What to use to shoot the breeze
48. French pronoun (pl.)
49. A stone's throw away
50. Arab noble
51. Pres. from MO
52. Gym gear

DOWN

1. Japanese fish
2. Up in years
3. ___ carpet
4. "Cleanse your ___, ye sinners" (James 4:8)
5. Jai ___
6. "For my people is foolish...they are ___ children" (Jeremiah 4:22)
7. "as natural ___ beasts made to be taken and destroyed" (2 Peter 2:12)
8. Wheel (comb. form)
9. Melville character
10. "___ the wicked from his wicked way" (Ezekiel 3:18)
12. "there is no ___ bread under mine hand" (1 Samuel 21:4)
19. Ever (poet.)
20. ___ mode
21. Hawaiian goose
22. "He it is to whom I shall give __ ___" (John 13:26)
24. "I will break also the ___ of Damascus" (Amos 1:5)
25. Inedible creature (Leviticus 11:19)
26. "this man [Job] was the greatest of all the men of the ___" (Job 1:3)
27. Preposition

28. Old English eel

30. "I humbly ___ thee that I may find grace in thy sight" (2 Samuel 16:4)

31. "ye shall neither be ___ nor unfruitful in the knowledge of our Lord" (2 Peter 1:8)

33. Research room

34. Digit

35. "thou art ____ and upon this rock I will build" (Matthew 16:18)

36. "Every day they ___ my words" (Psalm 56:5)

37. "___ no thought for your life" (Matthew 6:31)

38. City in the southern part of Judah

39. Island group off Timor

40. Greek god of war

44. "if any man be in Christ he is a ___ creature" (2 Corinthians 5:17)

45. Cask

46. Time periods (abbr.)

87

PUZZLE 43

ACROSS

1. Granitic rock layer underlying the continents
5. Document within a letter (abbr.)
8. From a distance
12. Father of Naum (Luke 3:25)
13. Recent (comb. form)
14. Put away
15. "And there we saw the giants, the sons of ___" (Numbers 13:33)
16. "Now the eyes of Israel were ___ for age" (Genesis 48:10)
17. A son of Jerahmeel (1 Chronicles 2)
18. "he did also predestinate __ __ __ to the image of his Son" (Romans 8:29)
21. Conjunction
22. ___ -liner
23. "There was a certain rich man which ___ sumptuously" (Luke 16:19)
26. To's companion
27. Actor Cobb
30. "There is __ __ here, which hath five barley loaves" (John 6:9)
31. Investigator (abbr.)
32. "the word of the Lord came unto the prophet Gad, David's ___" (2 Samuel 24:11)
33. Scottish topper
34. "That were graven with an iron___" (Job 19:24)
35. "Who provideth for the ___ his food?" (Job 38:41)
36. ___ Ten, collegiate sports division
37. Word always printed within brackets

38. "For we are ___ ___ of Christ, if we hold...stedfast unto the end" (Hebrews 3:14)
45. Tribe of Anna the prophetess
46. Moreover, in ancient times
47. Hillside (Scot.)
48. Imperfectly (prefix)
49. Vegetable portion
50. "The Pharisees began to ___ him vehemently" (Luke 11:53)
51. "And the Lord shall make thee the head, and not the ___" (Deuteronomy 28:13)
52. Former Pres.
53. Nicholas was one

DOWN

1. "And thou shalt make a mercy ___ of pure gold" (Exodus 25:17)
2. "Nay, my sons; for it __ __ good report that I [Eli] hear" (1 Samuel 2:24)
3. Home of the Crimson Tide (abbr., var.)
4. "The kingdom of heaven is ___ unto a man which sowed good seed" (Matthew 13:24)
5. Witch of ___
6. No (Ger.)
7. "the Father of mercies, and the God of all ___" (2 Corinthians 1:3)
8. "grass...which withereth ___it groweth up" (Psalm 129:6)
9. "His heart is as ___ as a stone" (Job 41:24)
10. Away from the wind
11. Tear
19. Food fish
20. City near Lod, in northwestern Judah (1 Chronicles 8:12)
23. "ye shall eat the ___ of the land" (Genesis 45:18)

1	2	3	4	■	5	6	7	■	8	9	10	11
12				■	13			■	14			
15				■	16			■	17			
18			19				20					
■	■	21			■	22			■	■	■	■
23	24	25			■	26			■	27	28	29
30			■	31			■	32				
33			■	34			■	35				
■	■	36			■	37			■	■	■	■
38	39	40			41				42	43	44
45			■	46			■	47			
48			■	49			■	50			
51			■	52			■	53			

24. In the manner of
25. Leviticus offering: "a ___ without a blemish"
26. Bog
27. Bk. of the Torah
28. Shoe size
29. Sea eagle
31. "I will raise up the ___ places thereof" (Isaiah 44:26)
32. An ancient stringed instrument (Daniel 3:5)
34. Baby food
35. Stream
36. "We got our bread with the ___ of our lives" (Lamentations 5:9)
37. Gape
38. "Thy tacklings are loosed; they could not well strengthen their ___" (Isaiah 33:23)
39. Adrift
40. ___-tasse
41. "___ my lips"
42. Misinterprets
43. ___ muffin
44. Prophet

89

ACROSS

1. Son of (Scot.)
4. Intelligence
7. "And they went...into the ark,...___of all flesh" (Genesis 7:15)
10. Atty.'s assn.
11. The daughter of Zechariah (2 Kings 18)
12. "Study to ___thyself approved unto God" (2 Timothy 2:15)
13. "Then hear thou in heaven their prayer and their ____" (1 Kings 8:45)
16. Cubic meters
17. First son of Bilhah and Jacob
18. Home (abbr.)
19. "the destruction of the poor is their ___" (Proverbs 10:15)
23. "Remember not the ___ of my youth" (Psalm 25:7)
25. "for a good man some would even ___ to die" (Romans 5:7)
26. Before (poet.)
27. Grandpas (Ger., familiar)
28. Gershwin
29. "And before the throne there was __ __ of glass" (Revelation 4:6)
30. Baton Rouge inst.
31. An early inhabitant of Palestine (Deuteronomy 2:23)
32. Colors
33. Woman of Athens converted by Paul (Acts 17)
35. Russian space station
36. Oxford college tutor
37. "I will harden the ___ of the Egyptians" (Exodus 14:17)

40. "A ___ ___ shall not be unpunished" (Proverbs 19:5)
43. Hillside (Scot.)
44. Lyric poem
45. Persian is one
46. A son of Bela (1 Chronicles 7:7)
47. Masculine nickname
48. Corp. administrators

DOWN

1. Bulk
2. Border
3. "Whatsoever we have heard done in ___, do also here" (Luke 4:23)
4. Part of British Isles
5. Large wading bird
6. Muscle spasm
7. "I will not take any thing that is ___" (Genesis 14:23)
8. Court
9. Purchase
12. Strip of metal or wood
14. "Then came to him his mother...and could not come at him for the ___" (Luke 8:19)
15. Shortened form of Adoniram
19. King of Troy (Gr. myth)
20. Bring back to life
21. Kilmer subject
22. Biblical affirmatives
23. "Are not two sparrows ___ for a farthing?" (Matthew 10:29)
24. It (Lat., var.)
25. "verily the first covenant had also ordinances of ___ service" (Hebrews 9:1)
29. A son of Shemidah (1 Chronicles 7:19)
31. Got up
34. First name of one-time presidential contender

35. "a nation ___ out and trodden
    down" (Isaiah 18:2)
37. Can be tanned
38. Russian ruler
39. Faster than speeding bullets
    (abbr.)
40. Law enforcement agcy.
41. (abbr.) seen in airports
42. "___ye not what the scripture
    saith of Elias?" (Romans 11:2)

PUZZLE 45

ACROSS

1. "praying...that God would open...a ___ of utterance" (Colossians 4:3)
5. Belonging to Victoria's hubby?
8. Daunting volume
12. Sea eagle
13. Aegean is one
14. Incite
15. "They that are whole have no ___ of a physician" (Mark 2:17)
16. Czech distance measure
17. Precious
18. Chemical suffix
20. "Thou hast with thine __ redeemed thy people" (Psalm 77:15)
22. Belonging to the Ithrite of 1 Chronicles 11:40
25. One-time host of TV's "Death Valley Days"
29. Swollen areas
30. Give assent
31. Rep. to convention
32. Masculine nickname
33. "And his feet shall stand...upon the Mount of ___" (Zechariah 14:4)
37. City six miles south of the Sea of Galilee
40. Wisconsin city
41. Ark's final resting place
42. Hwy.
43. "And the servant ___ to meet her" (Genesis 24:17)
44. "Is any merry? Let him ___" (James 5:13)
47. ___ Aviv

49. "Where are the gods of Sepharvaim, Hena, and ___?" (2 Kings 18:34)
53. The son of Chelub (1 Chronicles 27:26)
54. To the east of Abram's pitched tent (Genesis 12:8)
55. Ireland
56. To withdraw
57. Common (abbr.)
58. "It is vain for you to sit up ___" (Psalm 127:2)

DOWN

1. Eur. country
2. Mine product
3. ___-horse
4. "I will ___ you with a stretched out arm" (Exodus 6:6)
5. Evaluate
6. Bucolic setting
7. African desert
8. Airport runway
9. O.T. bk.
10. Debussy's "Le ___"
11. Dog days for Descartes
19. Pro sports org.
21. Popular room (abbr.)
22. Son of Penuel (1 Chronicles 4:4)
23. Ms. St. Johns
24. Souvenir
26. "And Abraham...sojourned in ___" (Genesis 20:1)
27. Maccabean name for Adoraim (2 Chronicles 11)
28. Father of Jeroboam (1 Kings 12)
34. "Behold a ___ shall conceive" (Isaiah 7:14)
35. Inner (comb. form)
36. To cook by boiling (KJV)

37. "leeks, the onions, and the ___"
    (Numbers 11:5)
38. A son of Jether (1 Chronicles 7)
39. Prophet whose name means
    "God's judge"
44. Baste
45. To resemble (suffix)
46. Powerful Washington lobby
    (abbr.)
48. Sup
50. By way of
51. "Thou __ the man"
    (2 Samuel 12:7)
52. Laughing sound

ACROSS

1. Kimono sashes
5. Years (Fr.)
8. "Thou hast enlarged my steps...that my feet did not ___"
   (Psalm 18:36)
12. "Be not __ with thy mouth"
    (Ecclesiastes 5:2)
13. Cask
14. Kingfish
15. Cordon ___
16. Vowel trio
17. "___, my daughter! Thou hast brought me very low"
    (Judges 11:35)
18. Son of Immer, father of Berechiah, head of children of Ephraim (2 Chronicles 28:12)
21. One-time gov't. agcy.
22. "they prophesy a ___ unto you"
    (Jeremiah 27:14)
23. Sired
26. Hied
27. She's about to come out (colloq.)
30. Member of the Eranites
    (Numbers 26)
31. Title
32. "___ twelve cakes thereof"
    (Leviticus 24:5)
33. "Pull me out of the __ that they have laid privily for me"
    (Psalm 31:4)
34. Evil
35. Syn. for "a roe"
36. River between SC and GA
37. Tin
38. Belonging to one of Jesus' disciples

44. Son of Rehoboam
    (1 Chronicles 3)
45. Out (Dutch)
46. ___ of clay
48. Half (prefix)
49. Feminine name
50. Dies ___
51. Utopia
52. Time periods (abbr.)
53. "I will...___thee all that is in thine heart" (1 Samuel 9:19)

DOWN

1. Globe
2. "Is there no ___ in Gilead?"
   (Jeremiah 8:22)
3. Understanding words
4. "king Ahasuerus sat on the throne...which was in ___ the palace" (Esther 1:2)
5. "foolish and unlearned questions ___" (2 Timothy 2:23)
6. "shall the ___ that is fastened in the sure place be removed"
   (Isaiah 22:25)
7. Exemplary
8. "So he returned with ___ of face to his own land"
   (2 Chronicles 32:21)
9. French composer
10. Silk fabric
11. "he shall ___ the people to the ends of the earth"
    (Deuteronomy 33:17)
19. Shack
20. German article
23. TV's Dr. Casey
24. Before (poet.)
25. Acquired (arch.)
26. "I will ___ you out of their bondage" (Exodus 6:6)

27. Small amount
28. Supplement, with "out"
29. Actress Barbara ___ Geddes
31. "And make me ___ meat" (Genesis 27:4)
32. "they are...partakers of the ___" (1 Timothy 6:2)
34. Word in Scrooge's vocabulary
35. Old Testament offering
36. "The Lord of hosts hath purposed it to ___ the pride of all glory" (Isaiah 23:9)
37. "stalls for beasts, and ___ for flocks" (2 Chronicles 32:28)

38. "They were children of fools, of ___ men" (Job 30:8)
39. Retired
40. Hoarfrost
41. "a ___ giveth ear to a naughty tongue" (Proverbs 17:4)
42. Used to be
43. "Write...in the king's name and ___ it with the king's ring" (Esther 8:8)
47. Wire (abbr.)

PUZZLE 47

ACROSS

1. Fire
4. "But I am a ___ and no man" (Psalm 22:6)
8. Kind of giver
12. Linking verb
13. "___in the year shall he make atonement upon it" (Exodus 30:10)
14. "The words of ___the son of Jakeh, even the prophecy" (Proverbs 30:1)
15. Capuchin monkey
16. Freshwater fish
17. "And Jonathan...had a son that was ___" (2 Samuel 4:3)
18. "He shall give his ___ charge concerning you" (Matthew 4:6)
20. John (Scot.)
22. Descendant of Asher (1 Chronicles 7:37)
23. "for he giveth not ___of any of his matters" (Job 33:13)
27. "All of ___ children were killed" (Job 1:19)
29. ___ Street
30. "But as the days of ___ were so shall the coming of the Son of man be" (Matthew 24:37)
31. Large volcanic crater in Japan (abbr.)
32. Swiss city (var.)
33. Actor Ameche
34. Southern state univ.
35. John or Jane (2 words)
36. "All ye that ___ the bow" (Jeremiah 50:14)
37. Anticipate

39. Pelt
40. Diminutive suffix
41. "there will I ___ all my fruits" (Luke 12:18)
44. Except
47. "straightway the spirit ___ him" (Mark 9:20)
49. Gardner
50. Raw materials
51. Father of Jesse (Ruth 4)
52. "And the ___ of the house of David will I lay upon his shoulder" (Isaiah 22:22)
53. "Mordecai the Jew was ___ to king Ahasuerus" (Esther 10:3)
54. Cincinnati team
55. Belonging to Judah's first son (Genesis 38)

DOWN

1. House (Sp.)
2. A son of Dishan (Genesis 36:28)
3. "Thou shalt love thy ___" (Matthew 19:19)
4. "And he shall judge the ___ in righteousness" (Psalm 9:8)
5. Burden of proof
6. Acknowledged, as payment (abbr.)
7. "A merry heart doeth good like ___" (Proverbs 17:22)
8. "Are not my princes altogether kings? Is not ___ as Carchemish?" (Isaiah 10:8,9)
9. Turkish title
10. Bay ___
11. Before (poet.)
19. Aurora
21. Teen concern
23. Brother of Moses
24. "O Lord, I am oppressed; ___ for me" (Isaiah 38:14)

25. "I will cause the sun to go down at ___" (Amos 8:9)
26. Care for
27. Door ___
28. Greek mountain
29. "one ___ between God and men" (1 Timothy 2:5)
32. "And they forsook the Lord and served ___" (Judges 2:13)
36. School ___
38. "he was gone to be ___ with a man that is a sinner" (Luke 19:7)
39. Gratifies
41. Produced
42. Preposition
43. "When a man's ___ please the Lord, he maketh even his enemies to be at peace" (Proverbs 16:7)
44. "Kiss the ___, lest he be angry" (Psalm 2:12)
45. Linking verb
46. "Thou shalt neither ___ a stranger nor oppress him" (Exodus 22:21)
48. Actor Vigoda

PUZZLE 48

ACROSS

1. "the sun and the ___ were darkened by...the smoke of the pit" (Revelation 9:2)
4. "the people imagine a ___ thing" (Psalm 2:1)
8. Subordinate officer at consulate (abbr.,var.)
12. 66 is one (abbr.)
13. Son of Shobal (Genesis 36:23)
14. Merit
15. N.T. bk.
16. "they also may without the word be ___" (1 Peter 3:1)
17. ___-eyed
18. Son of Jerahmeel (1 Chronicles 2:25)
20. "___ it in a book" (Isaiah 30:8)
22. "by grace are ye ___" (Ephesians 2:5)
24. "put forth a riddle and a ___ to the house of Israel" (Ezekiel 17:2)
27. "surely lend him sufficient for his ___" (Deuteronomy 15:8)
28. "and the beginning of his [Nimrod's] kingdom was ___" (Genesis 10:10)
29. Common hospital (abbr.)
30. Conjunction
31. ___ holiday
32. Chemical suffix
33. Astronomical research fac.
34. Deli fare
35. Ancient dry measure
36. "Even the rich shall ___ thy favour" (Psalm 45:12)
38. "a time to ___ and a time to pluck" (Ecclesiastes 3:2)
39. Small grove or wooded hill
40. ___ Day

41. "Write this for a memorial in a ___" (Exodus 17:4)
43. ___ culpa
44. Inhabitant (suffix)
47. "the ___ against the honourable" (Isaiah 3:5)
48. Monotonous
49. "if any man be in Christ, he is a ___ creature" (2 Corinthians 5:17)
50. British WWII weapon
51. Bore, with "of"
52. Chemical (suffix)

DOWN

1. Airport info.
2. News figure in 1995
3. "[Asa] ___ all the idols that his fathers had made" (1 Kings 15:12)
4. "pay that which thou hast ___" (Ecclesiastes 5:4)
5. Shortly
6. Author Fleming
7. Western state (abbr.)
8. Chaste
9. "Joshua and ___ ...searched the land" (Numbers 14:6)
10. Booty for Cortes
11. Compass dir.
19. "Feed me...with that same ___ pottage" (Genesis 25:30)
20. Husband of Abigail (1 Samuel 25)
21. First name of famed hurler
22. "wherefore thou layest a ___ for my life" (1 Samuel 28:9)
23. "And John was also baptizing in ___ near Salim" (John 3:23)
24. Actress Debra
25. "And David was clothed with a robe of fine ___" (1 Chronicles 15:27)
26. Tennis great

28. "Abraham ___ Isaac"
(Matthew 1:2)
31. Father of Eliasaph
(Numbers 3:24)
32. "let none of you ___ evil against
his brother" (Zechariah 7:10)
34. "For he...hath ___ down the middle
wall of partition"
(Ephesians 2:14)
35. Hello! (Sp., var.)
37. Pronoun
38. "And thou shalt make a ___ of pure
gold" (Exodus 28:36)
40. "___ye not, stand still and see the
salvation" (Exodus 14:13)

41. Business assn.
42. "And all that handle the ___...shall
come down from their ships"
(Ezekiel 27:29)
43. The year 1051, in Rome
45. Number of Haman's sons that
shared in his punishment
46. Mother of Mary's little lamb
48. ___ Knox (abbr.)

ACROSS

1. Solid geometric shape
5. Declare openly
8. "Thou hast enlarged my steps under me; so that my feet did not ___" (2 Samuel 22:37)
12. Middle East sultanate
13. Baseball stat.
14. Of gases (comb. form)
15. ___-a-brac
16. Gov't. agency
17. "Lord, __ __ I?" (Matthew 26:22)
18. "And ye shall dispossess the _____ of the land" (Numbers 33:53)
21. Linking verb
22. ___ hill
23. Specified area of activity
26. Genetic inits.
27. What Sylvester is
30. Relationship of Leah to Joseph
31. Spoil
32. "that he ___ his only begotten son" (John 3:16)
33. River in Northeast Scotland
34. "___ now whether my word shall come to pass" (Numbers 11:23)
35. "And David heard...that ___ did shear sheep" (1 Samuel 25:4)
36. "the spear smote him under the fifth ___" (2 Samuel 2:23)
37. Set
38. "For then shall be great _____" (Matthew 24:21)
43. In that manner
44. Equipment for an activity
45. "Eliasaph the son of ___" (Numbers 3:24)

47. Low land
48. The "mother of all living"
49. Gaelic
50. Solar disc
51. ___ Moines
52. This (Sp.)

DOWN

1. Corn ___
2. A king of Israel (1 Kings 16)
3. Where Jesus encountered distraught widow (Luke 7)
4. Charm
5. "of whose hand have I received any ___?" (1 Samuel 12:3)
6. A son of Merari (1 Chronicles 24:27)
7. "one board had two tenons equally ___ from one another" (Exodus 36:22)
8. French writer Antoine de ___-Exupery
9. For fear that
10. Eye membrane
11. "He maketh the deep to boil like a ___" (Job 41:30)
19. "How terrible ___ thou in thy works" (Psalm 66:3)
20. Actress Alicia
23. Hula hoop, for example
24. Regret
25. "Beloved, let us love __ another" (1 John 4:7)
26. Jane or John
27. Taxi
28. First name of Carolina-born actress
29. From a distance (comb. form)
31. "Thou hast _____ the heathen" (Psalm 9:5)

32. "Jesus, walking by the sea of ___ saw two brethren" (Matthew 4:18)
34. Bro. is one
35. Part of cyberspace (colloq.)
36. "And if Christ be not ___, then is our preaching vain" (1 Corinthians 15:14)
37. "Enter into his ___ with thanksgiving" (Psalm 100:4)
38. "___ Girl" (one-time sitcom)
39. "By me princes ___" (Proverbs 8:16)
40. Exist

41. "therein shall go no galley with ___" (Isaiah 33:21)
42. "As an eagle stirreth up her ___" (Deuteronomy 32:11)
43. Tennessee River project (abbr.)
46. Actress Remick

PUZZLE 50

ACROSS

1. Former Yugoslavian liquid measure
5. One of two epistles written by Paul (abbr.)
8. Exclamation of regret (var.)
12. ___-tasse
13. French article
14. Over there (Fr.)
15. "I have ___ God face to face" (Genesis 32:30)
16. Inhab.
17. A son of Jerahmeel (1 Chronicles 2:25)
18. "For whom he did foreknow, he also did ___ to be conformed to the image of his son" (Romans 8:29)
21. Zilpah and Jacob's son
22. To cause to become (suffix, var.)
23. Commenced
26. What goes boom!
27. Upperclasspersons (abbr.)
30. A son of Eliphaz (Genesis 36)
31. Gear tooth
32. "and man became a living ___" (Genesis 2:7)
33. Conjunction
34. Years and years
35. "the love of ___ is the root of all evil" (1 Timothy 6:10)
36. Bristly fibers on head of barley
37. "My Gal ___"
38. "what___ I endured: but out of them all the Lord delivered me" (2 Timothy 3:11)
44. Inflammatory disease (suffix)
45. First lady
46. Dole out
48. Powder ingredient
49. A person concerned with (suffix)
50. Ruth and Naomi's pride and joy
51. Pertaining to enzymes (suffix, pl.)
52. Author Amy
53. Law or custom (comb. form)

DOWN

1. "Classified" info.
2. "How long refuse ye to ___ my commandments?" (Exodus 16:28)
3. Hebrew dry measure
4. "dip thy morsel in the ___" (Ruth 2:14)
5. "the child was ___ from that very hour" (Matthew 17:18)
6. Cardinal numbers
7. "spoil not his ___ place" (Proverbs 24:15)
8. "It is not good that man should be ___" (Genesis 2:18)
9. Pasternak heroine
10. Incite
11. "Thou hast brought me no sweet ___" (Isaiah 43:24)
19. Son of Bilhah and Jacob
20. Adherent of (suffix)
23. Poor-___ (sandwich)
24. Crony (O.E.)
25. "they covered him with clothes, but he ___ no heat" (1 Kings 1:1)
26. Around 2000 pounds
27. "Chasten thy ___ while there is hope" (Proverbs 19:18)
28. Wish undone
29. Wily
31. "The rich man's wealth is...as an high wall in his own ___" (Proverbs 18:11)

32. "Then sat ___upon the throne of
    David his father" (1 Kings 1:12)
34. "But the poor man had nothing
    save one little ___ lamb"
    (2 Samuel 12:3)
35. Month in Marseilles
36. Organizations (abbr.)
37. Severe
38. Pocket bread
39. Greek letters
40. Get under one's skin
41. Layer of the eye
42. "Moses went up the mountain of
    ___" (Deuteronomy 34:1)
43. To stop up or plug
47. People of Nigeria

PUZZLE 51

ACROSS

1. "And he shall be like a ___ planted"
   (Psalm 1:3)
4. "___ me of things to come"
   (Isaiah 45:11)
6. "Make a joyful noise unto the ___"
   (Psalm 100:1)
9. Undergraduate degree (abbr.)
11. "O Lord, ___ thou my lips"
    (Psalm 51:15)
12. "through the ___ of their own hearts"
    (Romans 1:24)
14. "Take the ___ Train"
15. "Let the wicked fall into their own
    ___"(Psalm 141:10)
17. "and ___ out the valley of Succoth"
    (Psalm 60:6)
18. "___ iniquity unto their iniquity"
    (Psalm 69:27)
20. "shall eat bread ___ at my ___"
    (2 Samuel 9:10)
23. "___ thankful unto him"
    (Psalm 100:4)
25. "and ___ the sacrifices of the dead"
    (Psalm 106:28)
26. The son of Hur, of the tribe of Judah
    (Exodus 35:30)
28. "I am the Lord that brought thee out
    of ___" (Genesis 15:7)
29. "Howl, O Heshbon, for ___ is
    spoiled" (Jeremiah 49:3)
30. Canadian providence
31. "There is ___ speech nor language"
    (Psalm 19:3)
32. Latin (abbr.)
33. Org. concerned with early American
    genealogy
36. "Know ye that the Lord he is ___"
    (Psalm 100:3)
38. Nonmetallic element symbol
39. Baseball position (abbr.)

41. "took ___ the son of Saul"
    (2 Samuel 2:8)
45. "___ the ends of the earth have seen
    the salvation of our God (Psalm 98:3)
47. Darling
48. "And Solomon's son was Rehoboam,
    ___ his son" (1 Chronicles 3:10)
49. "and spreading himself like a green
    bay ___"(Psalm 37:35)
50. "a rod out of the ___ of Jesse"
    (Isaiah 11:1)
51. Pencil remnant
53. "All that ___ me whisper together"
    (Psalm 41:7)
54. "___ small and great beasts"
    (Psalm 104:25)
55. "___, though I walk through the val-
    ley of the shadow of death"
    (Psalm 23:4)
56. "beyond the tower of ___"
    (Genesis 35:21)

DOWN

1. "But Absalom fled, and went to ___"
   (2 Samuel 13:37)
2. "And the Lord God planted a garden
   ___ in Eden" (Genesis 2:8)
3. "before him to ___; but he said, I will
   not___" (Genesis 24:33)
5. Make unconscious, in boxing
6. "the borrower is servant to the ___"
   (Proverbs 22:7)
7. "doth every ___ speak of his glory"
   (Psalm 29:9)
8. PC system
10. Retirement assistance (abbr.)
13. "Maadai, Amram, and ___"
    (Ezra 10:34)
14. First man
16. "and dwelt in the land of ___"
    (Judges 11:3)
18. Hundredth of a kip
19. Computer storage and retrieval sys-
    tem (abbr.)
21. "Take me an heifer of three ___ old"
    (Genesis 15:9)

22. Breathing organ
24. "And Judah took a wife for ___ his first born" (Gen. 38:6)
27. "for we also forgive every one that is ___ to us" (Luke 11:4)
32. "For, ___, the kings were assembled" (Psalm 48:4)
34. "What ___ thee, Hagar?" (Genesis 21:17)
35. "and shall afflict ___, and he also shall perish for ever" (Numbers 24:24)
37. "___ my strength, ___ thee to help me" (Psalm 22:19)
38. "the son of Bani, the son of ___" (1 Chronicles 6:46)
40. "Be not ___ from me" (Psalm 22:11)
42. Equine strength (abbr.)
43. Bible section (abbr.)
44. "and ___ them about thy neck" (Proverbs 6:21)
46. "Slay them not, ___ my people forget" (Psalm 59:11)
49. Tool for doing laundry by hand
52. Eons (abbr.)
53. Laughter sound

ACROSS

1. "and whom he called, them he also ___" (Romans 8:30)
8. "And when he had dipped the ___" (John 13:26)
11. Troop entertainment org.
12. "and let us run with patience the ___" (Hebrews 12:1)
13. "but ye shall ___ away for your iniquities" (Ezekiel 24:23)
14. Mid-Atlantic st.
15. "so he paid the ___ thereof" (Jonah 1:3)
16. "And all that handle the ___" (Ezekiel 27:29)
17. "whether it be good or ___" (2 Corinthians 5:10)
18. "nor ___ other creature" (Romans 8:39)
19. Part of former Navigators Island (abbr.)
20. "shall be Ahira the son of ___" (Numbers 2:29)
22. "And they shall fall by the ___" (Luke 21:24)
24. "they had a great while ___ repented" (Luke 10:13)
25. "but the Spirit itself maketh ___ for us" (Romans 8:26)
27. "Then ___ hated her exceedingly" (2 Samuel 13:15)
28. "he also did ___ to be conformed" (Romans 8:29)
34. Average
35. "For the kingdom of God is not ___ and drink" (Romans 14:17)
36. Sweetheart (Scot.)
38. "___, thou that destroyed the temple" (Mark 15:29)
39. "If the whole body were an ___" (1 Corinthians 12:17)
40. "and stand in the ___ before me for the land" (Ezekiel 22:30)

41. "in that it ___ weak through the flesh" (Romans 8:3)
42. "And ___ bare Jabal" (Genesis 4:20)
44. "I ___ debtor" (Romans 1:14)
45. "beyond the tower of ___" (Genesis 35:21)
47. "that they have a zeal of ___" (Romans 10:2)
48. Before (prefix)
49. Actress Myrna
50. "and whom he justified, them he also ___" (Romans 8:30)

DOWN

1. "In the day when God shall ___ the secrets of men" (Romans 2:16)
2. "their women did change the natural ___" (Romans 1:26)
3. "And not only ___" (Romans 5:3)
4. "And unto Enoch was born ___" (Genesis 4:18)
5. "The night is ___ spent" (Romans 13:12)
6. "He casteth forth his ___ like morsels" (Psalm 147:17)
7. Sight organ (Scot.)
8. "___, give me this water" (John 4:15)
9. Canadian prov.
10. "God accepteth no man's ___" (Galatians 2:6)
13. "For this cause ___ ye tribute also" (Romans 13:6)
15. A humorous term for a state of anxiety
16. "as by ___ man ___ entered into the world" (Romans 5:12)
17. "Lift ye up a ___" (Isaiah 13:2)
18. "for she was of the ___ of twelve years" (Mark 5:42)
19. "because three days ___ I fell sick" (1 Samuel 30:13)
21. "Ataroth, and Dibon, and Jazer, and ___" (Numbers 32:3)
22. "And the sons of Judah; ___, and Onan" (Genesis 46:12)
23. Type of electrical flow (abbr.)
24. "And the king of ___ he hanged on a tree" (Joshua 8:29)

26. "If thou meet thine ___ ox" (Exodus 23:4)

27. "two men stood by them in white ___" (Acts 1:10)

29. "For I long to ___ you" (Romans 1:11)

30. Transportation org.

31. Mediterranean country (abbr.)

32. "both ___, and Anah" (Genesis 36:24)

33. "leaning upon the ___ of his staff" (Hebrews 11:21)

37. "not where Christ was ___" (Romans 15:20)

39. "And if the ___ shall say" (1 Corinthians 12:16)

40. "began Menahem the son of ___ to reign" (2 Kings 15:17)

41. "They are all gone out of the ___" (Romans 3:12)

42. "that Achaia was ready a year ___" (2 Corinthians 9:2)

43. "and in the borders of ___ on the west" (Joshua 11:2)

44. "that ye also ___ full of goodness" (Romans 15:14)

46. "but the evil which I would not, that I ___" (Romans 7:19)

48. Greek letter

ACROSS

1, "Why do the heathen ___" (Psalm 2:1)
5. "Praise him for his mighty ___" (Psalm 150:2)
9. More mentally sound)
10. "And when they came to ___" (Exodus 15:23)
12. Having no sight
13. Adores
15. Nickname (fem.)
16. Hoops org.
19. Bell sound
20. Object
22. "on the east side of ___" (Numbers 34:11)
23. "Naum, which was the son of ___" (Luke 3:25)
24. Disease that can cause paralysis (abbr.)
25. "He appointed the moon for ___" (Psalm 104:19)
28. Holy one (abbr.)
29. "Because in the night ___ of Moab" (Isaiah 15:1)
30. Compass point
31. "The ungodly are not ___" (Psalm 1:4)
33. "his ___ in the east" (Matthew 2:2)
35. Undergraduate degree (abbr.)
38. Gaelic
40. Popular kind of shirt
42. "Thou hast also turned the ___ of his sword" (Psalm 89:43)
45. "And ___, and Ramah" (Joshua 19:36)

46. "that the tabernacle was ___ up" (Numbers 9:15)
47. Group
48. Finished
49. "thou has broken ___ in pieces" (Psalm 89:10)
53. "as it were with a cart ___" (Isaiah 5:18)
54. "Let the wicked fall into their own ___" (Psalm 141:10)
55. "might observe his statutes, and keep his ___" (Psalm 105:45)

DOWN

1. "in three days I will ___ it up" (John 2:19)
2. Name (fem.)
3. Replacement for high school graduation (abbr.)
4. "And the sons of Judah; ___, and Onan" (Genesis 46:12)
5. "But I ___ poor and sorrowful" (Psalm 69:29)
6. West Coast st.
7. Figures of speech
8. Keeps
9. Narrow openings, slits
11. Restores
12. "and the ___ thereof was wrought" (1 Kings 7:26)
14. Cut
16. "and to ___, and came to Jericho" (Joshua 16:7)
17. Again, in music
18. Soon
21. What an author produces (abbr.)
26. "So they did ___" (Psalm 78:29)
27. Midwestern st.
31. "For he hath founded it upon the ___" (Psalm 24:2)

32. "___ my steps in thy word" (Psalm 119:133)

33. "son of ___, which was the son of Noe" (Luke 3:36)

34. Note of the musical scale

36. "and they fed in a ___" (Genesis 41:2)

37. "the first year of Darius the ___" (Daniel 11:1)

39. "the Lord said unto ___, Whence comest thou?" (Job 1:7)

41. Native of (suffix)

43. "For he maketh small the ___ of water" (Job 36:27)

44. DNA sequence

50. Hebrew letter

51. Radioactive element symbol

52. Undergrad deg.

53. Career military (abbr.)

ACROSS

1. "we should be made ___ according to the hope" (Titus 3:7)
6. "I . . . will bring them again to their ___" (Jeremiah 23:3)
11. "If sinners ___ thee, consent thou not" (Proverbs 1:10)
13. "the ark rested . . . upon the mountains of ___" (Genesis 8:4)
15. Paid notice
16. "ye shall be . . . ___ upon her knees" (Isaiah 66:12)
18. Pinetree St.
19. Chafe
21. "they traded . . .vessels of ___" (Ezekiel 27:13)
22. "The Lord spake unto Joshua the son of ___" (Joshua 1:1)
23. "For he hath founded it upon the ___" (Psalm 24:2)
25. "I took the little book . . . and ___ it up" (Revelation 10:10)
26. "And his ___ like unto fine brass" (Revelation 1:15)
27. Excavate
29. Repasts
30. "That was the ___ Light" (John 1:9)
31. "Love the brotherhood. ___ God." (1 Peter 2:17)
32. "let it be done with ___" (Ezra 6:12)
34. "those who . . . have their ___ exercised" (Hebrews 5:14)
36. Comb wool
37. "Blind, or broken, or maimed, or having a ___" (Leviticus 22:22)
38. Russian ruler
40. "thou shalt not plow with an ox and an ___ together" (Deuteronomy 22:10)
41. "not ___ the beginning of the world" (Matthew 24:21)
43. Aunt (Sp.)
44. Football position (abbr.)
45. "Thou art an ___ man" (Luke 19:21)
47. Chinese coin
48. Metal (abbr.)
49. Org. concerned with early American genealogy
50. Print measure
51. Armory (abbr.)
52. Opposite of him
53. "I am poor and ___" (Psalm 86:1)

DOWN

1. Hearkens
2. "God hath ___ me with a good dowry" (Genesis 30:20)
3. Mediterranean country (abbr.)
4. "___ me, and deliver me" (Psalm 144:7)
5. "the Lord will smite with a ___" (Isaiah 3:17)
6. "___ witnesses are risen up against me" (Psalm 27:12)
7. Crude metals
8. "There is a ___ here" (John 6:9)
9. Physician (abbr.)
10. Old Testament prophet
12. Anger
14. "Israel shall pitch their ___" (Numbers 1:52)
17. Specified time
20. Trades
22. Closest

The grid contains numbered cells: 1, 2, 3, 4, 5, 6, 7, 8, 9, 10, 11, 12, 13, 14, 15, 16, 17, 18, 19, 20, 21, 22, 23, 24, 25, 26, 27, 28, 29, 30, 31, 32, 33, 34, 35, 36, 37, 38, 39, 40, 41, 42, 43, 44, 45, 46, 47, 48, 49, 50, 51, 52, 53

24. "of ___, the family of the Sardites" (Numbers 26:26)

26. "in the day of a solemn ___" (Lamentations 2:7)

28. Defective bomb

29. "we persuade ___" (2 Corinthians 5:11)

31. "thou hast ___ me with bones and sinews" (Job 10:11)

32. Ascot

33. Gummy substance

34. "He ___ out our fathers first" (Acts 7:12)

35. "As they ___ he fell asleep" (Luke 8:23)

37. "he was ___ than all men" (1 Kings 4:31)

39. "A continual dropping in a very ___ day" (Proverbs 27:15)

41. "A third part shall be at the gate of ___" (2 Kings 11:6)

42. "of ___, the family of Eranites" (Numbers 26:36)

45. Long sigh

46. "how long will it be ___ they attain?" (Hosea 8:5)

ACROSS

1. Relative's nickname
4. Colonnade
8. "___we ourselves groan within ourselves" (Romans 8:23)
11. "he planteth an ___, and the rain doth nourish it" (Isaiah 44:14)
12. "he had . . . a ___ of brass between his shoulders" (1 Samuel 17:6)
14. "And thou shalt . . . shew them . . . the work that they must ___" (Exodus 18:20)
15. Foreboding
17. "he expelled thence the three sons of ___" (Judges 1:20)
19. "we are his people, and the ___ of his pasture" (Psalm 100:3)
21. Assist
22. "Which are blackish by reason of the ___" (Job 6:16)
24. "the ___ state of that man is worse than the first" (Matthew 12:45)
25. Beard of grain
26. Anecdote
27. Time zone
28. "Your fathers, where ___ they?" (Zechariah 1:5)
29. "be not dismayed at the ___of heaven" (Jeremiah 10:2)
31. "And the earth was without ___, and void" (Genesis 1:2)
33. "And thou shalt make ___ of shittim wood" (Exodus 26:26)
34. "if there be any praise, ___ on these things" (Philippians 4:8)
36. "the lapwing and the ___" (Leviticus 11:19)
37. Hawaiian hawk
38. "Go to the ___, thou sluggard" (Proverbs 6:6)
39. Coal scuttle
40. Folk song
42. Lyric poem
43. "That wast perfect . . . from the ___ that thou wast created" (Ezekiel 28:15)
44. "After these things did king Ahasuerus promote ___" (Esther 3:1)
45. "put a ___ on his hand" (Luke 15:22)
47. "some would even ___ to die" (Romans 5:7)
48. Print measure
50. "Now ___, captain of the host of the king of Syria" (2 Kings 5:1)
52. Arrest
55. "God shall . . . ___ it upon him while he is eating" (Job 20:23)
56. "And ___ your heart, and not your garments" (Joel 2:13)
57. "Give unto the Lord the glory ___ unto his name" (Psalm 29:2)

DOWN

1. Continent (abbr.)
2. "Nabal ___ his name" (1 Samuel 25:25)
3. "put off thy ___ from off thy feet (Exodus 3:5)
4. "If my ___ hath turned out of the way" (Job 31:7)
5. Light brown
6. West Coast state (abbr.)
7. "Whosoever drinketh of this water shall thirst ___" (John 4:13)
8. Greek letter
9. "the children of Gad called the altar ___" (Joshua 22:34)
10. "there is ___ upon earth that I desire beside thee" (Psalm 73:25)
13. "And he that . . . keepeth my works unto the ___" (Revelation 2:26)
16. "a place where two ways ___" (Mark 11:4)
18. "The ___ of the earth set themselves (Psalm 2:2)
19. "But while men ___, his enemy came" (Matthew 13:25)
20. Headgear
21. "Stand in ___ and sin not" (Psalm 4:4)
23. "How ___ a man be born when he is old?" (John 3:4)
25. "___ yourselves likewise with the same mind" (1 Peter 4:1)
26. "they cried out . . . and threw dust into the ___" (Acts 22:23)
28. "How shall I bring the ___ of God home?" (1 Chronicles 13:12)
29. "And he ___ down, and taught the people" (Luke 5:3)
30. "One ___ of ten shekels of gold" (Numbers 7:14)

31. "there shall come forth a vessel for the
    ___" (Proverbs 25:4)
32. Canadian province (abbr., var.)
33. "I may discern between good and ___"
    (1 Kings 3:9)
35. "Yea, he ___ power over the angel"
    (Hosea 12:4)
36. "And they have . . . given a ___ for an har-
    lot" (Joel 3:3)
37. Mountain in Crete
39. "And Sarah saw the son of ___"
    (Genesis 21:9)
40. "to be with Christ; which is ___ better"
    (Philippians 1:23)
41. "___ your ways and your doings"
    (Jeremiah 7:3)

42. "The eyes of the Lord are ___ the right-
    eous" (1 Peter 3:12)
43. Molecular base for heredity
44. "Deliver me . . out of the ___ of the
    wicked" (Psalm 71:4)
46. "[He] . . . brought to him an ___, and took
    care of him" (Luke 10:34)
47. "___ shall judge his people"
    (Genesis 49:16)
51. Bangor's state (abbr.)
53. Precious metal symbol
54. "these things ought not so to ___"
    (James 3:10)

ACROSS

1. Sailing term
5. Distant
7. "another angel ascending from the ___" (Revelation 7:2)
11. Gossip
13. "lo, I am ___ you alway" (Matthew 28:20)
14. Authorized Version (abbr.)
15. West Coast st.
16. "And ___ went and told them" (Mark 16:10)
18. Concerning
19. "Jachan and ___ and Heber" (1 Chronicles 5:13)
21. "whereunto was the city of ___" (Acts 27:8)
22. "for the ___ that is in the land of Assyria" (Isaiah 7:18)
23. Attack
25. "I will shoot ___ arrows" (1 Samuel 20:20)
28. PHD candidate
29. "To all the ___ in Christ Jesus" (Philippians 1:1)
30. Exclamation
33. Heading toward Antarctica (abbr.)
34. Paraphrase of First Commandment (2 words)
38. "thou sawest the feet and ___" (Daniel 2:41)
41. Locale
42. "from the kernels even to the ___" (Numbers 6:4)
43. Ear (comb. form)
44. Owl sound
45. Longing
48. Legal office (abbr.)

49. "Shimei, and ___, and the mighty men" (1 Kings 1:8)
50. Shelter
52. Where its charged to (abbr.)
53. Leer
55. Coporrate absorptions
57. "Whosoever shall ___ this writing" (Daniel 5:7)
58. Signal for help (abbr.)
59. Heraldric border

DOWN

1. "Moreover, the Lord spake again unto ___" (Isaiah 7:10)
2. "He . . . saw a publican, named ___" (Luke 5:27)
3. Apiece (abbr.)
4. Hospital place (abbr.)
5. Electrical unit
6. With me, an exclamation of sorrow
7. "One ___ lamb of the first year" (Leviticus 14:10)
8. "Arise, go up to ___" (Joshua 8:1)
9. "She uttereth her voice in the ___" (Proverbs 1:20)
10. "The transgressions of Israel were found in ___" (Micah 1:13)
12. Stable
16. Places
17. A sunken fence
20. "Pispah and ___" (1 Chronicles 7:38)
22. "Zechariah, ___, and Jaaziel" (1 Chronicles 15:18)
24. "Lord, who shall ___ in thy tabernacle?" (Psalm 15:1)
26. "according to all the ___ of it" (Numbers 9:3)
27. Worthless (prefix)
30. "thou art the ___ of God" (Matthew 14:33)

32. One held for ransom
35. Relating to (suffix)
36. Ottawa's prov.
37. "The Philistines . . . spread themselves in ___" (Judges 15:9)
38. Pegs
39. "But the children of the kingdom shall be cast out into ___ darkness" (Matthew 8:12)
40. "so many as the stars of the ___ in multitude" (Hebrews 11:12)
43. Scent
46. Nobleman
47. Snoop

50. "Look not upon the wine when it is ___" (Proverbs 23:31)
51. Self
54. West Coast city (abbr.)
55. Show Me St
56. Place providing medical aide (abbr.)

PUZZLE 57

ACROSS

1. "The Jephthah . . dwelt in he land of ___" (Judges 11:3)
4. "I will cleanse their ___" (Joel 3:21)
9. Decay
12. "There is none righteous, no, not ___" (Romans 3:10)
13. "the Lord will feed them as a lamb in a ___ place" (Hosea 4:16)
14. "And it came to pass by the way in the ___" (Exodus 4:24)
15. Midweek (abbr.)
16. "___ thou dash thy foot against a stone" (Psalm 91:12)
17. "look upon the ___ of thine anointed" (Psalm 84:9)
19. Midriff
21. "___ king of Egypt came up to fight" (2 Chronicles 35:20)
22. "They . . . took old ___ upon their asses" (Joshua 9:4)
23. "Joseph is without doubt ___ in pieces" (Genesis 37:33)
24. Compass point
26. "There dwelt men of ___ also therein" (Nehemiah 13:16)
27. "he preferred her and her ___" (Esther 2:9)
28. Lone Star st.
29. "Deliver thyself as a ___ from the hand of the hunter" (Proverbs 6:5)
30. New Zealand tree
31. "The sons of Shamer; ___ and Rohgah" (1 Chronicles 7:34)
32. "The children of ___ and Hushim" (1 Chronicles 7:12)
33. "But the ___ of the Lord stood in a path" (Numbers 22:24)
35. "we should not lust after ___ things" (1 Corinthians 10:6)
36. Italian river
37. "there was no ___ for them in the inn" (Luke 2:7)

38. "___ are the beginnings of sorrows" (Mark 13:8)
39. Guitar sound
41. Evades
42. "___ is the kingdom, and the power" (Matthew 6:13)
43. "the love of God is ___ abroad in our hearts" (Romans 5:5)
44. Midwestern st.
46. "The crowns shall be to . . . ___ the son of Zephaniah" (Zechariah 6:14)
47. "be cast out into ___ darkness" (Matthew 8:12)
49. "Why make ye this ___?" (Mark 5:39)
50. "Sir, come down ___ my child die" (John 4:49)
51. "For he knoweth our ___" (Psalm 103:14)
52. "In the first chariot were ___ horses" (Zechariah 6:2)

DOWN

1. "as a thread of ___ is broken" (Judges 16:9)
2. "Go thee ___" (Ezekiel 21:16) (4 words)
3. "How can these things ___?" (John 3:9)
4. "___ ye the Lord" (Psalm 103:21)
5. "the same shall be ___ of all" (Mark 9:35)
6. Table scrap
7. "___ king of Bashan" (1 Kings 4:19)
8. "There arose to ___ Israel Tola" (Judges 10:1)
9. "___ and poor, together" (Psalm 49:2)
10. "the ___ of the bank of the river" (Daniel 12:5) (4 words)
11. Southern st.
16. "___ as a lion" (Psalm 17:12)
18. "Praise him for his mighty ___" (Psalm 150:2)
20. "An half ___ of land" (1 Samuel 14:14)
21. "toward the north side of Bethemek, and ___" (Joshua 19:27)

116

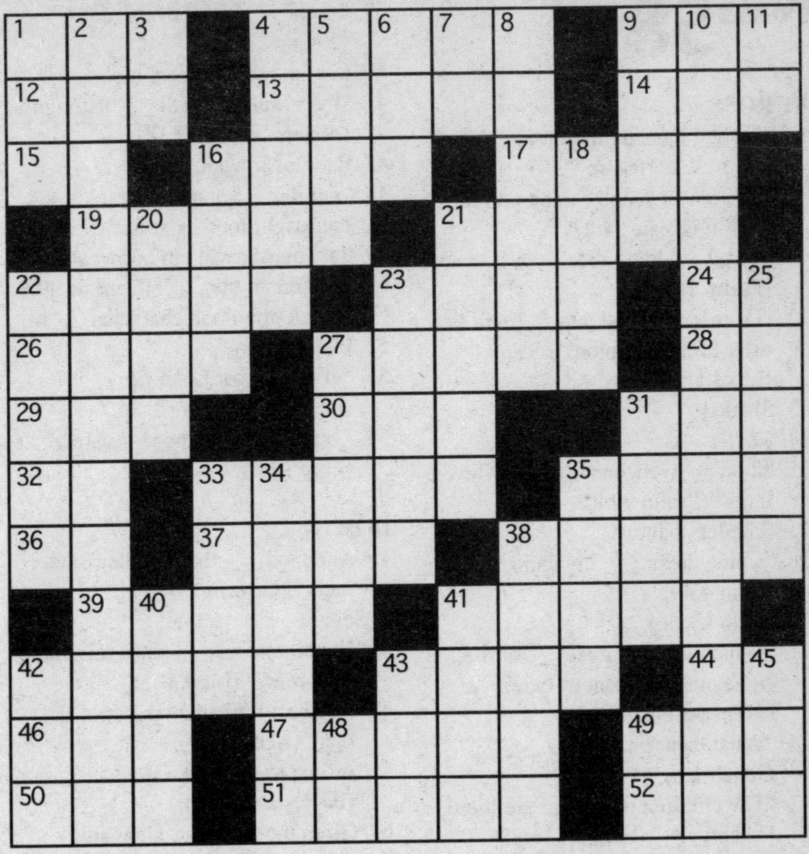
1 2 3 4 5 6 7 8 9 10 11
12 13 14
15 16 17 18
19 20 21
22 23 24 25
26 27 28
29 30 31
32 33 34 35
36 37 38
39 40 41
42 43 44 45
46 47 48 49
50 51 52

22. "___ you, and make you bare" (Isaiah 32:11)
23. "His sons were Ulam and ___" (1 Chronicles 7:16)
25. "The captive ___ hasteneth" (Isaiah 51:14)
27. "The sons of Japheth; Gomer and ___" (Genesis 10:2)
31. "The young men of ___ . . . shall fall by the sword" (Ezekiel 30:17)
33. "Uz and ___" (Genesis 36:28)
34. "Let ___ you imagine evil" (Zechariah 7:10, 2 words)
35. "But ___ made him a dagger" (Judges 3:16)
38. "that it may be ___ for a witness" (Deuteronomy 31:26)
40. "___ bottles, old, and rent" (Joshua 9:4)
41. "Noah begat ___, Ham, and Japheth" (Genesis 5:32)
42. God (comb. form)
43. Depot (abbr.)
45. "Cain . . . dwelt in the land of ___" (Genesis 4:16)
48. "___ of the Chaldees" (Nehemiah 9:7)
49. "It hath consumed ___ of Moab" (Numbers 21:28)

ACROSS

1. "He shall have dominion also from ___ to sea" (Psalm 72:8)
4. "The sons of Jacob came upon the ___" (Genesis 34:27)
9. "Lord, I ___ unto thee" (Psalm 141:1)
12. "Or if he shall ask an ___, will he offer him a scorpion?" (Luke 11:12)
13. Shaded
14. Caviar
15. "thou ___ vengeance of their inventions" (Psalm 99:8)
17. Smaller quantity
18. "Come down ___ my child die" (John 4:49)
19. Broth (Scot.)
21. "Which is a manifest ___ of the righteous judgment of God" (2 Thessalonians 1:5)
24. "What meanest thou, O ___?" (Jonah 1:6)
27. "The children of Dishan are these; Uz and ___" (Genesis 36:28)
28. "every idle word that men shall ___" (Matthew 12:36)
29. "I have ___ pleasure in you." (Malachi 1:10)
30. "And the ___, which the Lord God had taken from man" (Genesis 2:22)
31. "They ___ their days in wealth" (Job 21:13)
32. Greek letter
33. Message-s (abbr.)
34. Displayed
35. Holds in reverence
36. "ye have ___ at it" (Malachi 1:13)
38. Aware

39. "A daily ___ for every day" (2 Kings 25:30)
40. Length measurement (abbr.)
41. "there was no small ___ among the soldiers" (Acts 12:18)
43. Paint over again
48. "put it . . . upon the great ___ of their right foot" (Exodus 29:20)
49. "my master wotteth not what is with me in the ___" (Genesis 39:8)
51. Winnie-the-Pooh character
52. Piercing tool
53. "grievous words stir up ___" (Proverbs 15:1)
54. "yet ___ there is hope in Israel" (Ezra 10:2)

DOWN

1. "And God ___ them in the firmament" (Genesis 1:17)
2. Self
3. "How long is it ___ since this came unto him?" (Mark 9:21)
4. "they cast four anchors out of the ___" (Acts 27:29)
5. "A time to get, and a time to ___" (Ecclesiastes 3:6)
6. "Go to the ___, thou sluggard" (Proverbs 6:6)
7. That is (abbr.)
8. Midwestern st.
9. "For of this sort are they which ___ into houses" (2 Timothy 3:6)
10. Nickname (fem.)
11. Affirmative
16. Sharp
17. Garden herb
19. Mix together
20. "And he . . . stood up for to ___" (Luke 4:16)
21. Pastries
22. "Canst thou . . . loose the bands of ___" (Job 38:31)

23. Hebrew dry measure
24. "Come to him with all ___" (Acts 17:15)
25. "___ into his gates with thanksgiving" (Psalm 100:4)
26. "And thou shalt ___ and eat it" (Deuteronomy 16:7)
28. Period of unrestrained indulgence
31. "He may ___ you as wheat" (Luke 22:31)
32. "he shall take two he lambs . . . and one ___ lamb" (Leviticus 14:10)
34. "remember the Lord ___ off" (Jeremiah 51:50)
35. Singing part

37. "Tahath his son, ___ his son" (1 Chronicles 6:24)
38. "things . . . that shall come ___" (Ecclesiastes 1:11)
41. Depot (abbr.)
42. "He brake the withs, as a thread of ___ is broken" (Judges 16:9)
43. Carpet
44. Native of (suffix)
45. Vase
46. Dove's cry
47. Question word
49. "He saith among the trumpets, ___" (Job 39:25)
50. Canadian prov.

ACROSS

1. "cloven tongues like as of ___" (Acts 2:3)
5. "pertaining to the kingdom of ___" (Acts 1:3)
8. New Testament book
12. "and ___ with joy receiveth it" (Matthew 13:20)
13. "And Abraham set seven ___ lambs" (Genesis 21:28)
14. Send
15. "and the ___ of your god Remphan" (Acts 7:43)
16. "but ye have made it a ___ of thieves" (Luke 19:46)
17. "that I am ___ from the blood of all men" (Acts 20:26)
18. Popular vegetable
20. "The young lions roared upon him, and ___" (Jeremiah 2:15)
22. Of a seasoning (var.)
24. "But my servant ___" (Numbers 14:24)
27. Common abbr.
28. Several 16 oz. measures
31. Product (suffix)
32. "with a gold ___, . . . also a poor man" (James 2:2)
34. Verb form (abbr.)
35. "yet will I ___ make ___ full ___ of thee" (Jeremiah 30:11) (3 words)
37. "Hariph, Anathoth, ___" (Nehemiah 10:19)
39. "they went down into ___" (Acts 14:25)
41. "so that I might finish my ___ with joy" (Acts 20:24)
44. "began ___ to reign over Israel" (1 Kings 16:23)
46. Scandinavian country's capital
47. "___ while Paul waited for them at Athens" (Acts 17:16)
49. Throw
52. "yet will they ___ upon the Lord" (Micah 3:11)
53. Up to such a time (poet.)
54. "and smote the ___ into his temples" (Judges 4:21)
55. Not any
56. Sneaky
57. Liver secretion

DOWN

1. "and made their feet ___ in the stocks" (Acts 16:24)
2. "Arise and go ___ the city" (Acts 9:6)
3. Wander
4. Make very angry
5. "And ___, and Ahio, and Zacher" (1 Chronicles 8:31)
6. "___ no man any thing" (Romans 13:8)
7. "even ___ the Lord that bought them" (2 Peter 2:1)
8. Fully
9. "and will rend the ___ of their heart" (Hosea 13:8)
10. "bind the ___ of thine head upon thee" (Ezekiel 24:17)
11. Child's winter toy
19. "The mirth of ___ ceaseth" (Isaiah 24:8)
21. O.T. book (var.)
23. Yorba ___
24. "Neither ___ they prove the things" (Acts 24:13)
25. "Why make ye this ___, and weep?" (Mark 5:39)
26. Rent
28. Place for experimentation
29. Large snake

30. ___ Lanka
33. "of the thoughts and ___ of the heart" (Hebrews 4:12)
36. "and ___ rod that budded" (Hebrews 9:4)
37. Steal
40. "for I am meek and ___ in heart" (Matthew 11:29)
41. "present rain, and because of the ___" (Acts 28:2)
42. "As he saith also in ___" (Romans 9:25)
43. "and his sons were ___ and Rakem" (1 Chronicles 7:16)

45. "Sibbecai the Hushathite, ___ the Ahohite" (1 Chronicles 11:29)
48. "anointing him with ___" (James 5:14)
50. ___ cloth
51. Scottish is.
54. Canadian prov.

PUZZLE 60

ACROSS

1. "a stormy wind shall ___ it" (Ezekiel 13:11)
5. "Jonah was gone down ___ the sides of the ship" (Jonah 1:5)
9. Increase (arch.)
12. "my cup runneth ___" (Psalm 23:5)
13. Quatre (Fr.)
14. "A vineyard of ___ wine" (Isaiah 27:2)
15. Prevent
17. Will let know later (abbr.)
18. "Nathan the prophet, and Shimei, and ___ (1 Kings 1:8)
19. Air (comb. form)
21. "neither will I ___ an offering at your hand" (Malachi 1:10)
23. "those virgins arose, and ___ their lamps" (Matthew 25:7)
27. "the ___ was come to the place of the arrow" (1 Samuel 20:37)
28. Charged particles
29. "And after six days Jesus taketh ___, James, and John" (Matthew 17:1)
31. Year of Our Lord (abbr.)
33. "I have stretched out my hand, and no ___ regarded" (Proverbs 1:24)
34. "Number all the firstborn of the ___" (Numbers 3:40)
35. Exclamation of distaste
36. "The children of Gad called the altar ___" (Joshua 22:34)
37. "But ye are a chosen generation, a ___ priesthood" (1 Peter 2:9)
38. Act or process (suffix)
39. "A third part shall be at the gate of ___" (2 Kings 11:6)
40. Desire
42. "they shall take up a lamentation for thee, and ___ over thee" (Ezekiel 27:32)
45. Cup

DOWN

46. "___, even the ancient high places are ours in possession" (Ezekiel 36:2)
47. Anger
49. "___, Mahalaleel, Jered" (1 Chronicles 1:2)
53. "bring unto thee pure ___ olive beaten for the light" (Leviticus 24:2)
54. "I went down into the garden of ___ to see the fruits of the valley" (Song of Solomon 6:11)
56. "he went into a city called ___" (Luke 7:ll)
57. Peruvian money
58. Equipment
59. "And came to the strong hold of ___" (2 Samuel 24:7)

DOWN

1. "thy ___ and thy staff they comfort me" (Psalm 23:4)
2. "the serpent beguiled ___ through his subtilty" (2 Corinthians 11:3)
3. "the fishes that are taken in an evil ___" (Ecclesiates 9:12)
4. "the diviners . . . have told false ___" (Zechariah 10:2)
5. Inter. frequency
6. "___ by might, nor by power" (Zechariah 4:6)
7. Member of the brass section
8. "unto them were committed the ___ of God" (Romans 3:2)
9. "cause me to understand wherein I have ___" (Job 6:24)
10. "___ not thou silence" (Psalm 83:1)
11. Blue pencil
16. Radiation dosage
20. "I will ___ it" (Philemon 19)
22. Vehicle
23. "I will set him a ___" (Nehemiah 2:6)
24. "Whither have ye made a ___ today" (1 Samuel 27:10)
25. "There was no room for them in the ___" (Luke 2:7)
26. "Thou shalt not ___ to offer the first of thy ripe fruits" (Exodus 22:29)

30. "Ziph, and ___, and Bealoth" (Joshua 15:24)
31. Number of years
32. Graduate deg.
34. "thou shalt seek me in the ___" (Job 7:21)
35. Vase
37. "ye tithe mint and ___ and all manner of herbs" (Luke 11:42)
38. "the king's commandment was ___" (Daniel 3:22)
39. "I am ___ and despised" (Psalm 119:141)
41. Diving bird
42. Asian country

43. "Uzzah and ___, the sons of Abinadab, drave the new cart" (2 Samuel 6:3)
44. "That was the ___ Light" (John 1:9)
48. Greek letter
50. "I tell you ___; but rather division" (Luke 12:51)
51. "according to the prince of the power of the ___" (Ephesians 2:2)
52. Compass point
55. Older one (abbr.)

123

ACROSS

1. "I am the ___ of Sharon"
   (Song of Solomon 2:1)
5. Excavation site
9. "___ knoweth this man letters?"
   (John 7:15)
12. "And ___ they tell him of her"
    (Mark 1:30)
13. English river
14. "Stand in ___ and sin not" (Psalm 4:4)
15. East Coast st.
16. Temp. measurement
18. "as swift as the ___ flieth"
    (Deuteronomy 28:49)
20. Vandal
21. Satisfied
22. "The Lord called Samuel again the ___
    time" (1 Samuel 3:8)
24. "He was a burning and a ___ light"
    (John 5:35)
27. "Absalom ___ upon a mule"
    (2 Samuel 18:9)
28. "the waters were made ___ "
    (Exodus 15:25)
29. West Coast st.
30. "where ___ they?" (Zechariah 1:5)
31. "there appeared unto them Moses and
    ___ " (Matthew 17:3)
32. "The highways ___ waste"
    (Isaiah 33:8)
33. "Who ___ like unto thee?"
    (Psalm 35:10)
34. "they come up by the ___ of Ziz"
    (2 Chronicles 20:16)
35. "___ it, even to the foundation thereof"
    (Psalm 137:7)
36. "___ not the gift that is in thee"
    (1 Timothy 4:14)
38. "Then these men were bound in their
    coats, their ___, and their hats"
    (Daniel 3:21)
39. "a strong man to run a ___ "
    (Psalm 19:5)
40. "And ___ of checker work"
    (1 Kings 7:17)
41. Tilt
43. "A raven, which ___ forth to and fro"
    (Genesis 8:7)
44. Message-sending place (abbr.)
46. "I will not with ink and ___ write unto
    thee" (3 John 13)
47. female wool-bearing animals
49. "he placed at the east of the garden of
    ___ Cherubims" (Genesis 3:24)
51. "The Lord shall ___ to me another
    son" (Genesis 30:24)
52. "The lord of that servant . . . for-
    gave him the ___" (Matthew 18:27)
53. "there is ___ to help" (Psalm 22:11)

DOWN

1. "they offered a ___ of the flock for their
   trespass" (Ezra 10:19)
2. "For there is ___ God" (1 Timothy 2:5)
3. "And ___ all Israel shall be saved"
   (Romans 11:26)
4. "Thou therefore ___ hardness"
   (2 Timothy 2:3)
5. Reading material (abbr.)
6. Through blood vessels (abbr.)
7. "there shall ___ blood be shed for him"
   (Exodus 22:2)
8. "be avenged of the king's ___ "
   (1 Samuel 18:25)
9. "The sons of Gad; Ziphion and ___ "
   (Genesis 46:16)
10. "I am like an ___ of the desert"
    (Psalm 102:6)
11. Very small
17. "thy years shall have no ___ "
    (Psalm 102:27)
19. "She is thine ___ " (Leviticus 18:14)
20. "abide in a secret place, and ___ thy-
    self" (1 Samuel 19:2)
21. "like a torch of fire in a ___ "
    (Zechariah 12:6)
22. "and his ___ filled the temple"
    (Isaiah 6:1)
23. "And I saw, and behold a white ___ "
    (Revelation 6:2)

24. "feet that be ___ in running to mischief" (Proverbs 6:18)
25. "Make a joyful ___ unto the Lord" (Psalm 100:1)
26. "He maketh me to lie down in ___ pastures" (Psalm 23:2)
28. Slab
31. "The church that is at Babylon, ___ together with you" (1 Peter 5:13)
32. Girl
34. Tribe
35. "The seed is ___ under their clods" (Joel 1:17)
37. Lavish

38. "how often would I have gathered thy children together, as a ___" (Luke 13:34)
40. "There shall the great owl make her ___" (Isaiah 34:15)
41. Health resort
42. "And Jesus . . . was ___ by the Spirit into the wilderness" (Luke 4:1)
43. "If thou weavest the seven locks of my head with the ___" (Judges 16:13)
44. "___ virgins, which took their lamps" (Matthew 25:1)
45. "There is ___ God" (Mark 12:32)
48. Weekday (abbr.)
50. "___ all in the name of the Lord Jesus" (Colossians 3:17)

125

PUZZLE 62

ACROSS

1. To treat leather
4. "And he shall be like a ___ planted by the rivers" (Psalm 1:3)
8. Converse
12. "forgive, if you have aught against ___" (Mark 11:25)
13. "He that soweth iniquity shall ___ vanity" (Proverbs 22:8)
14. "___ thine enemy" (Matthew 5:43)
15. Football position (abbr.)
16. "___ the kine to the cart" (1 Samuel 6:7)
17. "Which are blackish by reason of the ___" (Job 6:16)
19. Printer's measure
20. "the walled city shall be ___ for ever" (Leviticus 25:30)
24. Crude metal
25. "with lower, second, and third ___ shalt thou make it" (Genesis 6:16)
28. "for a good man some would even ___ to die" (Romans 5:7)
30. Drink
31. "___ saith in her heart, I sit a queen" (Revelation 18:7)
32. Ins and ___
33. "let not ___ of them escape" (1 Kings 18:40)
34. "her great ___ went not forth out of her" (Ezekiel 24:12)
35. Wildebeest
36. Mil. decoration
37. Foot (comb. form)
38. "sell her unto a ___ nation" (Exodus 21:8)
40. "shut the doors, and ___ them" (Nehemiah 7:3)
41. "some have ___ angels unawares" (Hebrews 13:2)

45. Balloon gas symbol
47. "they were ___ strong for me" (Psalm 18:17)
48. "So they ___ both together" (John 20:4)
49. "from the beginning it was not ___" (Matthew 19:8)
50. "I was by the river of ___" (Daniel 8:2)
52. Russian mountain range
54. "the Lord shewed him all the land . . . unto ___" (Deuteronomy 34:1)
55. Bluish-white metal
56. Quick drink
57. "he should pay all that was ___ unto him" (Matthew 18:34)

DOWN

1. "as a ___ that is told" (Psalm 90:9)
2. "The ___ are a people not strong" (Proverbs 30:25)
3. East Coast st.
4. "I took . . . one of a ___" (Deuteronomy 1:23)
5. "They ___ to and fro" (Psalm 107:27)
6. Apiece (abbr.)
7. "they delivered the ___ (Acts 15:30)
8. "Son, be of good ___" (Matthew 9:2)
9. "He saith among the trumpets, ___" (Job 39:25)
10. "They . . . ___ the sacrifices of the dead" (Psalm 106:28)
11. "the kingdom of heaven be likened unto ___ virgins" (Matthew 25:1)
16. "his enemy came and sowed ___" (Matthew 13:25)
18. "they break their bones, and ___ them in pieces" (Micah 3:3)
21. Agony
22. "therefore what ___ thine hand?" (1 Samuel 21:3, 2 words)

126

23. "cannot my taste ___ perverse things?" (Job 6:30)
26. "the Lord raised them up a deliverer, ___" (Judges 3:15)
27. Incompletely
28. "Beware of ___, beware of evil workers" (Philippians 3:2)
29. "she is thine ___" (Leviticus 18:14)
30. "Herod. . . arrayed him in a ___ robe" (Luke 23:11)
34. "I take my journey into ___" (Romans 15:24)
36. Being (comb. Form)
39. Prank
40. Old Testament pagan god
42. "a ___ for him in the way" (Job 18:10)
43. "___ was a cunning hunter" (Genesis 25:27)
44. "He hath ___ all things well" (Mark 7:37)
45. "___ his firstborn" (Genesis 22:21)
46. "And the man came in hastily and told ___" (1 Samuel 4:14)
51. Year (abbr.)
53. New England st.
54. Minister's degree (abbr.)

PUZZLE 63

ACROSS

1. "Now after the ___ of Moses" (Joshua 1:1)
6. "over this Jordan, . . . ___ the land" (Joshua 1:2)
10. Morning (abbr.)
12. "which she had laid in ___ upon the roof" (Joshua 2:6)
13. "Come ___, put your feet upon the necks" (Joshua 10:24)
14. "___, every one that thirsteth" (Isaiah 55:1)
15. Toronto's prov.
16. "And Zebadiah, and Arad, and ___" (1 Chronicles 8:15)
17. Laughter sounds
18. " I ___ old and stricken in age" (Joshua 23:2)
20. "but he ___ the land to give the money" (2 Kings 23:35)
22. "Open the mouth of the ___" (Joshua 10:22)
23. "By ___ was their inheritance" (Joshua 14:2)
25. "and ___ the father of Abner" (1 Samuel 14:51)
26. Southern st.
27. Undergraduate deg.
28. "and as ___ the sun was down" (Joshua 8:29)
30. "And all that handle the ___" (Ezekiel 27:29)
32. Vegetable
34. "as it is also written in the second ___" (Acts 13:33)
37. "and they went to ___ in ambush" (Joshua 8:9)
38. Cords
39. ___-and-fro
41. Holy one (abbr.)
42. "And Joshua the son of ___" (Joshua 2:1)
45. Scottish river
46. "___ thou over us" (Judges 8:22)
48. "and dip it in the blood that is in the ___" (Exodus 12:22)
50. Southern st.

51. "the land which ___ do give ___ them" (Joshua 1:2)
52. "neither could any man ___ him" (Mark 5:4)
53. "All the kingdom of ___ in Bashan" (Joshua 13:12)
55. "We will ___ blameless of this thine oath" (Joshua 2:17)
56. "neither will I be with you any ___" (Joshua 7:12)
57. "and Dalaiah, and ___, seven" (1 Chronicles 3:24)
60. "and he called his name ___" (Genesis 38:3)
61." and to the fewer ye shall give the ___ inheritance" (Numbers 33:54)
62. Rock shelf

DOWN

1. "Thus shalt thou ___ six days" (Joshua 6:3)
2. "The sons of Judah were ___ and Onan" (Numbers 26:19)
3. "Why make ye this ___, and weep?" (Mark 5:39)
4. "and they ran unto the ___" (Joshua 7:22)
5. period of time (abbr.)
6. "and set it up there ___ an oak" (Joshua 24:26)
7. "and shalt surely lend him sufficient for his ___" (Deuteronomy 15:8)
8. "___ and feather"
9. Mt. Hood's st.
10. "Then we departed from the river of ___" (Ezra 8:31)
11. "as I was with ___" (Joshua 1:5)
16. "and now also the ___ is laid" (Luke 3:9)
17. "He saith among the trumpets, ___" (Job 39:25)
18. "The Lord ___ spake unto Joshua" (Joshua 20:1)
19. "and thou, ___, in the valley of Ajalon" (Joshua 10:12)
21. Relating to (suffix)
22. "The king of Dor in the ___ of Dor" (Joshua 12:23)
24. "they ___ not, neither do they spin" (Matthew 6:28)
26. Cleaning utensil

29. "nor make any ___ with your voice" (Joshua 6:10)
31. Foray
33. "My ___ also will I spread upon him" (Ezekiel 12:13)
35. "a feast of wines on the ___" (Isaiah 25:6)
36. Very small time unit (abbr.)
39. "out of every ___ a man" (Joshua 4:2)
40. "was heard even to the ___ court" (Ezekiel 10:5)
42. "and these are the ___ of his daughters" (Joshua 17:3)
43. "neither shall ye ___ enchantment" (Leviticus 19:26)
44. "they gave ___ part unto the Levites" (Joshua 14:4)

47. "and now, ___, I am this day" (Joshua 14:10)
48. "And he made ___ of shittim wood" (Exodus 36:31)
49. "so that they let ___ of them remain" (Joshua 8:22)
52. "and upon the great ___ of his right foot" (Leviticus 8:23)
54. "And out of the tribe of ___" (Joshua 21:38)
56. Reformation leader's initials
57. Southern st.
58. Unacceptable (abbr.)
59. That is (abbr.)

PUZZLE 64

ACROSS

1. "the children of Gad called the altar ___" (Joshua 22:34)
3. "I have trusted also in the Lord: therefore I shall not ___" (Psalm 26:1)
7. "The sons of Zibeon; ___ and Anah" (1 Chronicles 1:40)
10. "The seed is ___ under their clods" (Joel 1:17)
12. "And they ___ hands on them" (Acts 4:3)
14. "They are all ___ as an oven" (Hosea 7:7)
15. Lie
16. "broughtest him out of ___ of the Chaldees" (Nehemiah 9:7)
17. "they left their father Zebedee in the ___" (Mark 1:20)
19. "Praise the Lord, all ye Gentiles; and ___ him" (Romans 15:11)
20. "after he had offered ___ sacrifice for sins for ever" (Hebrews 10:12)
21. Bohemian Reformer, Jan ___
22. "The earth was without form, and ___" (Genesis 1:2)
23. "how ___ a man then understand" (Proverbs 20:24)
24. Mediterranean country (abbr.)
25. Wail
26. "turned from ___ eastward toward the sunrising" (Joshua 19:12)
28. "___ and all hills; fruitful trees, and all cedars" (Psalm 148:9)
30. "And round about the throne were four and twenty ___" (Revelation 4:4)
32. "___ it in a book" (Isaiah 30:8)
33. Midweek (abbr.)
34. Swedish money denomination
35. "In ___ and caves of the earth" (Hebrews 11:38)
36. "when Jesus ___ finished these parables, he departed" (Matthew 13:53)
37. "Is ___ sick among you?" (James 5:14)
38. "I will put my hook in thy ___" (2 Kings 19:28)
39. "Let me ___ through thy land" (Deuteronomy 2:27)
40. "Where ___ God my Maker" (Job 35:10)
41. "The ___ are a people not strong" (Proverbs 30:25)
42. "Rabbi, thou ___ the Son of God" (John 1:49)
43. "I saw, and behold, a ___ in the midst of the earth" (Daniel 4:10)
44. Eradicator
47. "Sallu, ___, Hilkiah, Jedaiah" (Nehemiah 12:7)
48. "Thou shall not ___ to offer the first of thy ripe fruits" (Exodus 22:29)
49. Symbol for sodium

DOWN

1. "The sons of Judah; ___, and Onan, and Shelah" (1 Chronicles 2:3)
2. "If thou ___ these things" (John 7:4)
3. "all iniquity shall ___ her mouth" (Psalm 107:42)
4. "And God said, ___ there be light" (Genesis 1:3)
5. Midwestern st.
6. "Achim begat ___" (Matthew 1:14)
7. "arise, go up to ___" (Joshua 8:1)
8. Body particle (suffix)
9. "turn aside, sit down ___" (Ruth 4:1)
11. "Lo ___, we have searched it" (Job 5:27)
13. Stomach area (abbr.)
15. "I will send a ___ into their hearts" (Leviticus 26:36)
16. "Babukiah and ___, their brethren" (Nehemiah 12:9)
17. "The ___ of Tarshish did sing of thee in thy market" (Ezekiel 27:25)
18. Small building
19. "The ___ which is lent to the Lord" (1 Samuel 2:20)
20. "Wherein shall go no galley with ___" (Isaiah 33:21)
22. You (Fr.)

23. "the sweet ___ from a far country?" (Jeremiah 6:20)
25. "And why beholdest thou the ___ that is in thy brother's eye?" (Luke 6:41)
26. Reclines
27. "to every man according to his ___" (Romans 2:6)
28. "Jacob begat Joseph the husband of ___" (Matthew 1:16)
29. Excellent (slang)
31. Eras
33. "the Lord ___ not in the wind" (1 Kings 19:11)
35. "she ___ on her lovers" (Ezekiel 23:5)
36. Berets
37. "The children also of Benjamin . . . dwelt at Michmash, and ___" (Nehemiah 11:31)
38. Compass point
39. "___ for the peace of Jerusalem" (Psalm 122:6)
41. "the ___ of the covenant" (Hebrews 9:4)
42. "The sons of Jether; Jepunneh, and Pispah, and ___" (1 Chronicles 7:38)
43. Message-sending place (abbr.)
44. Overhead railway
45. ___ passant, chess term
46. Career military (abbr.)

PUZZLE 65

ACROSS

1. Single
4. "He took him ___ from the multitude" (Mark 7:33)
8. One hundredth of a kip
10. "Ram the firstborn, and Bunah, and ___" (1 Chronicles 2:25)
12. "No man putteth a piece of a ___ garment upon an old" (Luke 5:36)
13. Opposite direction of no.
14. Southern st.
16. "Because that ___ hath dealt against the house of Judah" (Ezekiel 25:12)
18. "thou set thy ___ among the stars" (Obadiah 4)
20. "he that shall endure unto the ___, . . . shall be saved" (Mark 13:13)
22. "Ye blind guides, which strain at a ___" (Matthew 23:24)
24. "I will pour my Spirit upon thy ___" (Isaiah 44:3)
26. "unite my heart to fear thy ___" (Psalm 86:11)
28. "lest at any time we should ___ them slip" (Hebrews 2:1)
30. Threefold (comb. form)
31. "Call me not Naomi, call me ___" (Ruth 1:20)
32. "to Seth . . . there was born a son; and he called his name ___" (Genesis 4:26)
34. Compass point
35. Piece out
37. "the lapwing, and the ___" (Deuteronomy 14:18)
39. Hide-and-seek player
41. "This day is this scripture fulfilled in your ___" (Luke 4:21)
44. "The elder unto the elect ___ and her children" (2 John 1)
46. "Taanach and her towns, nor the inhabitants of ___ (Judges 1:27)
48. "___ the kine to the cart" (1 Samuel 6:7)
49. "I put thee in remembrance that thou ___ up the gift of God" (2 Timothy 1:6)
50. "the great owl, and the ___" (Deuteronomy 14:16)
52. "They ___ it with silver and with gold" (Jeremiah 10:4)
54. "a meat offering, mingled with oil, and one ___ of oil" (Leviticus 14:10)
56. "And over the host . . . was Ahira the son of ___" (Numbers 10:27)
58. Disturb
60. Italian river
61. Man's title (abbr.)
62. "The departed from ___" (Numbers 33:45)
64. "I have commanded my sanctified ___" (Isaiah 13:3)
66. Part of former Navigators Island (abbr.)
67. "we did eat in Egypt freely; the cucumbers . . . and the ___" (Numbers 11:5)
68. "And the Holy Ghost descended . . . like a ___ upon him" (Luke 3:22)

DOWN

1. "your heart shall ___ that seek God" (Psalm 69:32)
2. "There hath ___ temptation taken you" (1 Corinthians 10:13)
3. "Sir, come down ___ my child die" (John 4:49)
4. "___ they tell him of her" (Mark 1:30)
5. Not (prefix)
6. "Daniel was taken up out of the ___" (Daniel 6:23)
7. "thy ___ and thy she goats have not cast their young" (Genesis 31:38)
8. Fall flowers
9. ___-and-fro
11. "they shall fall by the ___ of the sword" (Luke 21:24)
15. "And there was one ___, a prophetess" (Luke 2:36)
17. "But cursed be the deceiver, which hath in his flock a ___" (Malachi 1:14)
19. "a throne was ___ in heaven" (Revelation 4:2)
21. "For we ___ not make ourselves of the number" (2 Corinthians 10:12)
23. "Were there not ___ cleansed?" (Luke 17:17)
25. God
27. "to ___ ourselves an ensample unto you to follow us" (2 Thessalonians 3:9)
29. "Jephthah fled . . ., and dwelt in the land of ___" (Judges 11:3)

132

Across/Down clues:

31. "her ___ shall lead her" (Nahum 2:7)
36. "Let us ___ and drink; for to morrow we die" (1 Corinthians 15:32)
38. "And his ___ drew the third part of the stars" (Revelation 12:4)
40. "They shall destroy the walls of Tyrus, and break down her ___" (Ezekiel 26:4)
42. "___ them out of the hand of the wicked" (Psalm 82:4)
43. "they . . . said unto them, is the ___ here?" (1 Samuel 9:11)
45. "The nations are as a ___ of a bucket" (Isaiah 40:15)
47. "his father . . . had compassion, and ___ , and fell on his neck" (Luke 15:20)
49. "John was clothed with . . . a girdle of ___" (Mark 1:6)

51. "I will fasten him as a ___" (Isaiah 22:23)
53. "we came with a straight course unto ___" (Acts 21:1)
55. "If an ox ___ a man or a woman" (Exodus 21:28)
57. Never (German)
59. "But if ye be ___ of the Spirit, ye are not under the law" (Galatians 5:18)
61. Mother
63. Northeastern st.
65. "if God ___ loved us, we ought also to love one another" (1 John 4:11)

ACROSS

1. "He smote them ___ and thigh" (Judges 15:8)
4. "Sir, come down ___ my child die" (John 4:49)
7. Org. nicknamed Wobblies
10. "The idols of the heathen ___ silver and gold (Psalm 135:15)
11. "For they shall ___ be cut down" (Psalm 37:2)
12. High sea
14. "to whom ye yield yourselves ___ to obey" (Romans 6:16)
16. Fruit seeds
17. "I brake the ___ of the wicked" (Job 29:17)
18. Having to do with ships (abbr.)
20. "For thou hast made . . . of a defenced city ___" (Isaiah 25:2, 2 words)
22. "What ___ thou here?" (Isaiah 22:16)
23. Mend
24. "the land was ___" (Exodus 10:15)
28. "I ___ no pleasant bread" (Daniel 10:3)
29. Memos
30. "The sons of Jether; . . . Pispah, and ___" (1 Chronicles 7:38)
31. "Christ hath ___ us from the curse of the law" (Galatians 3:13)
33. "The valley of the mountains shall reach unto" (Zechariah 14:5)
34. Dry
35. Silly
36. Possession of chattels

39. "And Zebadiah, and Arad, and ___" (1 Chronicles 8:15)
40. Helper (abbr.)
41. "and with ___ reproach" (Proverbs 18:3)
45. Sick
46. Aloud
47. "upon the great ___ of their right foot" (Exodus 29:20)
48. "why hath Satan filled thine heart to ___ to the Holy Ghost" (Acts 5:3)
49. Gaseous element symbol
50. Greek letter

DOWN

1. Owns
2. Fury
3. "for liars, for ___ persons" (1 Timothy 1:10)
4. Ages
5. "a tree that will not ___" (Isaiah 40:20)
6. "lest the people be ___" (Job 34:30)
7. "the Lord will not ___ sin" (Romans 4:8)
8. Hold off
9. Intelligence
11. "They were ___ asunder" (Hebrews 11:37)
13. Canadian prov.
15. "I hate ___ thoughts" (Psalm 119:113)
19. Interrogates
20. "the third day of the month ___" (Ezra 6:15)
21. "after a certain ___ every day" (2 Chronicles 8:13)
22. "the Lord saw that Leah was ___" (Genesis 29:31)

24. "let them have ___ over the fish of the sea" (Genesis 1:26)
25. "the child shall be a ___ unto God" (Judges 13:5)
26. "of ___, the family of Eranites" (Numbers 26:36)
27. "a pillar which is in the king's ___" (2 Samuel 18:18)
29. "Salathiel, which was the son of ___" (Luke 3:27)
32. "he placed at the ___ of the garden of Eden" (Genesis 3:24)
33. "and ___ with her suburbs" (1 Chronicles 6:73)

35. "Woe to the ___ shepherd" (Zechariah 11:17)
36. Travel by ship
37. "Naum, which was the son of ___" (Luke 3:25)
38. Land surrounded by water
39. Back (prefix)
42. Exam following BA or BS
43. "I command, ye, ___ I, but the Lord" (1 Corinthians 7:10)
44. "___, though I walk through the valley" (Psalm 23:4)

ACROSS

1. "We will ___ blameless of this thine oath" (Joshua 2:17)
3. Skin opening
7. "in their hands they shall ___ thee up" (Matthew 4:6)
11. Print measure
12. Therefore shall they ___ of the fruit" (Proverbs 1:31)
13. "Manasses begat ___" (Matthew 1:10)
14. "Dan shall be . . . an ___ in the path" (Genesis 49:17)
16. "I . . . dwelt as a king in the ___" (Job 29:25)
17. Twelve Steps group
18. "Of the sons of Bani; Maadai, Amram, and ___" (Ezra 10:34)
19. "high priest . . . tempted ___ as we are" (Hebrews 4:15)
20. Elder (abbr.) (Brit.)
21. Vase
22. "She weepeth ___ in the night" (Lamentations 1:2)
23. "all kinds of riches: with silver, iron, ___, and lead" (Ezekiel 27:12)
24. Place a step ahead of others (abbr.)
25. "The liberal soul shall be made ___" (Proverbs 11:25)
26. "the men of Cuth made ___" (2 Kings 17:30)
29. "A time to rend, and a time to ___" (Ecclesiastes 3:7)
30. Weapon
31. "Who shall ___ into the hill of the Lord" (Psalm 24:3)
34. "the whole ___ of Jacob was an hundred forty and seven years" (Genesis 47:28)
35. Baseball position (abbr.)
36. Chum
37. "Speak now in the ___ of the people" (Exodus 11:2)
39. Singing part (abbr.)
40. "that I may ___ Christ" (Philippians 3:8)
41. Step

42. "The sons of Benjamin were . . . Naaman, ___, and Rosh" (Genesis 46:21)
43. "Asenath the daughter of Potipherah priest of ___" (Genesis 41:45)
44. "tarry ye ___ and watch with me" (Matthew 26:38)
45. "Is Israel a servant? is he a homeborn ___?" (Jeremiah 2:14)
47. "he ___ his way into his own land" (Exodus 18:27)
48. Promise to pay
49. Overhead railway
50. Forest animal
51. "And the sons of Pharez were Hezron and ___" (Genesis 46:12)
52. Palm lily

DOWN

1. Nickname (fem.)
2. "Thou therefore ___ hardness, as a good soldier" (2 Timothy 2:3)
3. Pare
4. Row
5. Direction (abbr.)
6. "I will ___ the earth in the clear day" (Amos 8:9)
7. "They . . . have given a ___ for an harlot" (Joel 3:3)
8. ___ passant, chess term
9. Sound of rage
13. Woman's title (abbr.)
15. "ye have made it a ___ of thieves" (Mark 11:17)
16. "no ___ can come between them" (Job 41:16)
17. Monetary unit of India
19. "Cast in thy ___ among us" (Proverbs 1:14)
20. "establish the decree, and ___ the writing" (Daniel 6:8)
21. "The sons of ___; Arah, and Haniel" (1 Chronicles 7:39)
22. "they were ___ asunder" (Hebrews 11:37)
23. "all things that John spake of this man were ___" (John 10:41)
25. "they might ___ after him and find him" (Acts 17:27)

27. "As the partridge sitteth on ___"
(Jeremiah 17:11)

28. "Eutychus . . . fell down from the third
___" (Acts 20:9)

29. Examine

32. "they toil not, neither do they ___"
(Matthew 6:28)

33. "now there came a ___ over all the land
of Egypt" (Acts 7:11)

34. "The black horses which ___ therein go
forth" (Zechariah 6:6)

35. "Then returned they . . . from the mount
called ___" (Acts 1:12)

38. High card

39. "they . . . said Aha, ___, our eye hath
seen it" (Psalm 35:21)

40. "The ___ is nigh thee, even in thy
mouth" (Romans 10:8)

41. "I will not with ink and ___ write"
(3 John 13)

42. "The wall was finished in . . . the month
___" (Nehemiah 6:15)

44. Pageantry (abbr.)

45. Old French coin

46. "And they . . . brought the child to ___"
(1 Samuel 1:25)

47. Midweek (abbr.)

48. Not (prefix)

ACROSS

1. "The son of Mattathias, which was the son of ___" (Luke 3:26)
6. "He . . . made me a polished ___" (Isaiah 49:2)
11. Israel sang this song, ___ up, O well" (Numbers 21:17)
12. "none of the people ___ any food" (1 Samuel 14:24)
14. Eugene's st.
15. "who daily ___ us with benefits" (Psalm 68:19)
17. Orbit (abbr.)
18. "His eyes shall be ___ with wine" (Genesis 49:12)
20. "daubed it with ___ and with pitch" (Exodus 2:3)
21. "the children of ___" (Ezra 2:57)
22. "And it is a ___ thing" (Daniel 2:11)
24. "Eliasaph the son of ___" (Numbers 3:24)
25. Three feet (abbr.)
26. "___ the work of thine hands?" (Ecclesiastes 5:6)
31. Chief's asst.
32. "when thou walkest through the ___, thou shalt not be burned" (Isaiah 43:2)
33. "Eshtemoh, and ___" (Joshua 15:50)
34. Toward (prefix)
36. Independent workers
38. NA country
40. "I ___ the armies of Israel this day" (1 Samuel 17:10)
42. Cut
44. "Pispah and ___" (1 Chronicles 7:38)
45. "when thou ___ well to thyself" (Psalm 49:18)
49. New (comb. form)
50. Methane derivative (abbr.)

51. "According to the ___ of years thou shalt diminish the price" (Leviticus 25:16)
53. Its cap. is Dover
54. "Neither be dismayed, O ___" (Jeremiah 30:10)
56. "if the Lord be God, follow him: but if ___, then follow him" (1 Kings 18:21)
58. "The ___ of cattle are perplexed" (Joel 1:18)
59. "Shobab and ___" (1 Chronicles 2:18)

DOWN

1. "His branches shall ___" (Hosea 14:6)
2. "and he called his name ___" (Genesis 38:3)
3. Metric measure
4. "And ___ lived ninety years, and begat Cainan" (Genesis 5:9)
5. "___ the son of Nathan of Zobah" (2 Samuel 23:36)
6. "And there shall come forth a rod out of the ___ of Jesse" (Isaiah 11:1)
7. "I ___ every false way" (Psalm 119:104)
8. "he planteth an ___" (Isaiah 44:14)
9. Twelve inches (abbr.)
10. "neither shall thy land any more be ___ Desolate" (Isaiah 62:4)
11. "And the king was ___" (Matthew 14:9)
13. "And they continuing ___ with one accord in the temple" (Acts 2:46)
16. "I did cast them out as the ___ in the streets" (Psalm 18:42)
19. Physician (abbr.)
21. Writer's change (abbr.)
24. "A ___ tongue" (Proverbs 6:17)
27. "their lies caused them to ___" (Amos 2:4)
28. "Master, we would ___ a sign from thee" (Matthew 12:38)

29. "behold, behind him a ___ caught in a thicket" (Genesis 22:13)
30. Single
34. "From Allon to Zaanaannim and ___" (Joshua 19:33)
35. "The king's chamberlains, Bigthan and ___" (Esther 2:21)
37. "___ we ourselves groan within ourselves" (Romans 8:23)
38. The fat . . . may be ___ in any other use" (Leviticus 7:24)
39. "Put off thy ___ from thy feet" (Acts 7:33)
41. Note of the musical scale
43. Belonging to (suffix)

45. "And whatsoever ye do in word or ___" (Colossians 3:17)
46. "I will make . . . mourning as the ___" (Micah 1:8)
47. "Ethiopia and ___ for thee" (Isaiah 43:3)
48. Russian ruler
51. "Be it ___ from thee, Lord" (Matthew 16:22)
52. "as ye walk, and are ___" (Luke 24:17)
55. About
57. "___, I come: in the volume of the book" (Psalm 40:7)

PUZZLE 69

ACROSS

1. Spur
5. "I am ___ with my groaning" (Psalm 6:6)
9. "and ___ shall we ever be with the Lord" (1 Thessalonians 4:17)
11. "I . . . will ___ them as silver is refined" (Zechariah 13:9)
13. "___ them about thy neck" (Proverbs 6:21)
14. "Shuppim also, and Huppim, the children of ___" (1 Chronicles 7:12)
15. Paid notice
16. "Make thee a fiery serpent, and set it upon a ___" (Numbers 21:8)
18. "which have neither gates nor ___" (Jeremiah 49:31)
20. Of mice and ___
22. Ardor
24. Liturgy
26. "incline thine ___ unto me" (Psalm 17:6)
28. Weep
30. "they shall wet thee with the ___ of heaven" (Daniel 4:25)
31. "all Israel made ___ . . . king over Israel" (1 Kings 16:16)
32. "Hadar, and Tema, ___, Naphish, and Kedemah" (Genesis 25:15)
34. Concerning
35. "And ___ ran to meet him" (Genesis 33:4)
37. "The ___ of all wait upon thee" (Psalm 145:15)
39. Ancient Roman coin
41. "And on the seventh day God ___ his work" (Genesis 2:2)
43. Omaha's st.
44. Body part
46. Light brown
47. Make lace
49. Bucket
51. "Why withdrawest thou thy ___?" (Psalm 74:11)

54. Pig
56. "And he arose out of his ___" (Judges 3:20)
58. "And a ___ saw him again" (Mark 14:69)
60. Seattle's st.
61. "There hath ___ temptation taken you but such as is common to man" (1 Corinthians 10:13)
62. "peace, good will toward ___" (Luke 2:14)
64. Thin
66. Antibiotic (suffix)
67. "___ be to thine helpers" (1 Chronicles 12:18)
68. Average

DOWN

1. Baby carriage
2. "In famine he shall ___ thee from death" (Job 5:20)
3. Baseball position (abbr.)
4. "he . . . shall ___ them and the living bird" (Leviticus 14:6)
5. "Then Israel sang this song, Spring up, O ___" (Numbers 21:17)
6. Atmospheric hotness or coldness (abbr.)
7. "And the ___, which the Lord had taken from man" (Genesis 2:22)
8. "the ___ of my redeemed is come" (Isaiah 63:4)
9. "her treacherous ___ Judah feared not" (Jeremiah 3:8)
10. Surgeon's place in hospital (abbr.)
12. "as the days of ___ were" (Matthew 24:37)
17. "take thine ___, eat, drink, and be merry" (Luke 12:19)
19. "___ them out of the hand of the wicked" (Psalm 82:4)
21. "The king arose, and ___ his garments" (2 Samuel 13:31)
23. "that which is ___ in the scripture of truth" (Daniel 10:21)
25. "he shall take . . . one ___ lamb of the first year" (Leviticus 14:10)
27. "defend me from them that ___ up against me" (Psalm 59:1)

29. "his disciples were gone . . to ___ meat" (John 4:8)
32. "And he sent ___ before him unto Joseph" (Genesis 46:28)
33. Tamar put ashes on her head, and ___ her garment" (2 Samuel 13:19)
36. "Go to the ___, thou sluggard" (Proverbs 6:6)
38. "Thy borders are in the midst of the ___" (Ezekiel 27:4)
39. High mountain
40. "I will cause the shower to come down in his ___" (Ezekiel 34:26)
42. "Tappuah, and ___" (Joshua 15:34)
45. Present (Scot.)
48. "which of you, intending to build a ___" (Luke 14:28)
50. "Thy word is a ___ unto my feet" (Psalm 119:105)
52. "have we not prophesied in thy ___?" (Matthew 7:22)
53. "neither shall ye touch it, lest ye ___" (Genesis 3:3)
55. Heat up
57. Mound or peg
59. "why did ___ remain in ships?" (Judges 5:17)
61. Metallic element symbol
63. Symbol for sodium
65. "___ ye therefore, and teach all nations" (Matthew 28:19)

PUZZLE **70**

ACROSS

1. German river
4. Religious image
8. "the ruler of the land from ___ to the wilderness" (Isaiah 16:1)
12. "One . . . gathered thereof wild gourds his ___ full" (2 Kings 4:39)
13. "leaving Nazareth, he came and dwelt in ___" (Matthew 4:13)
15. Beast of burden
17. "yet my record is ___" (John 8:14)
18. Animal kingdom (comb. Form)
19. "turned to flight the armies of the ___" (Hebrews 11:34)
21. "And ___, and Abimael, and Sheba" (Genesis 10:28)
23. Ways of walking
25. "thick clouds of the ___" (Psalm 18:11)
28. Lung disease (abbr.)
30. "they called these days ___ after the name of Pur" (Esther 9:26)
32. Break
33. Assistance
35. Pals
37. Youth org.
38. "It is enough: ___ now thine hand" (2 Samuel 24:16)
40. Affirmatives
42. Printer's measure
43. "The children of ___, the children of Siaha" (Ezra 2:44)
45. "I laid me down and ___" (Psalm 3:5)
47. "Orpah kissed her mother in law; but ___ clave unto her" (Ruth 1:14)
49. Frightens
52. Near (prefix)
54. Crew

56. "I will walk within my house with a perfect ___" (Psalm 101:2)
57. "When they came nigh to Jerusalem, unto ___" (Mark 11:1)
60. Mom's apple ___
61. "their words unto the ___ of the world" (Romans 10:18)
62. "Ramoth with her suburbs, and ___ with her suburbs" (1 Chronicles 6:73)
63. "Arphaxad, which was the son of ___" (Luke 3:36)

DOWN

1. Napoleon's isle
2. "A man that beareth false witness against his neighbor is a ___" (Proverbs 25:18)
3. Plant division
4. "they . . . came unto ___" (Acts 13:51)
5. Golden St.
6. Choose
7. Roman emperor
8. Steals
9. Apiece (abbr.)
10. "the name of that city was called ___ at the first" (Genesis 28:19)
11. ___, amas, amat
14. Chafes
16. "For he . . . that soweth to the Spirit shall . . . ___ life everlasting" (Galatians 6:8)
20. Wander
22. Related to language (abbr.)
24. Locations
26. "I will ___ me of mine adversaries" (Isaiah 1:24)
27. "a ___ shall be the length thereof" (Exodus 28:16)
28. "Wherefore have ye not fulfilled your ___" (Exodus 5:14)

142

29. "a serpent shall ___ him" (Ecclesiastes 10:8)
31. Repasts
34. Black tern
36. "And Jacob came to Shalem, a city of ___" (Genesis 33:18)
39. "I discerned among the ___, a young man" (Proverbs 7:7)
41. Foretell (Scot.)
44. "If my ___ hath turned out of the way" (Job 31:7)
46. "they shall be snares and ___ unto you" (Joshua 23:13)
48. "He saith among the trumpets, ___" (Job 39:25, 2 words)

50. New York canal
51. "And there shall come forth a rod out of the ___ of Jesse" (Isaiah 11:1)
52. Nickname (masc.)
53. "he took ___ men of the elders of the city" (Ruth 4:2)
55. "he sent a ___ before them" (Psalm 105:17)
58. Football goal (abbr.)
59. Semiconductor element symbol

PUZZLE 71

ACROSS

1. "Where ___ thou?" (Genesis 3:9)
4. "Gideon the son of ___, a man of Israel" (Judges 7:14)
9. "He it is, to whom I shall give a ___" (John 13:26)
12. "they that ___ against thee shall be as nothing" (Isaiah 41:12)
13. "Moses called ___ the son of Nun Jehoshua" (Numbers 13:16)
14. "___ things I have required of thee" (Proverbs 30:7)
15. Moabite name for biblical giants
17. "There was no room for them in the ___" (Luke 2:7)
18. "though they be ___ like crimson, they shall be as wool" (Isaiah 1:18)
19. "there was a swarm of ___ and honey" (Judges 14:8)
21. "Zechariah the son of ___" (Ezra 6:14)
23. "He . . . set my ___ upon a rock" (Psalm 40:2)
25. "he lift up his eyes, being in ___" (Luke 16:23)
29. Government tax agency (abbr.)
30. Average
31. "An ___ spake to him" (John 12:29)
32. "The sons of Judah; ___, and Onan" (1 Chronicles 2:3)
33. "he ___ him, and he took it" (Genesis 33:11)
35. Symbol for sodium
36. "the waters of the ___ pool" (Isaiah 22:9)
39. "she was of the ___ of twelve years" (Mark 5:42)
40. Adherent (suffix)
41. "the contentions of a wife are a continual ___" (Proverbs 19:13)
43. "unto me every ___ shall bow" (Isaiah 45:23)

44. "I was delivered out of the mouth of the ___" (2 Timothy 4:17)
45. "It was planted in a good ___" (Ezekiel 17:8)
47. Roman numerals for fifty-four
49. "The trees of the Lord are full of ___" (Psalm 104:16)
51. "And after him was Shamgar the son of ___" (Judges 3:31)
54. "we . . . ___ helpers of your joy" (2 Corinthians 1:24)
55. "the house that I shall ___ into" (Nehemiah 2:8)
57. "as the days of ___ were" (Matthew 24:37)
58. "___ verily, their sound went into all the earth" (Romans 10:18)
59. "a book . . . sealed with seven ___" (Revelation 5:1)
60. "The son of Abinadab in all the region of ___" (1 Kings 4:11)

DOWN

1. "Stand in ___, and sin not" (Psalm 4:4)
2. "there stood before the river a ___" (Daniel 8:3)
3. "the ___ of the Lord" (Psalm 122:4)
4. "Which was the son of ___ which was the son of Eliezer" (Luke 3:29)
5. Bone
6. "___ the son of Abdiel" (1 Chronicles 5:15)
7. "They have made . . . boards of fir trees of ___" (Ezekiel 27:5)
8. "Hath not my ___ all these things?" (Acts 7:50, 2 words)
9. "be ___ in the Lord, and in the power of his might" (Ephesians 6:10)
10. "___ no man any thing" (Romans 13:8)
11. Hull
16. "much people ___ him" (Luke 9:37)
20. "the day ___ arise in your hearts" (2 Peter 1:19)
22. "He lieth in wait secretly as a lion in his ___" (Psalm 10:9)

144

23. "there were . . . shepherds abiding in the ___" (Luke 2:8)
24. "God smote him there for his ___" (2 Samuel 6:7)
26. "They . . . rejoice at the sound of the ___" (Job 21:12)
27. Taut
28. Blackboard
30. "Hear the counsel of the Lord . . . and his ___" (Jeremiah 49:20)
34. "Which leaveth her ___ in the earth" (Job 39:14)
37. "Her princes . . . are like ___ ravening the prey" (Ezekiel 22:27)
38. Upon (prefix)

40. Away from the coast
42. Silly
43. Relative
46. "a place. . . wherein shall go no galley with ___" (Isaiah 33:21)
47. "But ___ up for yourselves treasures in heaven" (Matthew 6:20)
48. Wrath
50. School org.
52. "Is any thing ___ hard for the Lord" (Genesis 18:14)
53. Armory (abbr.)
56. Small one (suffix)

ACROSS

1. "which is ___ the Lord" (Luke 2:11)
7. "Then he took unto him the ___" (Luke 18:31)
13. "while he is weary and weak ___" (2 Samuel 17:2)
14. Attack
15. Belonging to (suffix)
16. Sight organ (Scot.)
17. Political party member (abbr.)
18. What athletes want to break (abbr.)
19. Compass point
20. Rests
22. "and upon the great ___ of his right foot" (Leviticus 8:23)
24. Midwestern st.
25. "and ___ she asses laden with corn" (Genesis 45:23)
26. Hebrew letter
27. "and the land of ___ in the entrances thereof" (Micah 5:6)
29. Overhead railway
30. "Lord of ___ and earth" (Luke 10:21)
31. "it hath consumed ___ of Moab" (Numbers 21:28)
32. Doctor's deg.
33. Sweetheart (Scot.)
35. "And he ___ him" (Luke 22:57)
37. Greek letter
39. "And that which thou ___" (1 Corinthians 15:37)
41. Unusual
43. Undergraduate degree (abbr.)
44. Owns
46. Type of shark
47. Midweek (abbr.)
48. Midwestern st.
50. Extra work
51. "the children of Gad called the altar ___" (Joshua 22:34)
52. "could not come at him for the ___" (Luke 8:19)
54. Blob
56. "that they should come and ___ them" (Luke 5:7)
57. Chemical compound (suffix)

DOWN

1. "While they behold your ___ conversation" (1 Peter 3:2)
2. "Arah, and ___, and Rezia" (1 Chronicles 7:39)
3. Hospital staffer (abbr.)
4. Roman midmonth
5. "And all flesh shall ___ the salvation of God" (Luke 3:6)
6. Football goal (abbr.)
7. Professor's helper (abbr.)
8. Compass point
9. "which was the son of ___, which was the son of Phares" (Luke 3:33)
10. CA city
11. "and they perceived that he had seen a ___" (Luke 1:22)
12. "and Ezer, and ___" (1 Chronicles 7:21)
17. "Master, what shall we ___?" (Luke 3:12)
21. Great Smoky Mountains st.
22. "and it ___ him that he foameth again" (Luke 9:39)
23. "Love your ___" (Luke 6:27)
26. "and lift up your ___" (Luke 21:28)
28. Book part

33. "And ___ also went up from Galilee" (Luke 2:4)
34. Cry of pain
36. ___ swiss, fabric
37. "We have ___ unto you, and ye have not danced" (Matthew 11:17)
38. Made cold
39. "And when the Lord ___ her" (Luke 7:13)
40. "and Ishpan, and Heber, and ___" (1 Chronicles 8:22)
42. ___-and-fro
45. Year (abbr.)

49. "shall play on the hole of the ___" (Isaiah 11:8)
50. Kimono sash
53. Note on musical scale
55. One (Scot.)

ACROSS

1. "the Lord will deliver him ___ ___ of trouble" (Psalm 41:1)
7. "he fell into a ___" (Acts 10:10)
13. Declares
14. "The son of Gerber in ___-gilead" (1 Kings 4:13)
15. "Now when Jesus was born in ___ of Judea" (Matthew 2:1)
17. Hebrew letter
19. Measure of weight
20. "___, every one that thirsteth" (Isaiah 55:1)
22. Curvy shape
24. Cadge
26. What you write a memo on
27. Deed
29. "Then an ___ cried aloud" (Daniel 3:4)
31. Relating to flight
32. "God hath given ___ unto your brethren" (Joshua 22:4)
33. Hastens
35. "The seed is ___ under their clods" (Joel 1:17)
37. Vigor
38. "___ died without children" (1 Chronicles 2:30)
40. Had food
41. Three feet (abbr.)
43. Kin (abbr.)
45. Balloon gas symbol
46. "the Lord fulfill all thy ___" (Psalm 20:5)
50. "This Agar is mount Sinai in ___" (Galatians 4:25)
52. "we have had ___ to eat" (2 Chronicles 31:10)
55. "the ___ is not dead, but sleepeth" (Mark 5:39)
56. "but thou shalt utterly ___ it" (Deuteronomy 7:26)

DOWN

1. "For their rock ___ not as our Rock" (Deuteronomy 32:31)
2. The new covenant (abbr.)
3. Flap
4. Article
5. "the angels of God ___ him" (Genesis 32:1)
6. "Mehir which was the father of ___" (1 Chronicles 4:11)
7. "ae made a ___ about the altar" (1 Kings 18:32)
8. Cheer
9. "Surely I come quickly. ___" (Revelation 22:20)
10. ___ de plume
11. New England st.
12. Exclamation
16. Nickname (masc. or fem.)
17. Popular legume
18. "there ___ not a man of them" (1 Samuel 30:17)
20. "I will save her that ___" (Zephaniah 3:19)
21. "the ___ number of them is to be redeemed" (Numbers 3:48)
23. "the whole herd of swine ran violently down a ___ place" (Matthew 8:32)
24. Emotions
25. "they should not return to ___" (Matthew 2:12)
26. Sew temporarily
28. Anger
30. Take back (abbr.)

33. "who came in privily to ___ out our liberty" (Galatians 2:4)
34. Story appearing in parts
35. "they ___ upon the Lord God of their fathers" (2 Chronicles 13:18)
36. Born
39. "I will ___ you go" (Exodus 8:28)
42. "Their ___ shall not become garments" (Isaiah 59:6)
44. Nautical mile
46. Nickname (fem.)

47. "___ them about thy neck" (Proverbs 6:21)
48. "And they all with ___ consent began to make excuse" (Luke 14:18)
49. "And if any man will ___ thee at the law" (Matthew 5:40)
51. Year of our Lord (abbr.)
51. Symbol for Curie discovery
53. Working for the feds (abbr.)
54. Altitude (abbr.)

PUZZLE 74

ACROSS

1. "the Israelites went down to the Philistines, to sharpen every man his ___" (1 Samuel 13:20)
6. Refund
13. "Ezion-geber, which is beside ___" (1 Kings 9:26)
15. "And upon ___, and upon Nebo" (Jeremiah 48:22)
16. Roman numeral four
18. "Take now thy son, thine only son ___" (Genesis 22:2)
20. Peel
21. Hold up
23. "Heman, and Chalcol, and ___ the sons of Mahol" (1 Kings 4:31)
25. "Ahira, the son of ___" (Numbers 1:15)
26. Farm buildings
27. "He saith among the trumpets, ___" (Job 39:25)
29. "let tears ___ down like a river" (Lamentations 2:18)
30. "Jesus Christ the same yesterday, and ___, and forever" (Hebrews 13:8, 2 words)
31. "there came a woman having an alabaster ___" (Mark 14:3)
32. "he . . . came to a great well that is in ___" (1 Samuel 19:22)
34. "And ___ the father of Shechem went out" (Genesis 34:6)
37. "The Lord make his face ___ upon thee" (Numbers 6:25)
39. "Belshazzar the king made a great feast to a thousand of his ___" (Daniel 5:1)
41. One hundredth of a kip
43. Man (comb. form)
45. "as a ___ is shaken in the water" (1 Kings 14:15)

46. "I ___ my God through Christ Jesus for you all" (Romans 1:8)
48. Encouraged
50. Student's fear
51. Epic
52. ___-Do
54. "The ___ of truth shall be established for ever" (Proverbs 12:19)
55. Rested
56. Stimulate
58. Bitter vetch
59. Canadian prov.
60. Nickname (masc.)

DOWN

2. Balloon gas symbol
3. "The sons of Shobal; ___, and Manahath" (1 Chronicles 1:40)
4. Blushing
5. Greek letter
7. "the children of Gad called the altar ___" (Joshua 22:34)
8. "___ of the air have nests" (Luke 9:58)
9. "Roboam begat ___" (Matthew 1:7)
10. Weight measure
11. "I am Alpha nad Omega, the beginning and the ___" (Revelation 21:6)
12. "I will smite every horse with astonishment and his ___ with madness" (Zechariah 12:4)
14. "The children of Lod, ___, and Ono" (Ezra 2:33)
17. Earth's neighboring planet
19. "Resen between Nineveh and ___" (Genesis 10:12)
22. "Go out quickly into the streets and ___ of the city" (Luke 14:21)
24. But ye are a chosen generation, a ___ priesthood" (1 Peter 2:9)
26. "He heard the ___ of the trumpet" (Ezekiel 33:5)
27. Throng
28. Woodcutter's tool

30. "___ not with thyself that thou shalt escape" (Esther 4:13)
31. "Jehoida . . . ___ a hole in the lid of it" (2 Kings 12:9)
33. "That ___ to the sound of the viol" (Amos 6:5)
35. Additional
36. "the ___ is the Lord's" (1 Samuel 17:47)
38. Burst forth
40. Midwestern st.
42. "The covenant that I made with ___ fathers" (Hebrews 8:9)
44. Mouth (comb. Form)

47. "the poison of ___ is under their lips" (Romans 3:13)
49. Working for the feds (abbr.)
51. One that is (suffix)
52. Golf mound
53. "And he died in a good ___ age" (1 Chronicles 29:28)
55. "the heart of foolish doeth not ___" (Proverbs 15:7)
56. Type of books (abbr.)
57. "I am the Lord that brought thee out of ___ of the Chaldees" (Genesis 15:7)

ACROSS

1. Minute
4. "And ___ put ashes on her head" (2 Samuel 13:19)
9. "When he had dipped the ___, he gave it to Judas Iscariot" (John 13:26)
12. "I made myself servant unto ___" (1 Corinthians 9:19)
13. "The Lord . . . said unto him, ___ art thou?" (Genesis 3:9)
14. Entangle
15. "the Lord is among them, as in ___" (Psalm 68:17)
17. Make lace
18. Age
19. "she is thine ___" (Leviticus 18:14)
21. "he reared up altars for ___" (2 Kings 21:3)
23. "Sheshai, and Ahiman and Talmai, the children of ___" (Joshua 15:14)
25. "who hath ___ his will?" (Romans 9:19)
29. "behind him a ___ caught in a thicket" (Genesis 22:13)
30. "the fourth is like the ___ of God" (Daniel 3:25)
31. Mean
32. Input/Output (abbr., var.)
33. Worship
35. Hebrew letter
36. "thou hadst sent me away now ___" (Genesis 31:42)
39. Lump
40. Pageantry (abbr.)
41. Give a job
42. Pelts
43. "And out of the half tribe of Manasseh; ___ with her suburbs" (1 Chronicles 6:70)
46. Merit
48. "___ up for yourselves treasures in heaven" (Matthew 6:20)
50. Greek letter
52. Tiny amounts
55. Crude metal
56. Perfumed oil
58. Compass point
59. Through
60. Appears
61. Cereal grain

DOWN

1. "And, behold, there ___ a great earthquake" (Matthew 28:2)
2. "and he ran unto ___, and said, Here am I" (1 Samuel 3:5)
3. "Jeribai, and Joshaviah, the sons of ___" (1 Chronicles 11:46)
4. One of two
5. "___ Lord God! behold, thou hast made the heaven" (Jeremiah 32:17)
6. "Mercy and truth are ___ together" (Psalm 85:10)
7. Swift horses
8. "Whom I would have ___ with me" (Philemon 13)
9. Small fish
10. "All that handle the ___, the mariners" (Ezekiel 27:29)
11. School org.
16. Diving bird
20. Walked
22. "And ___ did that which was good and right" (2 Chronicles 14:2)
23. Pekah . . . smote him . . . with Argob and ___" (2 Kings 15:25)
24. "And ___ said, Turn again, my daughters" (Ruth 1:11)
26. Sufficient (arch.)
27. Heavens
28. Stainers

1	2	3		4	5	6	7	8		9	10	11
12				13						14		
15			16			17				18		
		19			20		21		22			
23	24				25	26					27	28
29				30				31				
32				33			34				35	
36		37	38			39				40		
41									42			
		43		44	45		46	47				
48	49			50		51		52			53	54
55				56			57			58		
59				60						61		

30. "I heard them ___, Let us go to Dothan" (Genesis 37:17)
34. "Why do the heathen ___?" (Psalm 2:1)
37. "And the ___ of faith shall save the sick" (James 5:15)
38. "Abram had dwelt ___ years in the land of Canaan" (Genesis 16:3)
40. "He was a mighty ___ before the Lord" (Genesis 10:9)
42. "the earth shall reel to and ___ like a drunkard" (Isaiah 24:20)
44. Greek letters
45. Scale of payment
47. Pretentious

48. "the Lord of hosts, shall ___ the bough with terror" (Isaiah 10:33)
49. "And they that ___ Christ's have crucified the flesh" (Galatians 5:24)
51. Earlier Utah
53. "forgive, if ye have ought against ___" (Mark 11:25)
54. "Elijah said, ___, thy son liveth" (1 Kings 17:23)
57. Morning (abbr.)

ACROSS

1. Owns
4. Spartan serf
9. "a ___ and his father will go"
   (Amos 2:7)
12. "Then ___ was wroth with the seer"
    (2 Chronicles 16:10)
13. "the king made a great throne of ___"
    (1 Kings 10:18)
14. Self
15. "they shall ___ every strong hold"
    (Habakkuk 1:10)
17. "they do ___ strifes"
    (2 Timothy 2:23)
19. "from the carrying away into Babylon
    unto Christ ___ fourteen generations"
    (Matthew 1:17)
20. Traveled
21. Music for three
23. "And she took a ___, and poured
    them out" (2 Samuel 13:9)
24. "Surely thou wilt ___ the wicked"
    (Psalm 139:19)
27. Apiece (abbr.)
28. "I will fasten him as a ___"
    (Isaiah 22:23)
30. Solid body (comb. form)
31. "___ them out of the hand of the
    wicked" (Psalm 82:4)
33. "he made narrowed ___ round about"
    (1 Kings 6:6)
35. Spanish woman (abbr.)
36. "When ye blow an ___"
    (Numbers 10:5)
38. New York canal
40. Surgeon's place (abbr.)
41. Greek letter
42. Wily
43. "And when the sun is ___, he shall be
    clean" (Leviticus 22:7)
45. "he . . . slew a lion in a pit in a ___
    day" (1 Chronicles 11:22)

47. Sheep's bleat
48. "God caused a deep ___ to fall upon
    Adam" (Genesis 2:21)
50. "And sold their possessions and
    goods, and ___ them" (Acts 2:45)
53. Conger
54. "Of Zebulun; ___ the son of Helon"
    (Numbers 1:9)
57. "Bethel on the west, and ___ on the
    east" (Genesis 12:8)
58. "In the beginning ___ the Word"
    (John 1:1)
59. Tell
60. "any man will ___ thee at the law"
    (Matthew 5:40)

DOWN

1. "he . . . went and sold all that he ___"
   (Matthew 13:46)
2. Enzyme (Suffix)
3. "the name of Abram's wife was ___"
   (Genesis 11:29)
4. "Jesus . . . did ___ himself from them"
   (John 12:36)
5. "the serpent beguiled ___"
   (2 Corinthians 11:3)
6. "and now, ___, I am this day"
   (Joshua 14:10)
7. "They . . . rejoice at the at the sound of
   the ___" (Job 21:12)
8. Category (var.)
9. Interferes
10. "from the ___ of fifty years they shall
    cease" (Numbers 8:25)
11. Scandinavian country (abbr.)
16. "he had nine hundred chariots of ___"
    (Judges 4:3)
18. "the swallow a ___ for herself"
    (Psalm 84:3)
20. "say all manner of evil against you
    ___" (Matthew 5:11)
21. Trillion (comb. form)
22. Revile
23. Pastry
25. "he shot an ___ beyond him"
    (1 Samuel 20:36)

26. "his bowels did ___ upon his brother" (Genesis 43:30)
29. "Thou hast a mighty ___" (Psalm 89:13)
30. Supplemental income
32. "among them were the ___ playing with timbrels" (Psalm 68:25)
34. "the fire shall ___ every man's work" (1 Corinthians 3:13)
37. Ancient alphabet letter
39. "Israel . . . spread his tent beyond the tower of ___" (Genesis 35:21)
42. Compass point
44. "according to the ___ of the tribes" (Habakkuk 3:9)

46. Uncloses (poet.)
47. "Ye shall find the ___ wrapped in swaddling clothes" (Luke 2:12)
48. "A time to rend, and a time to ___" (Ecclesiates 3:7)
49. Field
50. Dab
51. Water (Fr.)
52. "he should not ___ in the pit" (Isaiah 51:14)
55. Military officer (abbr.)
56. Hawkeye St.

PUZZLE 77

ACROSS

1. Kind of lettuce
4. "the measuring line shall yet go forth . . . upon the hill ___" (Jeremiah 31:39)
9. "He will finish the work, and ___ it short in righteousness" (Romans 9:28)
12. Eggs
13. "ye pay tithe of mint and ___ and cummin" (Matthew 23:23)
14. "not ___ thing hath failed" (Joshua 23:14)
15. Midweek (abbr.)
16. "bind this ___ of scarlet thread in the window" (Joshua 2:18)
17. Multitude
19. Queen (Sp.)
21. "He . . . keepeth silence, because he hath ___ it upon him" (Lamentations 3:28)
22. "the wild ___ quench their thirst" (Psalm 104:11)
23. Gael
24. Scope (abbr.)
26. "Have they not ___? have they not divided the prey?" (Judges 5:30)
27. Clupeid fishes
28. Compass point
29. "Make thee an ___ of gopher wood" (Genesis 6:14)
30. White metal
31. Professor's helper
32. Hebrew letter
33. Jogs
35. "And Caleb drove thence the three sons of ___" (Joshua 15:14)
37. "He saith among the trumpets, ___" (Job 39:25)
38. Pretentious
39. "lest thou dash thy foot against a ___" (Psalm 91:12)
40. "there was no water for the people to ___" (Exodus 17:1)
42. "he shall ___ at the latter day upon the earth" (Job 19:25)
43. Telephones
44. Snow vehicle
45. Venice's country (abbr.)
47. "[he] brought him to an ___, and took care of him" (Luke 10:34)
48. "Is not this Bathsheba, the daughter of ___?" (2 Samuel 11:3)
50. "let us meet . . . in the plain of ___" (Nehemiah 6:2)
51. "Is there any taste in the white of an ___?" (Job 6:6)
52. Depressions
53. "As for thine asses that were lost three days ___" (1 Samuel 9:20)

DOWN

1. "ye shall go out at the breaches, every ___ at that which is before her" (Amos 4:3)
2. "for the ___ of abominations he shall make it desolate" (Daniel 9:27)
3. Continent (abbr.)
4. "her masters saw that the hope of their ___ was gone" (Acts 16:19)
5. "There was one ___, a prophetess, the daughter of Phanuel" (Luke 2:36)
6. "the wheat and the ___ were not smitten" (Exodus 9:32)
7. Symbol for an artificially produced radioactive element
8. "that they may ___ my glory" (John 17:24)
9. "I will no more give thy ___ to be meat for thine enemies" (Isaiah 62:8)
10. "be ye of an ___ heart" (Proverbs 8:5)
11. Golf mound
16. "they ___ unto him with their tongues" (Psalm 78:36)
18. Scraps

20. "he called the name of the well ___; because they strove with him" (Genesis 26:20)
21. Legumes
22. "Then came . . . Joah, the son of ___ the recorder" (2 Kings 18:37)
23. Vouchers
25. "___, why sleepest thou, O Lord?" (Psalm 44:23)
27. "they had wings like the wings of a ___" (Zechariah 5:9)
33. "Samson . . . took firebrands, and turned ___ to tail" (Judges 15:4)
34. "every vessel of wood shall be ___ in water" (Leviticus 15:12)

35. "they came to the threshing floor of ___" (Genesis 50:10)
36. Worthless (prefix)
39. Originates
41. "the earth ___ again" (1 Samuel 4:5)
42. Lath
43. "come down ere my child ___" (John 4:49)
44. "if any man ___, we have an advocate" (1 John 2:1)
46. "Is any thing ___ hard for the Lord?" (Genesis 18:14)
49. Place a step ahead of others (abbr.)
50. Diphthong

PUZZLE 78

ACROSS

1. "named ___, a ruler of the Jews" (John 3:1)
9. "was Ahira the son of ___" (Numbers 10:27)
10. Camping equipment
11. "and he bowed his ___" (John 19:30)
13. One skilled in (suffix)
14. Bait
17. "for every one that ___" (Ezekiel 45:20)
19. To perceive (Fr.)
20. Periods
21. Coyote St.
22. "Of the tribe of Benjamin, ___" (Numbers 34:21)
25. Simple
27. Mien
28. "Go ye up unto this ___" (John 7:8)
30. Water vapor
32. "___ thy peace, and come out of him" (Luke 4:35)
34. Apiece (abbr.)
35. "throughout all his ___" (Esther 1:20)
38. Those who question
41. "I sent you to ___ that" (John 4:38)
42. "___, and Rohgah" (1 Chronicles 7:34)
44. "the generations of Esau, who is ___" (Genesis 36:1)
45. Relating to a messenger
49. "and brought him to an ___" (Luke 10:34)

DOWN

1. "___ to the parcel of ground" (John 4:5)
2. "Behold, an Israelite ___" (John 1:47)
3. St. Sutter colonized (abbr.)
4. "as ___ that ___ authority" (Mark 1:22)
5. Volcano
6. Mt. Katahdin's st.
7. "___ the Lord had been my help" (Psalm 94:17)
8. Stout
11. "___ ye shall see heaven open" (John 1:51)
12. "The sons of Judah; ___, and Onan" (1 Chronicles 2:3)
15. Disaster-aid group (abbr.)
16. Inoffensive expression
18. "which also was the ___" (Luke 6:16)
23. Untruth
24. "captain for the sixth month was ___" (1 Chronicles 27:9)
29. "and Ziza the son of ___" (1 Chronicles 4:37)
31. Opposite of givers
33. "this only would I ___ of you" (Galatians 3:2)
36. "I write unto you, young ___" (1 John 2:13)
37. Father
38. To suffer ill health
39. Alter
40. Taiwan, until 1997
43. Laughter sound
46. Printer's measure
47. Boot-camp staffer (abbr.)

ACROSS

1. Pure (abbr.)
4. "the measuring line shall yet go forth . . . upon the hill ___" (Jeremiah 31:39)
9. "the just shall ___ it on" (Job 27:17)
12. Chum
13. "The captive ___ hasteneth that he may be loosed" (Isaiah 51:14)
14. Shelter
15. Bothers
17. "that which cometh of the ___ of his patrimony" (Deuteronomy 18:8)
18. "Hew down the ___" (Daniel 4:14)
19. "The sons of Benjamin were . . . Naaman, ___, and Rosh" (Genesis 46:21)
20. "We have an ___, whereof they have no right to eat" (Hebrews 13:10)
22. Sips
25. "Suffer me that I may ___ the pillars" (Judges 16:26)
26. "Take my yoke upon you, and ___ of me" (Matthew 11:29)
28. "do my prophets ___ harm" (Psalm 105:15)
29. Youngster
30. "I have seen thy ___: behold, I will heal thee" (2 Kings 20:5)
31. Nickname (masc. or fem.)
32. Symbol for an artificially produced radioactive element
33. "Hushim and ___ were his wives" (1 Chronicles 8:8)
34. "Speak unto every feathered ___" (Ezekiel 39:17)
35. "___ to thine own house" (Luke 8:39)
37. Parts of speech
38. "inwardly they ___ ravening wolves" (Matthew 7:15)
39. Mythological being

40. "the ___ also filleth the pools" (Psalm 84:6)
42. "when he had ___ Jesus, he delivered him" (Matthew 27:26)
46. Pointed tool
47. "Come ye yourselves ___ into a desert place" (Mark 6:31)
48. Woman's name
49. "___, Lord: yet the dogs under the table eat" (Mark 7:28)
50. "Behold, he is in thine ___" (Job 2:6)
51. "though they be ___ like crimson, they shall be as wool" (Isaiah 1:18)

DOWN

1. "given to hospitality, ___ to teach" (1 Timothy 3:2)
2. "shut the doors, and ___ them" (Nehemiah 7:3)
3. Grooved
4. "___ the son of Uri was in the country of Gilead" (1 Kings 4:19)
5. Wheel shaft
6. "the wheat and the ___ were not smitten" (Exodus 9:32)
7. Overhead railways
8. "Let this mind ___ in you" (Philippians 2:5)
9. "Jacob was a ___ man" (Genesis 25:27)
10. "Of the sons of Bani; Maadei, Amram, and ___" (Ezra 10:34)
11. Golf mound
16. Russian mountain range
17. Shank
19. Blunders
20. "___ I am waxed old shall I have pleasure" (Genesis 18:12)
21. Rent
22. "The sons of Zerah; . . . Calcol, and ___" (1 Chronicles 2:6)
23. "he himself seeketh to be ___ openly" (John 7:4)
24. "ye shall find rest for your ___" (Jeremiah 6:16)

26. "The pillars whereupon the house
   standeth, that I may ___ upon them"
   (Judges 16:26)
27. "incline thine ___ unto me"
   (Psalm 17:6)
30. "the devil threw him down, and ___
   him" (Luke 9:42)
31. Loiterer
33. "___ their graven images with fire"
   (Deuteronomy 7:5)
34. "Fill ___ barrels with water"
   (1 Kings 18:33)
36. "Samson . . . put a firebrand in the
   midst between two ___" Judges 15:4)
37. Having to do with ships (abbr.)

39. "He . . . passed over the ___ Jabbok"
   (Genesis 32:22)
40. Flat fish
41. "stand in ___ and sin not"
   (Psalm 4:4)
42. Health resort
43. "How ___ these things be?"
   (John 3:9)
44. "the serpent beguiled ___ through his
   subtilty" (2 Corinthians 11:3)
45. Father
47. "___ Lord God! behold, thou hast
   made the heaven" (Jeremiah 32:17)

ACROSS

1. Pointed tool
4. "Of Naphtali, ___ the son of Enan" (Numbers 1:15)
9. "Moses sent to ___ out Jaazer" (Numbers 21:32)
12. "Let her be as the loving hind and pleasant ___" (Proverbs 5:19)
13. "And ___ stilled the people before Moses" (Numbers 13:30)
14. Turnover
15. "O Lord; ___ me thy paths" (Psalm 25:4)
17. "Noah . . . offered ___ offerings on the altar" (Genesis 8:20)
19. "the ___ is full, the fats overflow" (Joel 3:13)
22. One (Scot.)
23. "his life shall be unto him for a ___" (Jeremiah 21:9)
25. Air (prefix)
27. Golden ____
30. Opposite of followed
31. "we have a great high ___" (Hebrews 4:14)
33. Sodium symbol
34. The Wizard of ___
35. Tablet
36. "as it was in the days of ___" (Luke 17:26)
37. Hoosier St.
38. Palm lily
39. Tour
41. "the priest shall put it . . . upon the great ___ of his right foot" (Leviticus 14:14)
42. "Heber, which was the son of ___" (Luke 3:35)
44. "What is that to us? ___ thou to that" (Matthew 27:4)
45. Jokes

46. "Love worketh no ___ to his neighbor" (Romans 13:10)
48. "they shall ___ in the name of the Lord" (Zephaniah 3:12)
50. Quake
53. "the Lord sent ___ among them" (2 Kings 17:25)
56. One skilled in (suffix)
57. "Hushim and ___ were his wives" (1 Chronicles 8:8)
60. Shimei, and ___, and the mighty men which belonged to David" (1 Kings 1:8)
61. Sighs
62. "The sons of ___ the Netophathite" (Jeremiah 40:8)
63. "the king . . . ___ his heart on Daniel to deliver him" (Daniel 6:14)

DOWN

1. "___ not thou our God? (2 Chronicles 20:7)
2. "Who hath ___? Who hath sorrow?" (Proverbs 23:29)
3. "he ___ and walked" (Acts 14:10)
4. Pain
5. "He saith among the trumpets, ___" (Job 39:25)
6. Not (prefix)
7. Concerning
8. "whereby we cry, ___, Father" (Romans 8:15)
9. Banquet
10. "will men take a ___ of it?" (Ezekiel 15:3)
11. "when we were ___ without strength . . . Christ died for the ungodly" (Romans 5:6)
16. "Unto thee will I ___, O Lord" (Psalm 28:1)
18. Come together
20. "unto Thyatira and unto ___, and unto Philadelphia" (Revelation 1:11)

21. ____ whale
23. Plans
24. "The sons of Ulla; Arah, and Haniel, and ___" (1 Chronicles 7:39)
26. One who hires
28. Shallot
29. Paths
31. Nickname (masc. or fem.)
32. Distress call
35. "Take a ___, and bring hither the timbrel" (Psalm 81:2)
40. "I will spread my ___ upon them" (Hosea 7:12)
41. "But is under ___ and governors" (Galatians 4:2)

43. Claims
45. Greek letter
47. Part of the ear
49. "I was by the river of ___" (Daniel 8:2)
50. Beverage
51. Cheer
52. Strike
54. Born (Fr.)
55. "many shall come . . . and shall ___ down with Abraham" (Matthew 8:11)

ACROSS

1. "and ___ the wife of Chuza"
   (Luke 8:3)
7. "After this ___ did thy servant to me"
   (Genesis 39:19)
11. "The Lord shall ___ to me another
    son" (Genesis 30:24)
12. "And the sons of Shemidah were . . .
    and Likhi, and ___"
    (1 Chronicles 7:19)
14. "and he took ___ of his ribs"
    (Genesis 2:21)
15. Investment option (abbr.)
16. "Joab . . . ___ the king"
    (2 Samuel 14:22)
18. Wilmington's st.
19. "And ___ the son of Omri did evil"
    (1 Kings 16:30)
20. "Tappuah, and ___" (Joshua 15:34)
22. "Therefore is the name of it called
    ___" (Genesis 11:9)
25. "and one thousand ___ of gold"
    (Ezra 2:69)
26. Former Yugoslavian republic
29. Southern st.
30. "___ the son of Ikkesh the Tekoite"
    (2 Samuel 23:26)
31. "And he said, ___, it is yet high
    day" (Genesis 29:7)
32. Part of West Indies (abbr.)
34. Nix
35. Interjection
36. "from the house of ___"
    (Exodus 13:14)
40. "and thou shalt call his name ___"
    (Genesis 17:19)
43. Odors
45. "And who whosoever shall compel
    thee to go a ___" (Matthew 5:41)
47. Trim off

48. "the children of Gad called the altar
    ___" (Joshua 22:34)
50. "Understandest thou what thou
    ___?" (Acts 8:30)
52. Balloon gas symbol
53. "Of fowls also of the ___ by sevens"
    (Genesis 7:3)
55. Tedious
56. "whose mouth must be held in with
    ___ and bridle" (Psalm 32:9)
57. Discovers
58. "the noise of them that rejoice ___"
    (Isaiah 24:8)

DOWN

1. "And Rebekah spake unto ___ her
   son" (Genesis 27:6)
2. "wherewith the ___ number of them"
   (Numbers 3:48)
3. Year of our Lord (abbr.)
4. "___ with her suburbs, four cities"
   (Joshua 21:35)
5. "And ___, and Eshtemoh, and Anim"
   (Joshua 15:50)
6. "Let us ___ man in our image"
   (Genesis 1:26)
7. "___ your ways and your doings"
   (Jeremiah 7:3)
8. "Now Sarai Abram's wife bare him
   ___ children" (Genesis 16:1)
9. "The ___ of all flesh is come before
   me" (Genesis 6:13)
10. "The paper ___ by the brooks"
    (Isaiah 19:7)
13. Hoosier st.
16. God (comb. form)
17. "Till a ___ strike through his liver"
    (Proverbs 7:23)
19. "that God remembered ___"
    (Genesis 19:29)
21. "There was a ___ in the land of Uz"
    (Job 1:1)
23. "Yea, ten ___ of vineyard"
    (Isaiah 5:10)
25. Greeting

27. "and dwelt in the land of ___"
(Judges 11:3)
28. Aircraft related field (abbr.)
33. "Turn ye not unto ___"
(Leviticus 19:4)
34. "and ___ the father of Abner"
(1 Samuel 14:51)
37. Beaver St.
38. Ingress
39. Elephant's political assn.
40. "Hattush, and ___, and Bariah"
(1 Chronicles 3:22)
41. Attitude
42. "Of every ___ beast thou shalt take"
(Genesis 7:2)

44. "not as man ___; for man looketh"
(1 Samuel 16:7)
46. "And the seven thin ___ devoureth"
(Genesis 41:7)
47. Yield
49. "thou shalt surely ___"
(Genesis 2:17)
51. Boot-camp staffer
52. "and the archers ___ him"
(1 Samuel 31:3)
54. Symbol for Curie discovery
56. "She shall ___ called Woman"
(Genesis 2:23)

ACROSS

1. "lest thou ___ thy foot against a stone" (Psalm 91:12)
5. Average
8. "Heber, which was the son of ___" (Luke 3:35)
12. Being (comb. Form)
13. "And his sisters, ___ they not all with us?" (Matthew 13:56)
14. "I ___ not" (Luke 17:9)
15. Greek letter
16. "Who changed the truth of God into a ___" (Romans 1:25)
17. "He that hath the ___ is the bridegroom" (John 3:29)
18. "God be merciful to me a ___" (Luke 18:13)
20. Crystallized rock
21. Mote
22. "to ___ the book, neither to look thereon" (Revelation 5:4)
23. "found one of his fellow servants, which ___ him an hundred pence" (Matthew 18:28)
25. "I knew that thou ___ me always" (John 11:42)
28. Petrol
29. Boscs
30. Go
32. Wanders
34. "Jotham ran away, and fled, and went to ___" (Judges 9:21)
35. "they turned about with a very small ___" (James 3:4)
36. "if it be possible, let this ___ pass from me" (Matthew 26:39)
37. Picture
39. Dry measure
42. "took joyfully the spoiling of your ___" (Hebrews 10:34)

43. Pat
44. "Sir, come down ___ my child die" (John 4:49)
45. "I am, and none ___ beside me" (Isaiah 47:8)
46. "Gathered the good into vessels, but cast the ___ away" (Matthew 13:48)
47. Italian river
48. "punish the men that are settled on their ___" (Zephaniah 1:12)
49. "___ hath not seen, nor ear heard" (1 Corinthians 2:9)
50. "all the trees of ___, the choice and best of Lebanon" (Ezekiel 31:16)

DOWN

1. Accomplishes
2. Opposing (prefix)
3. "the place where thou ___ is holy ground" (Acts 7:33)
4. "___, every one that thirsteth" (Isaiah 55:1)
5. "A ___ of turtledoves, or two young pigeons" (Luke 2:24)
6. "Sirs, ye ___ brethren" (Acts 7:26)
7. Concerning
8. Walked
9. Dry
10. Ore vein
11. "Stand in ___, and sin not" (Psalm 4:4)
16. "the king of Egypt will not ___ you go" (Exodus 3:19)
17. "there came forth two she ___ out of the wood" (2 Kings 2:24)
19. "Dwelt in the land of ___" (Genesis 4:16)
20. Cogs
22. "all the magicians and astrologers that were in all his ___" (Daniel 1:20)

23. "___ king of Bashan"
    (1 Kings 4:19)
24. "It ___ very good" (Genesis 1:31)
25. Greeting
26. "The Lord is my ___" (Psalm 23:1)
27. "___ them about thy neck"
    (Proverbs 6:21)
29. "as certain also of your own ___"
    (Acts 17:28)
31. "The sons of Judah; ___, and
    Onan" (1 Chronicles 2:3)
33. "We came. . . the day following
    unto ___" (Acts 21:1)
34. Public vehicle
36. Young bear

37. "Moses made a serpent of brass,
    and put it upon a ___"
    (Numbers 21:9)
38. Stockings
39. "And the Spirit ___ me go with
    them" (Acts 11:12)
40. Bird of prey
41. Name (masc.)
42. Set
43. "one ___ is with the Lord as a
    thousand years" (2 Peter 3:8)
46. "Obey my voice, and I will ___
    your God" (Jeremiah 7:23)
47. One (Scot.)

ACROSS

1. "of ___ from under heaven" (Exodus 17:14)
6. "land of ___ to buy food" (Genesis 42:7)
11. "Call me not Naomi, call me ___" (Ruth 1:20)
12. "Judah took a wife for ___ his firstborn" (Genesis 38:6)
13. Government agency (abbr.)
14. Egg
15. Enlisted man
16. Publisher's abbreviation
17. Edge
18. "save the ___ the inhabitants of Gibeon" (Joshua 11:19)
21. Length measurement (abbr.)
22. "it doth ___ yet" (1 John 3:2)
23. Ammunition
25. Mineral's raw state
26. Decline
27. CA city
28. Adam's wife
31. Norway's capital
33. "is it not ___?" (Malachi 1:8)
34. "the borders of Tyre and ___" (Mark 7:24)
36. A definite amount
38. Symbol for element used in electronic devices
39. "Let her be as the loving ___ and pleasant roe" (Proverbs 5:19)
40. Iran's ex-sovereign
41. Sicily's nation (abbr.)
42. "an ___ soul shall suffer hunger" (Proverbs 19:15)
43. Symbol for poisonous element
44. Shout of contempt

46. Tall shade tree
48. Styptic
50. "And ___ also the Jairite" (2 Samuel 20:26)
51. Year (abbr.)
52. "and ___ greedily after the error" (Jude 11)
54. "regions of ___ and Cilicia" (Galatians 1:21)
55. Stomach area (abbr.)

DOWN

1. "Egyptians, and the ___" (Ezra 9:1)
2. Expert
3. Taro
4. Strike
5. "the ___ that came of Hemath" (1 Chronicles 2:55)
7. "son of ___, was the ruler of the house of God" (Nehemiah 11:11)
8. One (Scot.)
9. "given to hospitality, ___ to teach" (1 Timothy 3:2)
10. "and the princes of ___" (Psalm 68:27)
15. "In ___ the Lord appeared" (1 Kings 3:5)
18. "When Sanballat the ___" (Nehemiah 2:10)
19. "and called the place ___" (Genesis 35:7)
20. Barely (abbr.)
22. "___ room for them in the inn" (Luke 2:7)
24. "___ the son of Ammihud" (Numbers 1:10)
29. "the ___ over the beast" (Revelation 15:2)
30. "called the altar ___" (Joshua 22:34)

32. "And Mizraim begat ___"
    (1 Chronicles 1:11)
35. Exclamation
37. "He shall deliver the ___"
    (Job 22:30)
41. Egyptian wading bird
45. "And all that handle the ___"
    (Ezekiel 27:29)
47. "For, ___, the winter is past"
    (Song of Solomon 2:11)
49. "Shallum, and Telem, and ___"
    (Ezra 10:24)
51. Canadian province
53. Tar Heel State (abbr.)

ACROSS

1. "a Branch shall grow out of his ___" (Isaiah 11:1)
6. Heir
11. Same (comb. form)
12. Secular
14. Mouth
15. "a ravening and a ___ lion" (Psalm 22:13)
17. Part of year (abbr.)
18. "Amram, and ___" (Ezra 10:34)
20. "they shall be snares and ___ unto you" (Joshua 23:13)
21. Graduate degree (abbr.)
22. "His hand was leprous as ___" (Exodus 4:6)
24. Sere
25. "the children of Gad called the altar ___" (Joshua 22:34)
26. "___ the horses" (Jeremiah 46:4)
31. For architects, ability to bear stress (abbr.)
32. "He that findeth his life shall ___ it" (Matthew 10:39)
33. "counteth the ___, whether he have sufficient to finish it?" (Luke 14:28)
34. "if God ___ loved us" (1 John 4:11)
36. "the son of Zechariah, the son of ___" (Nehemiah 11:5)
38. "what must I ___ to be saved?" (Acts 16:30)
40. "Saul abode in Gibeah under a ___" (1 Samuel 22:6)
42. Shoal
44. Fruit drink (suffix)
45. "Furthermore ___ answered" (Job 34:1)

49. "Go to the ___, thou sluggard" (Proverbs 6:6)
50. Pine Tree St.
51. "He ___ up the poor" (Psalm 113:7)
53. That is (abbr.)
54. "___ ye the Lord" (Psalm 150:1)
56. "Then thus came every ___ unto the king" (Esther 2:13)
58. "mount Zion, on the ___ of the north" (Psalm 48:2)
59. "there shall not be found in the bursting of it a ___" (Isaiah 30:14)

DOWN

1. Mail again
2. First Covenant
3. Above (poet.)
4. Horse's gait
5. Fly high
6. "that my footsteps ___ not" (Psalm 17:5)
7. "thou shalt make his ___ to receive his ashes" (Exodus 27:3)
8. Equip
9. Characterized by (suffix)
10. Ruse
11. "Martha received him into her ___" (Luke 10:38)
13. Burdens
16. "I have withholden the ___ from you" (Amos 4:7)
19. "___, I come unto thee in a thick cloud" (Exodus 19:9)
21. Man's title (abbr.)
23. "the God in ___ hand thy breath is" (Daniel 5:23)
24. "the sons of Korah: ___, and Elkanah" (Exodus 6:24)
27. "he planteth an ___" (Isaiah 44:14)
28. "Shimei, and ___, and the mighty men" (1 Kings 1:8)
29. Habitat (comb. form)

30. "Kiss the ___, lest he be angry" (Psalm 2:12)
34. "___ with thy foot" (Ezekiel 6:11)
35. Decrees
37. "unfeigned faith . . . dwelt first in thy grandmother ___" (2 Timothy 1:5)
38. "But ye ___ the Holy One" (Acts 3:14)
39. "He, that being ___ reproved hardeneth his neck" (Proverbs 29:1)
41. Sight organ (Scot.)
43. Apiece (abbr.)

45. "And among these nations shalt thou find no ___" (Deuteronomy 28:65)
46. "thou hast . . . told me ___" (Judges 16:10)
47. "And they made upon the ___ of the robe pomegranates" (Exodus 39:24)
48. Beehive State
51. "___ them out of the hand of the wicked" (Psalm 82:4)
52. Hurry
55. "they fled before the men of ___" (Joshua 7:4)
57. Physician (abbr.)

ACROSS

1. "Isaac called ___, and blessed him". (Genesis 28:1)
6. "the next day we arrived at ___, and tarried at Trogyllium" (Acts 20:15)
11. Announcement
12. "And God created great ___" (Genesis 1:21)
14. "As he saith also in ___" (Romans 9:25)
15. "Elijah said, ___, thy son liveth" (1 Kings 17:23)
17. "and sparks of fire ___ out" (Job 41:19)
18. Blackbird
19. Bravo
20. Pearl diver
21. Upon (prefix)
22. "The sun shall not ___ thee by day" (Psalm 121:6)
24. Hospital place
25. Great room
28. "whom God hath raised from the ___" (Acts 3:15)
31. "The Jews departed, and had great ___ among themselves" (Acts 28:29)
32. "___, which was the son of Joseph" (Luke 3:26)
34. Touches
37. "Good ___ the word of the Lord" (2 Kings 20:19)
38. "the right of the ___ do they not judge" (Jeremiah 5:28)
41. "as soon as the sun is ___, thou shalt rise" (Judges 9:33)

42. "Who can utter the mighty ___ of the Lord?" (Psalm 106:2)
45. "Joshua . . . sent out of Shittim two men to ___" (Joshua 2:1)
46. "thou shalt in any ___ bring them again" (Deuteronomy 22:1)
48. "the ___, because he cheweth the cud" (Leviticus 11:6)
49. God (comb. form)
50. Before (prefix)
51. "Neither have two coats ___" (Luke 9:3)
53. Leased
55. "Abraham bought . . . of the sons of ___ the father of Sychem" (Acts 7:16)
56. "if your soul were in my soul's ___" (Job 16:4)

DOWN

1. "Mary was espoused to ___" (Matthew 1:18)
2. "The children of ___ of Hezekiah" (Ezra 2:16)
3. Heaven (Fr.)
4. Body of water (abbr.)
5. Broom
6. "Salome, had bought ___ spices" (Mark 16:1)
7. "Then said I, ___ Lord God!" (Ezekiel 4:14)
8. Evil (Fr.)
9. Olives
10. Joined by sewing
11. Seward Peninsula cape
13. Bowsprit
16. "___ and Ahiah, the sons of Shisha" (1 Kings 4:3)
22. "The beauty of Israel is ___ upon thy high places" (2 Samuel 1:19)

23. "things wherewith one may ___ another" (Romans 14:19)
26. "he shall gather the lambs with his ___" (Isaiah 40:11)
27. Name (masc. or fem.)
29. Compass point
30. "the Levites were numbered from the ___ of thirty years" (1 Chronicles 23:3)
32. "The children of Keros, the children of ___" (Ezra 2:44)
33. "I would hasten my ___ from the windy storm" (Psalm 55:8)

35. "the fruits that thy soul ___ after are departed" (Revelation 18:14)
36. "neither bid him God ___" (2 John 10)
39. Organic compound
40. Tinters
43. Prune
44. "if any man ___ to be contentious" (1 Corinthians 11:16)
46. "the sweet ___ from a far country" (Jeremiah 6:20)
47. Pier
52. Business (abbr.)
54. Sicily's nation (abbr.)

ACROSS

1. "His mother's name also was ___" (2 Kings 18:2)
4. "And ___ searched all the tent" (Genesis 31:34)
9. "the lapwing, and the ___" (Leviticus 11:19)
12. Sleep phenomenon
13. "I will ___ thee, I will praise thy name" (Isaiah 25:1)
14. Fuss
15. "___ and war are against me" (Job 10:17)
17. "The children of Dishan are these: Uz and ___" (Genesis 36:28)
18. "thine asses that were lost three days ___" (1 Samuel 9:20)
19. "___ thou as man seeth?" (Job 10:4)
22. Turn inside out
24. Interjection
25. Age
28. Twice (comb. form)
29. Southeast Asians
31. "He saith, ___" (Matthew 17:25)
32. Architecture style
34. "He that refuseth reproof ___" (Proverbs 10:17)
37. Continent (abbr.)
38. Large (abbr.)
39. Mauna ___
40. One (Scot.)
41. "he walketh through ___ places" (Luke 11:24)
42. Fiery
44. Dye

46. "In the first chariot were ___ horses" (Zechariah 6:2)
48. Yet
49. Hooklike part
53. Louder
56. "Encamp . . . between Migdol and the ___" (Exodus 14:2)
57. Dull finish
59. Graduate degree (abbr.)
60. "God created man in his ___ image" (Genesis 1:27)
61. Theater employee
62. Interjection

DOWN

1. Circle part
2. "A bishop then must be . . . of good ___" (1 Timothy 3:2)
3. "they have made them a molten ___" (Deuteronomy 9:12)
4. "make bare the ___" (Isaiah 47:2)
5. "they shall . . . come against her with ___" (Jeremiah 46:22)
6. Vile
7. Alcohol radical
8. Part of the Bible
9. "shut the doors, and ___ them" (Nehemiah 7:3)
10. Girl's name
11. Two thousand pounds
16. "And gathered them out of the lands . . . from the west, from the ___" (Psalm 107:3)
17. Laotian money
20. Artist's tool
21. Compass point
22. Sharp
23. "Jacob's ___ was out of joint" (Genesis 32:25)
25. "He that winketh with the ___ causeth sorrow" (Proverbs 10:10)

174

26. "happy is every one that ___ her" (Proverbs 3:18)
27. Pallid
30. Performer
33. "I . . . will ___ them as gold is tried" (Zechariah 13:9)
35. Irish county (abbr.)
36. Rodent
43. "But yet in it shall be a ___, and it shall return" (Isaiah 6:13)
45. Unfruitful
47. "A sword is upon the liars; and they shall ___" (Jeremiah 50:36)
49. Serviceman's org.

50. "I saw a new heaven and a ___ earth" (Revelation 21:1)
51. Container
52. Southwestern univ.
54. Comparative ending
55. Greek letter
58. Ancient Roman coin

PUZZLE 87

ACROSS

1. "the dead in Christ shall ___ first" (1 Thessalonians 4:16)
5. "that city was called ___ at the first" (Genesis 28:19)
8. Cable car
12. "Arad, and ___" (1 Chronicles 8:15)
13. "They...brought the child to ___" (1 Samuel 1:25)
14. Seize (arch.)
15. "he doeth whatsoever ___ him" (Ecclesiates 8:3)
17. "___ we ourselves groan within ourselves" (Romans 8:23)
18. Judgment
19. "For the ___ of the Almighty are within me" (Job 6:4)
21. "Speak now in the ___ of the people" (Exodus 11:2)
24. "Maadai, Amram, and ___" (Ezra 10:34)
25. "let us not love in word . . . but in ___" (1 John 3:18)
28. "There came wise men from the ___" (Matthew 2:1)
30. "Jephthah . . . dwelt in the land of ___" (Judges 11:3)
33. "thy king cometh . . . riding upon an ___" (Zechariah 9:9)
34. "Avim, and ___, and Ophrah" (Joshua 18:23)
35. "how long will it be ___ they attain to innocency?" (Hosea 8:5)
36. "the angels of God ___ him" (Genesis 32:1)
37. "And ___ gave names to all cattle" (Genesis 2:20)
38. "the land is as the garden of ___" (Joel 2:3)
39. "The sons of Caleb . . . ___, Elah, and Naam" (1 Chronicles 4:15)

41. "This is the __; come, let us kill him" (Mark 12:7)
43. "a great ___ from the Lord shall be among them" (Zechariah 14:13)
46. "take up the ___, and follow me" (Mark 10:21)
50. "the valley of the mountains shall reach unto ___" (Zechariah 14:5)
51. "Behold, a man of ___, an eunuch" (Acts 8:27)
54. "his violent dealing shall come down upon his own ___" (Psalm 7:16)
55. "He maketh me to ___ down in green pastures" (Psalm 23:2)
56. Rail
57. Snow vehicle
58. "So Joshua ___ the people depart" (Joshua 24:28)
59. Pump

DOWN

1. Strikes
2. "for they be ___" (Exodus 5:8)
3. "We have ___ his star in the East" (Matthew 2:2)
4. Deleted
5. Shelter
6. Ultimo (abbr.)
7. "The Nethinims: the children of ___" (Nehemiah 7:46)
8. "they are ___ unto this day" (Joshua 4:9)
9. "In his days Edom ___ from under the hand of Judah" (2 Kings 8:20)
10. Afresh
11. Alps (abbr.)
16. "shall ye encamp by the ___" (Exodus 14:2)
20. "the name of the other ___" (Ruth 1:4)
22. "he shall ___ therein all the days of his life" (Deuteronomy 17:19)
23. "Therefore ___ laughed within herself" (Genesis 18:12)
25. "the ___ sitting upon the young" (Deuteronomy 22:6)

26. Compass point
27. "the priest shall ___ it"
(Leviticus 27:14)
29. "there are differences of administrations, but the ___ Lord"
(1 Corinthians 12:5)
31. Crude metal
32. "Zechariah, ___, and Jaaziel"
(1 Chronicles 15:18)
34. "And at midnight ___ and Silas prayed" (Acts 16:25)
38. "Who can understand his ___?"
(Psalm 19:12)
40. "He that ___ the nations in anger"
(Isaiah 14:6)

42. Here (Fr.)
43. Faucets
44. "Hadoram, and ___, and Diklah"
(Genesis 10:27)
45. "I . . . will ___ thee all that is in thine heart" (1 Samuel 9:19)
47. Fish (
48. Chinese (comb. Form)
49. Fill
52. "___ them about thy neck"
(Proverbs 6:21)
53. Chicken

PUZZLE 88

ACROSS

1. "___, make haste, and come down" (Luke 19:5)
2. Balloon gas symbol
9. "the children of Shobal . . . Manahath, and ___" (Genesis 36:23)
10. "frogs . . . shall go . . . into thine ___" (Exodus 8:3)
13. Buffalo
15. A son of Joktan (Genesis 10:27)
17. "let ___ stand at his right hand" (Psalm 109:6)
19. Parent
20. "Now unto him that is able to ___" (Ephesians 3:20)
22. "___ the son of Kishi, the son of Abdi" (1 Chronicles 6:44)
23. "shall all the families of the ___" (Genesis 28:14)
25. "___ not Moses his chosen stood" (Psalm 106:23)
27. When plane's due
28. Name (fem.)
30. Denial
31. Title for Queen Elizabeth (abbr.)
32. Where details are not spelled out (abbr.)
33. Rims
36. "And ___ his son reigned in his stead" (1 Kings 15:8)
37. "___ Lord God! behold, I cannot speak" (Jeremiah 1:6)
38. "Samuel arose and went to ___" (1 Samuel 3:6)
39. Cooking measure (abbr.)
42. "the voice of the ___ is heard" (Song of Solomon 2:12)

45. "And the sons of Gomer; ___, and Riphath" (Genesis 10:3)
48. Dainty
50. Thermocouple element symbol
51. "these are the sons of Shuthelah: of ___" (Numbers 26:36)
53. Parley (abbr.)
54. Nasty
55. Slate

DOWN

1. "James the son of ___, and John his brother" (Mark 1:19)
2. "His mother's name also was ___" (2 Kings 18:2)
3. Financial professionals (abbr.)
4. "and the bride out of her ___" (Joel 2:16)
5. Undergraduate deg.
6. "And Jacob ___ pottage" (Genesis 25:29)
7. Pagentry (abbr.)
8. "Tappuah, and ___" (Joshua 15:34)
11. "She is empty, and ___" (Nahum 2:10)
12. "___ and great are there" (Job 3:19)
14. Prophet who spoke to David
15. "And Naarah bare him . . . Temeni, and ___" (1 Chronicles 4:6)
16. "there was one ___, a prophetess" (Luke 2:36)
18. Weekday (abbr.)
21. "for his ___ sake" (Mark 6:26)
24. "___ of the south" (Joshua 19:8)
26. "Barzillai the Gileadite of ___" (2 Samuel 17:27)
29. Federal agency
30. Sioux St.

33. Continent (abbr.)
34. Choose
35. Symbol for element used in electronic devices
36. "___ against the fenced cities" (Zephaniah 1:16)
40. "sewed sackcloth upon my ___" (Job 16:15)
41. Coach's courses (abbr.)
43. Brother of 15 Across
44. Memphis's st.
46. "___ that ye refuse not him" (Hebrews 12:25)
47. Seine

49. Self
52. Symbol for element used to make signs

ACROSS

1. "Why go ye ___ to kill me?"
   (John 7:19)
6. Currents
11. Tunnel
13. Kidnap
15. "the heart of fools ___ in the house
    of mirth" (Ecclesiastes 7:4)
16. "Defile not . . . the land which ye
    shall ___" (Numbers 35:34)
18. Scope (abbr.)
19. "the sons of Benjamin were . . .
    ___ and Rosh" (Genesis 46:21)
21. Vends
22. Noise
23. "Friend, ___ me three loaves"
    (Luke 11:5)
25. "As the days of ___ were"
    (Matthew 24:37)
26. Headland
27. "Jacob was yet ___ gone out"
    (Genesis 27:30)
29. "she ___ on her lovers"
    (Ezekiel 23:5)
30. Great Lake
31. "As the ___ panteth after the water
    brooks" (Psalm 42:1)
32. "Not that I speak in respect of ___"
    (Philippians 4:ll)
34. "Every man's ___ of money was in
    his sack" (Genesis 42:35)
36. "the Lord shall ___ for the fly"
    (Isaiah 7:18)
37. "incline thine ___ unto me"
    (Psalm 17:6)
38. "the coat was without ___"
    (John 19:23)
40. Island (Fr.)
41. "Restore . . . to them . . . their ___"
    (Nehemiah 5:11)

43. Compass point
44. "we should ___ them slip
    (Hebrews 2:1)
45. "thou shalt make for them ___"
    (Exodus 28:40)
47. Professor's helper
48. "The sons of Helah were Zereth,
    and Jezoar, and ___"
    (1 Chronicles 4:7)
50. "Peter, standing up with the ___"
    (Acts 2:14)
52. "Are there not twelve ___ in the
    day? (John 11:9)
53. "he . . . delivered me from all my
    ___" (Psalm 34:4)

DOWN

1. "Kish, the son of ___"
   (1 Samuel 9:1)
2. "Who cut up mallows by the ___"
   (Job 30:4)
3. Webfoot St.
4. "I have called by name Bezaleel, the
   son of ___" (Exodus 31:2)
5. Heavy weights
6. "he asked for a writing ___"
   (Luke 1:63)
7. Wading bird
8. Insecticide (abbr.)
9. Well (comb. Form)
10. "he took him a potsherd to ___
    himself (Job 2:8)
12. "___ come ye?" (Genesis 42:7)
14. "For every kind of beasts . . . is
    ___" (James 3:7)
17. Healing plant
20. "in every place ___ shall be
    offered" (Malachi 1:11)
22. "Fight the Lord's ___"
    (1 Samuel 18:17)
24. "He took three ___ in his hand"
    (2 Samuel 18:14)

26. "they bound him with two new ___" (Judges 15:13)
28. State Roger Williams founded (abbr.)
29. "he . . .pursued them unto ___" (Genesis 14:14)
31. Obstacle
32. During
33. "What ___ thee, Hagar?" (Genesis 21:17)
34. "There went with him a ___ of men" (1 Samuel 10:26)
35. "Intending after ___ to bring him forth to the people" (Acts 12:4)

37. Merits
39. "Thou shalt by no ___ come out thence" (Matthew 5:26)
41. "who will make me a ___?" (Job 24:25)
42. "I can of mine own ___ do nothing" (John 5:30)
45. African antelope
46. "we shall ___ him as he is" (1 John 3:2)
49. "___, every one that thirsteth" (Isaiah 55:1)
51. Old Dominion (abbr.)

PUZZLE 90

ACROSS

1. Big ___, California region
4. "the ___ thereof shall be as the wine of Lebanon" (Hosea 14:7)
9. "Lamech took unto him ___ wives" (Genesis 4:19)
12. "the ___ of violence is in their hands" (Isaiah 59:6)
13. "ye bear witness that ye ___ the deeds of your fathers" (Luke 11:48)
14. "her ___ was to light on a part of the field" (Ruth 2:3)
15. Symbol for sodium
16. "___ the Ahohite" (1 Chronicles 11:29)
17. "Pay me that thou ___" (Matthew 18:28)
19. "Herod . . . heard him ___" (Mark 6:20)
21. "I will fetch my knowledge from ___" (Job 36:3)
22. Crafty
23. "Jerusalem, which killest the prophets, and ___ them" (Luke 13:34)
26. Clarified butter
28. "thy king cometh . . . riding upon an ass, and upon a ___" (Zechariah 9:9)
29. "The sons of Judah; ___, and Onan" (1 Chronicles 2:3)
30. One that is (suffix)
31. Gaudy
33. Greek letter
34. Soldier
35. Solitary
36. "the deceiver, which hath in his flock a ___" (Malachi 1:14)
37. "why ___ thou thyself alone" (Exodus 18:14)
39. Musical note
40. Wings
41. "Yea, I have ___ it" (Isaiah 46:11)

45. "To whom then will ye ___ God" (Isaiah 40:18)
46. Leg part
47. Concerning
48. "How amiable ___ thy tabernacles" (Psalm 84:1)
49. "Bread ___ in secret is pleasant" (Proverbs 9:17)
51. Pat
52. "the ___ of the scribes is in vain" (Jeremiah 8:8)
53. Small amounts
54. "Lod and ___ the valley of craftsmen" (Nehemiah 11:35)

DOWN

1. "at midnight Paul and Silas prayed, and ___ praises" (Acts 16:25)
2. "the man spake unto Ithiel, even unto Ithiel and ___" (Proverbs 30:1)
3. Direction (abbr.)
4. Leap forth
5. "as the ___ is in the potter's hand" (Jeremiah 18:6)
6. "there came a man of God unto ___" (1 Samuel 2:27)
7. "___ flesh should be saved" (Mark 13:20)
8. "ye make him ___ more the child of hell" (Matthew 23:15)
9. "he worshipped the Lord ___" (1 Samuel 1:28)
10. "___ not Esau Jacob's brother?" (Malachi 1:2)
11. Choose
16. "every ___ word that men shall speak" (Matthew 12:36)
18. "he began to be in ___" (Luke 15:14)
20. "Of the tribe of ___ were sealed twelve thousand" (Revelation 7:6)
21. Expiate
23. "the ___ measure that is abominable" (Micha 6:10)
24. "___ up those things which the seven thunders uttered" (Revelation 10:4)

25. "Thou . . . gavest them right judg-
    ments, and ___ laws"
    (Nehemiah 9:13)
26. Tops
27. Hawaiian fern
31. "she went, and came, and ___ in the
    field" (Ruth 2:3)
32. "her smoke ___ up for ever and ever"
    (Revelation 19:3)
33. "how they might entangle him in his
    ___" (Matthew 22:15)
35. Tamarisk
36. "Behold, even to the ___, and it
    shineth not" (Job 25:5)
38. "thine iniquity is ___ away"
    (Isaiah 6:7)

39. Whirls
41. "Blessed be the Lord God of ___"
    (Genesis 9:26)
42. "of ___, the family of Eranites"
    (Numbers 26:36)
43. "Bel boweth down, ___ stoopeth"
    (Isaiah 46:1)
44. "The lot is cast into the ___"
    (Proverbs 16:33)
45. Anger
46. Depot (abbr.)
50. "It hath consumed ___ of Moab"
    (Numbers 21:28)
51. "What have I to ___ any more with
    idols?" (Hosea 14:8)

ACROSS

2. "For this Agar is ___ ___"
(Galatians 4:25)
11. "all thy borders with ___"
(Exodus 8:2)
12. "Peter, an ___ of Jesus Christ"
(1 Peter 1:1)
15. A unit of length
16. "sons of Eliab; ___"
(Numbers 26:9)
21. Large rodent
22. "an ___ of grace unto"
(Proverbs 1:9)
26. "river of Arnon unto ___ ___"
(Deuteronomy 3:8)
28. "and ___ greedily after the error"
(Jude 11)
29. Note of the musical scale
30. Long-bodied fish
31. "Lebbaeus, whose surname was
___" (Matthew 10:3)
34. Bill of exchange (abbr.)
35. "the ___ leaped in her womb"
(Luke 1:41)
36. Symbol for element used in
alloys
38. Discount
41. "by his name ___, and rejoice
before him" (Psalm 68:4)
42. "David himself followed the
___" (2 Samuel 3:31)
44. Undergraduate degree (abbr.)
45. Small one (suffix)
46. "came to Joel the ___ of
Penthuel" (Joel 1:1)
47. Repetition of sound
49. Incite, with up

50. "Henoch, and ___, and Eldaah"
(1 Chronicles 1:33)

DOWN

1. "___ on the altar" (Genesis 8:20)
2. "the house of the Lord at
Jerusalem in ___ ___"
(2 Chronicles 3:1)
3. "and ___ the king of Bashan"
(Numbers 21:33)
4. As above (abbr.)
5. Symbol for element in vanadium
family
6. Where you can spend a paseta
(abbr.)
7. Electrically charged particle
8. Halifax's province (abbr.)
9. "I ___ no pleasant bread"
(Daniel 10:3)
10. "it shall go ___ with him"
(Job 20:26)
13. Tall shade tree
14. "___ away thine eyes"
(Song of Solomon 6:5)
17. "unto ___, which is in the land of
Moab" (Deuteronomy 32:49,
2 words)
18. "know our ___ in unto you"
(1 Thessalonians 2:1)
19. "Jahath begat Ahumai, and ___"
(1 Chronicles 4:2)
20. Pagentry (abbr.)
23. "brass to ___ the house of the
Lord" (2 Chronicles 24:12)
24. Sunshine State (abbr.)
25. Bean curd
27. Military installation (abbr.)
32. "Both how to be ___"
(Philippians 4:12)
33. Medical test (abbr.)

35. "The ephah and the ___"
(Ezekiel 45:11)
37. "brought the heads of ___"
(Judges 7:25)
39. Somewhat (suffix)
40. Woodwind instrument
41. Israelite
43. Length measurement (abbr.)
46. Roadway (abbr.)
48. Symbol for element in milk

PUZZLE 92

ACROSS

1. "unto the angel of the church in ___ write" (Revelation 3:1)
7. "And before the ___ there was a sea of glass" (Revelation 4:6)
13. "___ our God" (Revelation 19:5)
14. "I saw a star fall from ___" (Revelation 9:1)
15. Brat
16. Medical test
18. Yankees, Cowboys, or Lakers
19. Rosters
21. French king's name
22. Purdue's st.
23. Pester
26. Small one (suffix)
27. "and ___ them about thy neck" (Proverbs 6:21)
29 "I am ___ and Omega" (Revelation 1:8)
30. "to ___ them that dwell upon the earth" (Revelation 3:10)
31. Currant
32. "the son in law of Shechaniah the son of ___" (Nehemiah 6:18)
33. "even as a ___ tree casteth" (Revelation 6:13)
35. Million (comb. Form)
37. Ran into
40. Ancient Roman coin
41. "the mighty ___ which belonged to David" (1 Kings 1:8)
42. "They shall hunger ___ more" (Revelation 7:16)
43. Requires
46. "Thy silver is become ___" (Isaiah 1:22)
48. Go

49. "an half ___ of land" (1 Samuel 14:14)
52. Relative's nickname (abbr.)
53. "and why ___ thou not?" (1 Samuel 1:8)
55. Negative word
58. Semiconductor element symbol
59. "and the day following unto ___" (Acts 21:1)
60. "the pillar and ___ of the truth" (1 Timothy 3:15)

DOWN

1. "let him hear what the ___ saith" (Revelation 3:6)
2. "___ and Mephibosheth" (2 Samuel 21:8)
3. Intent
4. Double (comb. form)
5. "blessed ___ he that keepeth the sayings" (Revelation 22:7)
6. "son of ___, which was the son of Noe" (Luke 3:36)
7. Containing sulfur (comb. form)
8. Hebrew letter
9. "Even after a certain ___ every day" (2 Chronicles 8:13)
10. "and to morrow is cast into the ___" (Luke 12:28)
11. "for now is our salvation ___" (Romans 13:11)
12. "Because the carnal mind is ___ against God" (Romans 8:7)
17. "Thrust in thy sickle, and ___" (Revelation 14:15)
20. Remain
21. "if any man ___ my voice, ___ open the door" (Revelation 3:20)
24. "Go up, O ___; besiege, O Media" (Isaiah 21:2)

25. "Jonathan the son of ___ the Hararite" (1 Chronicles 11:34)
28. "Or if he shall ask an ___" (Luke 11:12)
30. Graduate degree (abbr.)
33. "and am set down with my ___ in his throne" (Revelation 3:21)
34. "The vision of ___ the son of Amoz" (Isaiah 1:1)
36. Ruler
38. "lifted up as an ___ upon his land" (Zechariah 9:16)
39. "I am ___ up and down as the locust" (Psalm 109:23)

44. Acetone-related group
45. Return postage container (abbr.)
47. Mouth
50. Licensed educators
51. England (abbr.)
54. Past ending (suffix)
56. West Coast st.
57. Message-sending place (abbr.)

ACROSS

1. "the lapwing, and the ___"
   (Leviticus 11:19)
4. Strips of land between rivers
9. "The king . . . brought men from
   Babylon, and from Cuthah and from
   ___" (2 Kings 17:24)
12. Age
13. "the sons of ___ the Netophathite"
    (Jeremiah 40:8)
14. "your father . . . changed my wages
    ___ times" (Genesis 31:7)
15. "their ___ things shall not profit"
    (Isaiah 44:9)
18. Semiconductor element symbol
19. "they . . . brought the child to ___"
    (1 Samuel 1:25)
20. "It is ___ for a camel to go through
    the eye of a needle"
    (Matthew 19:24)
22. Dwells
26. "Ye are the ___ of the earth"
    (Matthew 5:13)
27. Overhead railway
28. Rhythm
30. "his sons were ___ and Rakem"
    (1 Chronicles 7:16)
32. "___, I have no man . . . to put me
    into the pool" (John 5:7)
34. Tropical fruits
36. Distributor's woe (abbr.)
37. Melt
39. "like a torch of fire in a ___"
    (Zechariah 12:6)
41. "___, I am with you alway"
    (Matthew 28:20)
42. Great Barrier Island
44. "I am ___ with comfort"
    (2 Corinthians 7:4)
46. "___ believe me for the very works'
    sake" (John 14:11, 2 words)

48. Teacher's group
49. Concerning
50. "he cried with a ___ voice unto
    Daniel" (Daniel 6:20)
55. Ear of grain
57. "We gat our bread with the ___ of
    our lives" (Lamentations 5:9)
58. "the birds of the ___"
    (2 Samuel 21:10)
59. Leaf (Abbr.)
60. ___-burly
61. Born (Fr.)

DOWN

1. "Arise, take up thy ___"
   (Matthew 9:6)
2. "ye ___ gone away from mine ordinances" (Malachi 3:7)
3. "In thee are men that carry ___ to
   shed blood" (Ezekiel 22:9)
4. "thyself hast ___ it" (1 Kings 20:40)
5. Choose
6. "___, our eye hath seen it"
   (Psalm 35:21)
7. "Ye shall find the ___ wrapped in
   swaddling clothes" (Luke 2:12)
8. "it pleased ___ to abide there"
   (Acts 15:34)
9. Near (prefix)
10. Legume
11. "And out of the half tribe of
    Manasseh; ___ with her suburbs"
    (1 Chronicles 6:70)
16. "they removed from Marah, and
    came unto ___" (Numbers 33:9)
17. "they called his name ___"
    (Genesis 25:25)
21. Artist (abbr.)
22. "Had I as yet told it to . . . the
    nobles, nor to the rulers, nor to the
    ___" (Nehemiah 2:16)
23. "___ and Ahiah, the sons of Shisha"
    (1 Kings 4:3)
24. Greek letters

25. "of Adam after he had begotten ___"
(Genesis 5:4)
29. Sand bar
31. Disposition
33. "The people shall go out and gather
a certain ___ every day"
(Exodus 16:4)
35. Pious
38. Water source
40. "after a dead dog, after a ___"
(1 Samuel 24:14)
43. "Joah, the son of ___, the recorder"
(Isaiah 36:22)
45. "And ___ went to shear his sheep"
(Genesis 31:19)

46. Crude metals
47. Ostrichlike bird
51. "You do ___, not knowing the scriptures" (Matthew 22:29)
52. Nothing
53. "they ___ in wait to deceive"
(Ephesians 4:14)
54. "how long will it be ___ they
believe me" (Numbers 14:11)
56. Apennines country

ACROSS

1. "tribulation worketh ___"
   (Romans 5:3)
6. Hebrew month
10. Teacher's org.
11. Flank
12. "neither do the aged ___ judgment" (Job 32:9)
15. Inside (abbr.)
16. Cow's milk bag
17. Female deer
19. "The ___ lifteth up" (Nahum 3:3)
21. "___ verily, their sound went into all the earth" (Romans 10:18)
23. "and black as a ___"
   (Song of Solomon 5:11)
26. Symbol for lime's element
28. "___ wind in my fury"
   (Ezekiel 13:13)
30. "___ than the heavens"
   (Hebrews 7:26)
34. "ye to do with me, O ___"
   (Joel 3:4)
35. "___ the Ahohite"
   (1 Chronicles 11:29)
36. Large salt-water body
38. Continent (abbr.)
39. "as a ___ robbed of her whelps in the field" (2 Samuel 17:8)
41. "___ that I had wings"
   (Psalm 55:6)
42. "as a thread of ___ is broken"
   (Judges 16:9)
44. "royal apparel of ___ and white"
   (Esther 8:15)
45. "and ___, that draw the bow"
   (Isaiah 66:19)
47. Incarcerated vet.

49. Symbol for Curie discovery
50. Symbol for salt
51. "And not only ___"
   (Romans 5:3)
52. "___ the West was won"
53. Pawtuxet River's state (abbr.)
54. Football goal (abbr.)

DOWN

1. "in spirit, in faith, in ___"
   (1 Timothy 4:12)
2. "For the ___ sake" (2 John 1:2)
3. "we count them happy which ___"
   (James 5:11)
4. "must ___ be borne"
   (Jeremiah 10:5)
5. One who combs wool for spinning
6. "And ___ did that which was good and right" (2 Chronicles 14:2)
7. "he will ___ us up" (Hosea 6:1)
8. "Ahinadab the son of ___"
   (1 Kings 4:14)
9. "___ thankful unto him"
   (Psalm 100:4)
13. "strong men, Elihu, and ___"
   (1 Chronicles 26:7)
14. "a woman in ___" (Micah 4:9)
18. "to ___ of the tree of life"
   (Revelation 2:7)
20. Symbol for element used to make signs
22. "young man named ___, being fallen into a deep sleep"
   (Acts 20:9)
24. Negotiate
25. "the apple of his ___"
   (Zechariah 2:8)
27. Midweek (abbr.)
28. "a ___, and a candlestick"
   (2 Kings 4:10)
29. Mineral in a raw state

31. "And after him ___"
    (Nehemiah 11:8)
32. "In his days did ___ the
    Bethelite" (1 Kings 16:34)
33. Peruse again
37. "___ shall have distresses daily"
    (Ezekiel 30:16)
40. "she is thine ___"
    (Leviticus 18:14)
43. Court
46. "Now unto him that is able to
    ___" (Ephesians 3:20)
48. Extended conflict (abbr.)
49. Part of postal address (abbr.)

PUZZLE 95

ACROSS

1. "he that gathered least gathered ___ homers" (Numbers 11:32)
4. "they ___ upon horses" (Jeremiah 6:23)
8. "that which cometh of the ___ of his patrimony" (Deuteronomy 18:8)
12. "Go your way, ___ the fat" (Nehemiah 8:10)
13. "Ram the firstborn, and Bunah, and ___" (1 Chronicles 2:25)
14. Cultivate
15. "The word ___ nigh thee" (Romans 10:8)
16. Having a visual defect (comb. form)
17. Vocal
18. "the ___ of the tree were for the healing of the nations" (Revelation 22:2)
20. "in the black and ___ night" (Proverbs 7:9)
21. Intermediate (comb. form)
22. "him that ___ understanding" (Proverbs 9:4)
25. "The fire shall ___ be burning" (Leviticus 6:13)
27. "glorify ye the Lord in the ___" (Isaiah 24:15)
28. Concerning
29. "the fourth part of an ___ of wine for a drink offering" (Exodus 29:40)
30. "he had forty sons and thirty nephews, that rode on threescore and ten ass ___" (Judges 12:14)
31. "he . . . rebuked the winds and the ___" (Matthew 8:26)
32. Not (prefix)
33. "her princes are become like ___" (Lamentations 1:6)
34. "They ___ to and fro" (Psalm 107:27)
35. "they wandered in ___" (Hebrews 11:38)

37. "upon the great ___ of their right foot" (Exodus 29:20)
38. "Casting all your ___ upon him" (1 Peter 5:7)
39. "a ___ and a commander to the people" (Isaiah 55:4)
42. "A ___ heart doeth good" (Proverbs 17:22)
44. "Come hither, and ___ the words of the Lord" (Joshua 3:9)
45. "we will ___ as thou sayest" (Nehemiah 5:12)
46. Leave out
47. Back
48. "And he ___ them forth" (Psalm 107:7)
49. Young dogs
50. Electric units
51. "Onesimus . . . who is ___ of you" (Colossians 4:9)

DOWN

1. "it . . . shall be eaten: as a ___ tree" (Isaiah 6:13)
2. "His soul shall dwell at ___" (Psalm 25:13)
3. Bible part (abbr.)
4. "the soldiers cut off the ___" (Acts 27:32)
5. Rainbow
6. Gov't agency
7. Printer's measure
8. Games
9. Similar
10. ___ cit
11. "And Abraham set seven ___ lambs" (Genesis 21:28)
16. Remaining
17. Feather parts
19. "Surely I come quickly. ___" (Revelation 22:20)
20. "quench all the fiery ___ of the wicked" (Ephesians 6:16)
22. Droops
23. "And he shall be like a ___ planted by the rivers" (Psalm 1:3)

192

24. "O Lord, ___ me; for my bones are vexed" (Psalm 6:2)
25. "the Lord raised them up a deliverer, ___" (Judges 3:15)
26. "I am the true ___" (John 15:1)
27. Loud (musical)
30. "to ___ him to Babylon" (Jeremiah 39:7)
31. "I will bring forth a ___ out of Jacob" (Isaiah 65:9)
33. "The ___ of the children of men" (Proverbs 15:11)
34. "Let the sea ___" (Psalm 96:11)
36. "let him take it, and likewise his ___" (Luke 22:36)
37. "The Lord God will wipe away ___" (Isaiah 25:8)
39. "Why ___ ye, ye high hills?" (Psalm 68:16)
40. "The Lord God . . . put him into the garden of ___" (Genesis 2:15)
41. "they ___ upon the camels" (Genesis 24:61)
42. Swab
43. Australian bird
44. "A woman . . . touched the ___ of his garment" (Matthew 9:20)
47. Scope (abbr.)
48. "and, ___, I am with you alway" (Matthew 28:20)

PUZZLE 96

ACROSS

1. Edmonton's province (abbr.)
3. "word of the Lord to Israel by ___" (Malachi 1:1)
9. Greek letter
11. "and Mary the mother of James, and ___" (Mark 16:1)
13. "Purge me with ___" (Psalm 51:7)
15. "For the waters of ___ shall be" (Isaiah 15:9)
16. Amlah
17. "that ___ may set his ___ on high" (Habakkuk 2:9)
18. "and the ___, and the garlick" (Numbers 11:5)
20. Printer's measure
21. "for the harvest ___ ripe" (Joel 3:13)
22. Transportation method (abbr.)
23. "and he that ministered to my ___" (Philippians 2:25)
26. "the son of ___, which as the son of Zorobabel" (Luke 3:27)
28. "called the altar ___" (Joshua 22:34)
29. "that we should sail into ___" (Acts 27:1)
30. "I ___ jealous for Jerusalem" (Zechariah 1:14)
31. "And thou, O ___ of the flock" (Micah 4:8)
34. "He shall come as an ___ against" (Hosea 8:1)
37. Toronto's province (abbr.)
38. Saco River state (abbr.)
39. Show Me St.
40. Fosse

42. "I will redeem them from ___" (Hosea 13:14)
43. Summer month (abbr.)
44. "Go to the ___, thou sluggard" (Proverbs 6:6)
45. Burns
48. Skills
49. Totonto's prov.
50. "whose ___ reached unto the heaven" (Daniel 4:20)

DOWN

1. Part of former Navigators Island (abbr.)
2. "and some ___ me kill thee" (1 Samuel 24:10)
3. "I will water it every ___" (Isaiah 27:3)
4. "The words of ___" (Amos 1:1)
5. "I have neither ___ on usury" (Jeremiah 15:10)
6. Disruption
7. "when they had sung an ___" (Matthew 26:30)
8. "The vision of ___ the son of Amoz" (Isaiah 1:1)
9. Wail
10. Soar
12. "I heard the man clothed in ___" (Daniel 12:7)
14. Angle
17. "he that ___ him out" (Isaiah 22:16)
19. "a companion of riotous men ___ his father" (Proverbs 28:7)
21. "and the molten ___" (Nahum 1:14)
24. "Why make ye this ___, and weep?" (Mark 5:39)
25. "saying, ___, we would see Jesus" (John 12:21)

194

26. Grain
27. Nickname (masc. or fem.)
32. "like a ___ in travail" (Micah 4:10)
33. "till they had ___?" (Obadiah 5)
35. Gosling
36. "and I punished the ___" (Zechariah 10:3)
38. Man's title (abbr.)
41. Askew
42. "Till a ___ strike through his liver" (Proverbs 7:23)
45. "What have we spoken ___ much" (Malachi 3:13)
46. Miami Indian state (Abbr.)
47. Symbol for element used in electronic devices
48. "___ Lord God! behold, thou hast made the heaven" (Jeremiah 32:17)

ACROSS

1. Expires
5. "to sail by the coasts of ___" (Acts 27:2)
9. "an half ___ of land" (1 Samuel 14:14)
10. "There is ___ holy as the Lord" (1 Samuel 2:2)
11. "and he made the ___ of brass" (Exodus 38:8)
13. "The ___ to Jesuah" (1 Chronicles 24:11)
16. "and Naaman, ___, and Rosh" (Genesis 46:21)
17. "Command ___ and his sons" (Leviticus 6:9)
20. Metal source
21. "Thou art my ___ place" (Psalm 32:7)
22. More nasty
24. Computer abbreviation
25. Cranes
26. Electrical engineer (abbr.)
28. Hebrew letter
30. "The ___ of one curtain" (Exodus 26:2)
34. "That the saying of ___ the prophet" (John 12:38)
36. "and why ___ thou not?" (1 Samuel 1:8)
39. "had told Samuel in his ___ a day before" (1 Samuel 9:15)
40. "borders of gold with ___ of silver" (Song of Solomon 1:11)
41. Return mail (abbr.)
42. "that ___ presume" (Esther 7:5)
44. Breakfast item

46. "upon Azariah the son of ___" (2 Chronicles 15:1)
48. Diets
49. Cable
50. "and all the little ___ that were with him" (2 Samuel 15:22)

DOWN

1. "send me ___ thy son" (1 Samuel 16:19)
2. "He casteth forth his ___ like morsels" (Psalm 147:17)
3. "I have a secret ___ unto thee" (Judges 3:19)
4. Compass point
5. Relating to (suffix)
6. Poem
7. Chemical substance (suffix)
8. "was baptizing in ___ near to Salim" (John 3:23)
11. "And when he came unto ___" (Judges 15:14)
12. "and ___ went before the ark" (2 Samuel 6:4)
14. "I saw, and behold, a ___ in the midst of the earth" (Daniel 4:10)
15. This place
18. "We have sinned ___ the Lord" (1 Samuel 7:6)
19. "and have ___ the weightier matters" (Matthew 23:23)
23. "shall play on the hole of the ___" (Isaiah 11:8)
27. "and the two sons of ___" (1 Samuel 4:11)
28. "take ___ to thyself until the morning" (1 Samuel 19:2)
29. "And I gave unto Isaac Jacob and ___" (Joshua 24:4)
31. "intending after ___ to bring him forth" (Acts 12:4)

196

32. "___ hither Micaiah the son of Imlah" (1 Kings 22:9)
33. Printer's notation
35. "he shot an ___ beyond him" (1 Samuel 20:36)
37. "His hand took hold of ___ heel" (Genesis 25:26)
38. Back talk
43. Missile plan (abbr.)
45. "And David called ___ of the young men" (2 Samuel 1:15)
47. First State (abbr.)
48. Its capital is St. Louis (abbr.)

PUZZLE 98

ACROSS

1. "his grace . . . which is ___ to build you up" (Acts 20:32)
5. Hebrew month
9. Laughter sounds
12. "do not even the ___ the same?" (Matthew 5:46)
14. Greek letter
15. Smoky Mountains St.
16. Tripoli measure
17. Dairy department item
18. "that which cometh of the ___ of his patrimony" (Deuteronomy 18:8)
20. "he was about to ___ into Syria" (Acts 20:3)
22. "they look and ___ upon me" (Psalm 22:17)
24. "thou shalt say, I ___ flesh" (Deuteronomy 12:20, 2 words)
27. "The legs of the ___ are not equal" (Proverbs 26:7)
28. God (comb. form)
29. Compass point
30. Tumor (suffix)
31. "In the same day shall the Lord ___ with a razor that is hired" (Isaiah 7:20)
32. John (Sc.)
33. "All that handle the ___, the mariners" (Ezekiel 27:29)
34. Shaft
35. Arteries (abbr.)
36. W. Indies island
37. Feather part
38. "ye pay ___ of mint and anise and cummin" (Matthew 23:23)
40. Gather
41. Jolts
42. Fault
44. Very well
45. "he said, ___, such a one!" (Ruth 4:1)
47. Biblical well
48. Council of Jewish elders
52. Thing (Latin)
53. "the land is as the garden of ___" (Joel 2:3)
54. Attar

DOWN

1. "A bishop then must be blameless . . . ___ to teach" (1 Timothy 3:2)
2. Roll
3. Pound (abbr.)
4. Overhead railway
5. "as it were an half ___ of land" (1 Samuel 14:14)
6. Sheep's cry
7. "as corn is sifted ___" (Amos 9:9) (3 words)
8. Undergraduate degree (abbr.)
9. Experts in Greek language and literature
10. "I ___ no pleasant bread" (Daniel 10:3)
11. ___ Paulo
13. "every ___ word that men shall speak, they shall give account thereof" (Matthew 12:36)
17. "Jacob . . . took the stone . . . and poured ___ upon the top of it" (Genesis 28:18)
18. Philippine island
19. "Blessed ___ the poor in spirit" (Matthew 5:3)
21. Helm position
22. Sailing vessel
23. "Absalom . . . had a fair sister, whose name was ___" (2 Samuel 13:1)

198

24. "thou art as a ___ in the seas" (Ezekiel 32:2)
25. "After him was Shamgar the son of ___" (Judges 3:31)
26. Taut
28. Strap
31. "children of a ___ long" (Lamentations 2:20)
37. Promise
38. "the Lord will ___ me up" (Psalm 27:10)
39. Within (prefix)
41. "His name is ___" (Luke 1:63)

42. "Remove thy way ___ from her" (Proverbs 5:8)
43. "___ thou also upon thy left side" (Ezekiel 4:4)
44. One (Sc.)
45. "the archers ___ him" (1 Samuel 31:3)
46. "Let us meet . . . in the plain of ___" (Nehemiah 6:2)
48. Compass point
49. Toward (suffix)
50. "ye shall not fast as ye ___ this day" (Isaiah 58:4)
51. Football position (abbr.)

ACROSS

1. "___ your beasts, and go" (Genesis 45:17)
4. Greek letters
8. "whether it be ___ or ewe, ye shall not kill it" (Leviticus 22:28)
11. Laotian money
12. "According as his ___ power hath given unto us" (2 Peter 1:3)
14. "to what ___ they like?" (Luke 7:31)
15. "the clouds drop down the ___" (Proverbs 3:20)
17. "ye shall be hated of all ___" (Matthew 10:22)
18. "all the people ___ together" (Acts 3:11)
20. "teachers, having itching ___" (2 Timothy 4:3)
22. Fifty-six, in ancient Rome
23. Milan's nation (abbr.)
24. "He begat of Hodesh his wife, Jobab and ___" (1 Chronicles 8:9)
26. Paid attention
28. ___ passant, chess term
29. Blood factor
30. "I am Alpha and Omega, the beginning and the ___" (Revelation 21:6)
31. Carpet
33. Continent (abbr.)
35. "discern between good and ___" (1 Kings 3:9)
36. Flightless bird
37. Nickname (masc. or fem.)
38. "thy mighty in the ___" (Isaiah 3:25)
39. "all that ___ within me" (Psalm 103:1)
41. Apiece (abbr.)
42. "a full ___ be given thee" (Ruth 2:12)
44. "They shall lay hold on bow and ___" (Jeremiah 6:23)
46. "I ___ the good shepherd" (John 10:14)
47. Crude metal
48. Lath

49. "as a ___ doth gather her brood" (Luke 13:34)
50. Mimic
51. Small lizard
54. "they . . . brought the child to ___" (1 Samuel 1:25)
56. Entangle
59. That is (abbr.)
60. "While we look ___ at the things which are seen" (2 Corinthians 4:18)
61. "What ___ is this that ye have done?" (Genesis 44:15)
62. Win

DOWN

1. "There is a ___ here, which hath five barley loaves" (John 6:9)
2. "They . . . ___ the sacrifices of the dead" (Psalms 106:28)
3. "the children of Gad called the altar ___" (Joshua 22:34)
4. Times before
5. "with silver, iron, ___, and lead they traded in thy fairs" (Ezekiel 27:12)
6. Belonging to (suffix)
7. "he . . . went and ___ Baal, and worshipped him" (1 Kings 16:31)
8. "Who then ___ be saved?" (Matthew 19:25)
9. Its capital is Salem
10. "he took them, and ___ aside" (Luke 9:10)
13. "The sons of Zophah; . . . Beri, and ___" (1 Chronicles 7:36)
16. "They . . . weave the spider's ___" (Isaiah 59:5)
19. Relief
21. "the birds of the ___ have nests" (Matthew 8:20)
22. "Do good, and ___, hoping for nothing again" (Luke 6:35)
23. thou shall be desolate, O Mount Seir, and all ___" (Ezekiel 35:15)
24. "what vehement desire, yea, what ___" (2 Corinthians 7:11)
25. "do according to all that they ___ thee" (Deuteronomy 17:10)

26. "he ___ my voice out of his temple" (Psalm 18:6)
27. "how long will it be ___ thou be quiet?" (Jeremiah 47:6)
32. Forage plant
34. "ye tithe mint and ___ and all manner of herbs" (Luke 11:42)
35. "Himself took our infirmities, and ___ our sicknesses" (Matthew 8:17)
38. "Cornelius . . . was ___ from God by an holy angel" (Acts 10:22)
39. "All the inhabitants of the ___ shall be astonished" (Ezekiel 27:35)
40. Health resort
43. "___ to thee, Moab!" (Numbers 21:29)
45. Summer (Fr.)

46. "all the promises of God in him are yea, and in him ___" (2 Corinthians 1:20)
48. "Have they not ___?" (Judges 5:30)
49. "the archers ___ him" (1 Samuel 31:3)
50. Soul (Fr.)
52. "our rafters of ___" (Song of Solomon 1:17)
53. "Abram had dwelt ___ years in the land of Canaan" (Genesis 16:3)
55. "___, I am with you alway" (Matthew 28:20)
57. Compass point
58. Balloon gas symbol

201

ACROSS

1. Nickname (masc.)
2. "The gathering together of the waters called he ___" (Genesis 1:10)
9. Part of a circle
12. Cony
13. "the tongue can no man ___" (James 3:8)
14. "After this manner will I ___ the pride of Judah" (Jeremiah 13:9)
15. "the children of Gad called the altar ___" (Joshua 22:34)
16. "the twelfth month, which is the month of ___" (Esther 3:13)
18. "thou hast been . . . a strong tower from the ___" (Psalm 61:3)
20. "___ without ceasing" (1 Thessalonians 5:17)
21. "John was clothed . . . with a girdle of ___" (Mark 1:6)
22. "Her grapes are ___ ripe" (Revelation 14:18)
24. Consumer
27. Guatamalan fruit
28. Stockings
29. Bangor's st.
30. "all they are brass, and ___, and iron, and lead" (Ezekiel 22:18)
31. "the time is ___" (1 Corinthians 7:29)
33. Opposite (prefix)
34. Near (prefix)
35. "a certain vessel descending . . . as it had been a great ___" (Acts 10:11)
36. "they brought every man his present . . . mules, a ___ year by year" (1 Kings 10:25)
37. "How knoweth this man ___, having never learned?" (John 7:15)
39. "Take up the fish that ___ cometh up" (Matthew 17:27)
40. Harsh breathing
41. "Thou ___ faith, and I have works" (James 2:18)
42. Blouse
44. Parch
45. Apiece (abbr.)
47. Pinnacle
48. "Shem also, the father of all the children of ___" (Genesis 10:21)
50. "I will ___ praise to thy name, O thou most High" (Psalm 9:2)
52. One (Sc.)
53. "a stormy wind shall ___ it" (Ezekiel 13:11)
54. "Saul tarried . . . under a pomegranate ___" (1 Samuel 14:2)

DOWN

1. God (comb. form)
2. "he ___ horns coming out of his hand" (Habakkuk 3:4)
3. Its capital is Little Rock (abbr.)
4. Fondly
5. "none can ___ his hand" (Daniel 4:35)
6. "If thou wilt . . . give ___ to his commandments" (Exodus 15:26)
7. "I ___ God, even thy God" (Psalm 50:7)
8. "No man said, What ___ thou?" (John 4:27)
9. "___ your ways and your doings" (Jeremiah 7:3)
10. "the ___ of atonement, whereby an atonement shall be made for him" (Numbers 5:8)
11. "Arise, ___ out in the night" (Lamentations 2:19)
17. "in that ___ will I make a covenant for them" (Hosea 2:18)
19. "This is the number of them . . . ___ and twenty knives" (Ezra 1:9)
20. Plot
21. "It is as ___ to a fool to do mischief" (Proverbs 10:23)

Across / Down Clues

22. Deadly
23. "___ my heart to fear thy name" (Psalm 86:11)
24. "put off thy ___ from off thy feet" (Exodus 3:5)
25. Discharges
26. Readjust
31. "Thou hast been a ___ for me" (Psalm 61:3)
32. "turn aside, sit down ___" (Ruth 4:1)
33. "Till a ___ strike through his liver" (Proverbs 7:23)
35. "There shall come a ___ out of Jacob" (Numbers 24:17)
36. "when thou liest down, and when thou ___ up" (Deuteronomy 6:7)
38. Worthless stuff
41. "Abraham ran unto the ___" (Genesis 18:7)
42. Depot (abbr.)
43. Liquid measure (Heb.)
44. Japanese coin
45. Compass point
46. "Strong meat belongeth to them that are of full ___" (Hebrews 5:14)
49. "Let this mind ___ in you" (Philippians 2:5)
51. "Shuppim also, and Huppim, the children of ___" (1 Chronicles 7:12)

PUZZLE **101**

ACROSS

2. Home of Elimelech and Naomi
8. Groupie's god
9. "A time to get, and a time to
   _____"(Ecclesiastes 3:6)
11. "that I may ____Christ"
    (Philippians 3:8)
13. Time (abbr.)
15. "...call me ____" (Ruth 1:20)
16. Color of pink
18. Age
19. Linkletter
22. Around (prefix)
23. " ___kissed her mother-in-law"
    (Ruth 1:14)
25. Conjunction
26. Memo
28. "Intreat _____not to leave thee"
    (Ruth 1:16)
29. U.S. state
30. Preposition
31. Son of Naomi (var.) (Ruth 1:2)
33. Elders' pronouncement: "____are
    witnesses" (Ruth 4:11)
34. Fifth letter of the Hebrew
    alphabet
37. Part of psyche
38. Wife of Mahlon
40. Objective
41. We
43. That is to say (abbr.)
44. Part of tennis term
45. "and they came to Bethlehem in
    the beginning of barley ____"
    (Ruth 1:22)
48. What Boaz gave as a testimony to
    his neighbor (Ruth 4:7)
49. Buy back

DOWN

1. "And Naomi had a _____"
   (Ruth 2:1)
2. Rose, for one
3. Naomi's husband
4. "And she ____at his feet"
   (Ruth 3:14)
5. Hardy shade tree
6. Where Elimelech died
7. "And she [Ruth]...gleaned in the
   field after the _____"(Ruth 2:3)
10. Yr. in HS
12. And not
14. Gain or obtain, as a reward
17. Reaction of Bethlehemites: "Is
    this _____?"(Ruth 1:19)
20. Biblical harlot
21. "And in that day it shall come to
    pass, that the glory of Jacob shall
    be made____"(Isaiah 17:4)
22. Naomi's kinsman
24. Family member
27. Father of Jesse
32. Pronoun
33. "under whose _____thou art
    come to trust"(Ruth 2:12)
35. Jehovah
36. Boaz's command: "Let her
    _____" (Ruth 2:15)
39. Jonathan to David: "take ____to
    thyself" (1 Samuel 19:2)
40. Where Boaz went up to and sat
    beside (Ruth 4:1)
42. Pronoun used for ships
46. Farm address (abbr.)
47. Dir.

by
Ruth Tatham Nottage

ACROSS

1. Smart
6. "God created the _____"
   (Genesis 1:1)
11. "And a _____ went out of
    Eden" (Genesis 2:10)
12. "To everything there is a
    _____" (Ecclesiastes 3:1)
13. Splendid
15. "And God saw the light,...___was
    good" (Genesis 1:4)
16. "And Joshua burnt ___, and made
    it an heap for ever" (Joshua 8:28)
17. Twelve-step group
18. Regulated by the moon
20. Exam
22. Messrs. (sing.)
23. Ruthenium (abbr.)
24. "Who remembered us in our low
    _____" (Psalm 136:23)
26. "For the Lord shall comfort
    Zion:...he will make her wilder-
    ness like ___" (Isaiah 51:3)
28. Nancy Hanks's son, familiarly
29. _____ Book
30. Clay oven
31. First child
35. River or sea
36. Wt.
37. Planted
40. Baseball stat.
42. The first heaven
44. Northern food fish
45. _____ story
48. Blooms
49. "...and all the _____ of the field
    shall clap their hands"
    (Isaiah 55:12)

50. MLB div.
51. Made in His own image
52. First word declaring Trinity
    (Genesis 1:26)
53. Appeared the third day
    (Genesis 1:9)

DOWN

1. Made out of nothing (Genesis 1:1)
2. Flowers of the field
   (Matthew 6:28)
3. First lady
4. Fruit of the earth
5. Age
6. Pronoun
7. "And the _____was without
   form" (Genesis 1:2)
8. ___ is condition
9. Total emptiness (Genesis 1:2)
10. "Wherefore, as by one man sin
    _____into the world"
    (Romans 5:12)
12. "There shall come a ____ out of
    Jacob" (Numbers 24:17)
14. What Adam gave every living
    creature (Genesis 2:19)
19. The greater light (Genesis 1:16)
21. Way or case
25. Cares for
26. Ages
27. Certain doctor (abbr.)
29. Soldier (abbr.)
31. Precipices
32. Second son of Adam
33. "so is thy praise unto the____of
    the earth" (Psalms 48:10)
34. Trade agreement (abbr.)
38. Indian, for example
39. "...and the whole ____lieth in
    wickedness" (1 John 5:19)
41. ____ house

43. Smirch
46. Galilee, for one
47. Border

by
Ruth Tatham Nottage

ACROSS

1. Man called by Luke "chief among the publicans"
8. Pastry
11. Justice Fortas, to friends
12. Solution
14. Continent (abbr.)
15. Swinging bed
16. Redact
18. Owns
19. To tear out by the roots
22. Attention!
23. Timothy was one
24. Radium (abbr.)
25. KJV pronoun
26. JFK arrival
28. Drive forward
32. Mental health
35. Swift one with antlers
38. Dixie state (abbr.)
39. Alone
41. Endure
43. To attack physically, with "into"
44. Preposition
45. Above
46. Deep and intense, vivid
48. Pronoun
50. Fifth is famous (abbr.)
51. Symbol of Asherah
53. Word used in similes
55. Compass dir.
56. Supped
57. Retreat

DOWN

1. Father of John the Baptist
2. Patriarch
3. Halt
4. Robust
5. Zest
6. Pronoun
7. Scandinavian
8. Deceive
9. TLC provider
10. To make less intense
13. Once married to Ernie
17. Bye (Brit.)
20. Is
21. One with a legally valid will
26. Affirmative for Arturo
27. Tenth U.S. president
29. Solomon had one
30. "By faith _____ was translated that he should not see death" (Hebrews 11:5)
31. Mil. mainstay
32. David's successor
33. Mimic
34. Roman emperor
36. French conjunction
37. Saved from Sodom
40. _____ press
42. Thoroughfare (abbr.)
46. Raced
47. Mature
49. Mother of Seth
52. Plural ending
54. Ed.'s abbr.

by
Susan Oliver

ACROSS

1. Moses' successor
6. Sea ____
11. Reed instrument
12. He brought Saul to Antioch
14. Concerning
15. That "je ne sais quoi" quality
16. List elements
17. Colorist, crudely
19. Dry
21. Abijah's successor
22. Stood out
23. Tresses
24. "...and when he saw him, straightway the spirit ___ him" (Mark 9:20)
26. Noah's son
28. Morsel of food
29. Musical syllable
31. Midwest state (abbr.)
32. Portico
34. Exists
36. Emporium
38. Clement
40. Masada is one
41. Council
42. "The legs of the ___ are not equal" (Proverbs 26:7)
44. Conjunction
45. Where Joshua was defeated
46. Family
48. He died twice
49. Even, in poesy

DOWN

1. Site of baptisms
2. Complies
3. Ergo
4. ____say
5. Son of Terah
6. Malicious
7. Topper
8. Ruth's son
9. Ewe's mate
10. John the Baptist was one
13. Moses' spokesman
18. Be all ____
20. Feminine suffix
22. To refine ore
24. Judas, for one
25. Preposition
27. King of Tyre
28. Mrs. Chaplin
30. Feminine name
32. Gets some shut-eye
33. ____commandments
34. Elected
35. Masculine name
37. Much honored king of 2 Chronicles 14-16
39. Weird
43. What God never does
45. Genius, to friends
47. Live

by
Susan Oliver

ACROSS

1. M.D.'s forte
3. Kin (abbr., pl.)
7. Sister-in-law of Orpah
11. City which means "house of bread"
15. ___Grande
16. Uncanny
17. Hot ____
19. Form of address (abbr.)
20. Timpani
21. About
22. Preposition
23. Dir.
24. Trespass
27. Musical notations
29. Exclamation
31. Priestly tribe
32. Sigh
33. Serpent
35. Creative, tasteful
37. Heed
38. ___ of reason
40. Preposition
42. Fathoms
44. Perfect place
46. Judah's son
47. City close by Nahor
49. College deg.
50. Designate
52. Prefix meaning "not"
53. Conjunction
54. ___ out
55. Aka Dorcas
56. Stalk

DOWN

1. David's ancestor
2. "Well of the covenant" city
3. Hallow
4. Musical syllable
5. Exclamations of surprise
6. Behold
8. Chaldean city
9. Paul's "son"
10. Part of altar
12. Nonfiction
13. Pronoun
14. First institution
18. Kind of shot
25. Indisposed
26. Born
28. Sabb. day
29. Gold, to Goya
30. Pen
34. Aka Cephas
36. Changes one's ways
38. Asp
39. Honor
41. Lair
43. Characteristic
45. Surrealist
47. Boffo show
48. In the style of
49. Anaconda
51. Parisienne (abbr.)

by
Susan Oliver

ACROSS

1. Queen of Judah
8. Exclamation of success
11. Jezebel's folly
12. Destroyed
15. Midwest state (abbr.)
16. Fissure
17. Artery
18. Dad, in Dogpatch
19. Levi's grandson
21. _____salts
23. Lutetium (abbr.)
24. Chicago fixture (abbr.)
26. Door____
27. Strange
29. Bacteria
32. Prefix meaning "to"
34. Elijah's successor
36. Hero of Uris's Exodus
38. Grandfather of David
39. Clergyman
40. Offspring
41. Parseghian, formerly of NFL
43. Paddle
44. Enid's state (abbr.)
46. Against
47. Strip of wood
49. Musical syllable
50. Extension or wing (var.)
51. Solomon had one
54. Style
55. Instant _____
56. Like

DOWN

1. David's son
2. Sacred book
3. Samson's secret
4. ____dena, CA
5. Major proph.
6. Healing plant
7. David had one
9. Leap
10. Infamous king
13. Possessive
14. Orpah's mother-in-law
20. Where Ahaziah was slain
   (2 Kings 9)
22. Last minor prophet
25. ___Miserables
28. Judge of Israel
30. Ostrich
31. Dogpatch doyenne?
33. What faith can accomplish
35. Masculine name
37. Chem. element
38. ____ surgery
39. Repeated word in Ecclesiastes
40. Foreman
42. Informer
45. Guard
48. Pitch
50. Airport abbr.
52. 1,050 to Cicero
53. Milliliter (abbr.)

by
Susan Oliver

ACROSS

1. Jesus' earthly mother
7. Exclamation
11. Sarah's son
12. Savior
14. Everlasting
16. Prophet
17. Procedure (abbr.)
18. Article
19. Athens is here (abbr.)
20. Circle
22. Negative
24. Decorated again
26. ___Paso
27. Member of AMA
28. Father of the Edomites
30. David's ammo
32. Peak
34. Member of AARP
35. Soothing plant
36. God killed him (1 Chronicles 13)
37. Aka Tabitha
39. Ventilate
40. It borders NJ (abbr.)
41 Finesse
42. Robert or Alan
43. Exclamation
45. Lines of verse
46. Chemical suffix
48. Crumb of food
49. Porch
50. Speck of dust

DOWN

1. What John had on Patmos
2. Lives
3. Harlot recorded in Joshua
4. Peachy place (abbr.)
5. Geological epoch
6. Biblical mount
7. He followed Abijah
8. Feminine nickname
9. Its members are on a first-name basis (abbr.)
10. Avoid
12. East. seaboard state
13. Nighttime noise
15. Apostle
18. Reference book
21. Plural suffix
23. Spotted cat
24. Laban's sister
25. West. state
28. Joseph's son
29. Bathsheba's husband
30. Cushion
31. Fierce dry wind
32. Shrub of Rhododendron family
33. Placed
38. Preposition
40. Bard
44. Musical syllable
45. Part of paycheck? (abbr.)
47. Coif

by
Susan Oliver

ACROSS
1. Yeast
5. Attract
10. Large animal similar to buffalo
11. More than somnolent
13. Small town
16. Law (abbr.)
17. "____ye not unequally yoked" (2 Corinthians 6:14)
18. Name meaning "God of Judah"
19. What some need to make
22. "...a man's ____ are the men of his own house" (Micah 7:6)
24. ____ Moline, IL
27. At some time
28. Bread
29. Mr. _____
31. Midwest state (abbr.)
33. Olive, for one
34. Rocks, slangily
35. Not clergy
38. "in the wall of the house he [Solomon] made narrowed ____"(1 Kings 6:6)
40. Disbelief
42. Bible abbr.
43. Reporter's question
45. To and ____
46. Prefix meaning reversal
47. Work in garden
49. Conjunction
50. Album successor
51. Island in the East Indies (abbr.)
53. Tea steeped for a minute?
54. Grain
56. Fabric
57. Ogle

58. "forgive them; they know ____what they do" (Luke 23:34)

DOWN
1. Charity
2. John, for example
3. Worth
4. Bother
5. Dixie state (abbr.)
6. "____ is more"
7. Epistle
8. ___ the Down Staircase, Kaufman classic
9. Chosen
12. Picked out from a group
14. Crosspieces over a door
15. Reproof
20. Suffix meaning "to cause to become" (Brit.)
21. Uttered (arch.)
23. Elected
25. Dispersed
26. Disdain
30. Rested (arch.)
32. As I Lay _____, Faulkner classic
35. To stagger
36. Residence
39. Sparrow sound
41. Preposition
44. Ox _____
46. "my peace I give ___ you" (John 14:27)
48. Nocturnal bird
52. ___ and when
54. Not them
55. Article

by
JoAnn Horn

ACROSS

1. Heirs
7. Odor
10. "and whosoever shall say to his brother,___, shall be in danger of the council" (Matthew 5:22)
11. Not at any time
12. No matter when
14. Teaching standard of right and wrong
17. "Which all are to perish with the _____"(Colossians 2:22)
19. Proceed slowly
20. Pronoun
22. Door parts
24. Certainly
26. Quick, alert
27. Digit
28. Violent attack
32. "____is finished" (John 19:30)
33. Sumptuous meal
35. "nothing common____unclean hath... entered into my mouth" (Acts 11:8)
36. Raves
37. Plunge, immerse
39. Ungodly
41. Spiritual
43. Unmarried women (arch.)
47. Conceit
50. "___ye into all the world" (Mark 16:15)
51. Affirmative
52. Quick, active

DOWN

1. Talk to God
2. Tore
3. Slippery
4. "Doth not even _____ itself teach you..."(1 Corinthians 11:14)
5. Hostility
6. "For mine eyes have ____ thy salvation" (Luke 2:30)
7. Theol. school
8. Reward
9. _____ a good line
13. Linking verb
15. Son of Phalec (Luke 3:35)
16. ____ wife
18. The ____ and Mrs. Muir, film classic
20. Forage
21. Before, in poesy
23. Electees
24. Stained
25. Claim on property
28. Ice hockey statistic
29. "whereby we cry, _____, Father" (Romans 8:15)
30. Master
31. Stab
33. Not real
34. "the day is ____hand" (Romans 13:12)
36. Edge
38. Receptacle
40. Bucolic region (arch.)
42. "Be not ___ in thine own eyes" (Proverbs 3:7)
44. Urge, with on
45. Exclamation
46. Happiness
48. "ye believe ____God" (John 14:1)
49. Liquid metric measure

by
JoAnn Horn

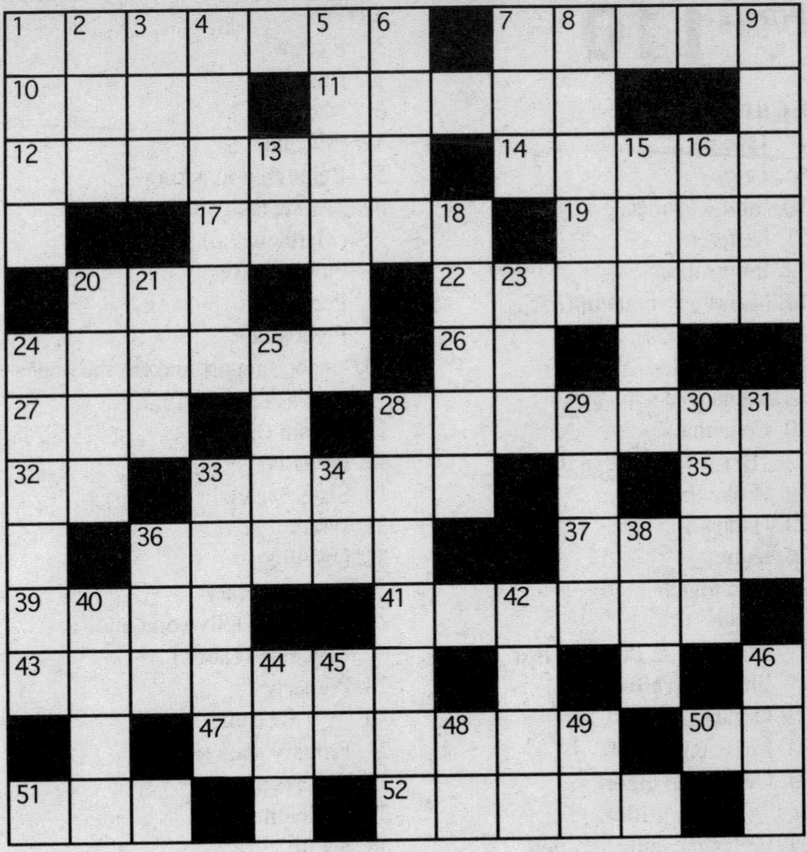

ACROSS

1. Late meal
6. Felony
10. Simile syntax
11. Different
12. Preposition
14. "Elias ___ cometh first" (Mark 9:12)
16. Time period
18. Bathsheba's husband
20. Consume
22. "But whom say ye that I ___?" (Luke 9:20)
23. Happy
24. Saute ___
25. Two together
27. Fence
29. "The law of the wise is a ____ of life" (Proverbs 13:14)
32. Organs
33. Luke, e.g.
34. One or the other
36. ____ Rev. (title)
37. Prefix meaning "around"
38. Cease
40. One entitled to discounts (abbr.)
41. One who drives away demons
45. Without vegetation
47. On the ___
48. ___ Hague (city in The Netherlands)
49. On thin ___
50. ____ code
51. Dispatched
52. "Behold___mother" (Mark 3:34)
53. Snare

DOWN

1. Except
2. Employ
3. Match
4. Educate
5. Belonging to a king
6. "Arise, take up ___bed" (Matthew 9:6)
7. Pay attention
8. Period
9. Preposition
13. "a good report maketh the bones ___" (Proverbs 15:30)
15. Gossip (Brit.)
17. Prepared
19. Sister's garb
21. Wrath
22. Dwelling
24. Contemporary
26. Home of Dollywood and Graceland (abbr.)
28. Property
30. ____ de camp
31. Primary state (abbr.)
35. Deserved
37. Skeleton
38. Set up
39. "He brought me up also out of an horrible ___" (Psalm 40:2)
40. ____ deep
42. Dr.'s tool
43. "____ Father which art in heaven" (Matthew 6:9)
44. Horse adjunct
46. Undoing (prefix)

by
JoAnn Horn

ACROSS

1. Divine favor
5. "I will raise unto David a right-eous ____" (Jeremiah 23:5)
10. Safflower, for one
11. Virus
14. "For my people is foolish...they are _____children" (Jeremiah 4:22)
15. "_____is the kingdom" (Matthew 6:13)
17. School org.
18. Spiritual belief
19. El Shaddai
20. Sweet potato
21. Pronoun
22. "And __the heavens were opened" (Matthew 3:16)
25. Baby bed
28. Not all
31. "The Spirit like a ___ descending upon him" (Mark 1:10)
33. ____ egg
34. ___end
35. "No mention shall be made of _____, or of pearls"(Job 28:18)
36. Inert gas (suffix)
37. _____ magnetism
39. Article
40. U.S. Congress building
43." ___ chance!"
44. Undergarment
47. "He shall be called a _____" (Matthew 2:23)
48. Not used
50. Western state (abbr.)
51. Not lt.

52. "but one ____ destroyeth much good" (Ecclesiastes 9:18)

DOWN

1. Good News
2. Public uproar
3. Elevated holy table
4. Educate spiritually
5. "they shall__ one flesh" (Genesis 2:24)
6. Instead of
7. Hardwood
8. "And who is my _____?" (Luke 10:29)
9. Obey
12. Abraham's son
13. To wedge
16. "But as the days of ___ were" (Matthew 24:37)
23. _____ air (market)
24. Biblical verb
26. Baal, for example
27. Dissolve
29. "___ if!" (colloq.)
30. ___ fire
32. Conceited
33. "If ye have faith, and doubt ___" (Matthew 21:21)
34. Marry
35. Minister's need
37. Separated
38. Husband of Zipporah
41. From a distance
42. Damage
45. Hostel
46. Sty
47. Tot's first word
49. The royal ___

by
JoAnn Horn

PUZZLE 112

ACROSS

1. "And I will...cover you with ___" (Ezekiel 37:6)
4. Endeavored
10. Conjunction
11. "I have glorified thee on the ___" (John 17:4)
12. In debt
13. Tune
14. "which of them will love him ___" (Luke 7:42)
16. Reverential fear
17. Missing
18. Preposition
19. Pertaining to the heavens
22. Hanker
25. Grain
26. River formed at Khartoum
28. "Thou feedest them with the bread of ___" (Psalm 80:5)
30. Give off light
31. Tool of blacksmith
32. Article
35. Pronoun
36. Oldest son of Rebekkah
38. Exclamation
41. Prickly sensation
42. Hosp. abbr.
44. "She is come...to ___ my body" (Mark 14:8)
46. Medium (abbr.)
47. Part of truck
49. Village in Galilee
50. Preposition
52. "She crieth at the gates, at the ___ of the city" (Proverbs 8:3)
54. "And Jesus... ___ up straight-way" (Matthew 3:16)
55. Proboscis

DOWN

1. "And fell down on his face... giving him thanks: and he was a ___" (Luke 17:16)
2. "I never ___ you: depart from me" (Matthew 7:23)
3. Not working
4. Dialogue beginning
5. Conjunction
6. Highest degree
7. Ebenezer Scrooge saw this
8. Small child
9. "Jesus ___" (John 11:35)
11. Rim
15. Sharp pain
17. Smallest amount
18. Let happen
19. "Almost thou persuadest me to be a ___" (Acts 26:28)
20. "___, I am with you" (Matthew 28:20)
21. Suffer
23. Singing part (abbr.)
24. Chamber in mountain
27. Some of BoPeep's brood
29. Killed
33. Stop
34. Number on a cricket team
37. Preposition
39. Groups of people with same beliefs
40. Chew
43. "And it is a ___ thing that the king requireth" (Daniel 2:11)
44. Characteristic of (suffix)
45. ___ way
48. ___ way
51. Musical syllable
53. Nyet (Eng.)

by
JoAnn Horn

ACROSS

1. "Sing unto him a new ___" (Psalm 33:3)
5. Star nearest the earth
7. "If thou doest not well, sin lieth at the _____" (Genesis 4:7)
10. Home of the Reds and the Cavaliers
11. "But I suffer not a woman...to _____ authority over the man" (1 Timothy 2:12)
12. Mournful sound
14. Prefix for join
16. "there will your _____ be also" (Matthew 6:21)
18. Make amends
20. Position
21. Preposition
22. Pronoun
23. "I am the bread ___ life" (John 6:35)
24. Time period
25. TV show
27. Not them
28. Delight
29. Chess piece
31. "that so labouring ye ought to support the ___" (Acts 20:35)
32. Simile syntax
35. Worth
36. To ponder
38. Adversary
41. Red or Dead
42. "_____ you there?" (question asked by famous hymn)
43. Cutting side of blade
45. Suffix meaning "little"
46. _____ Island
49. Bucolic blast
50. Place of worship

DOWN

1. "that the ___ be without knowledge, it is not good" (Proverbs 19:2)
2. Exclamation
3. "But if a man walk in the ___, he stumbleth" (John 11:10)
4. "___ ye into all the world and preach the gospel" (Mark 16:15)
5. Weapon
6. Creature of habit?
7. "shake off the _____ under your feet" (Mark 6:11)
8. Conjunction
9. _____ ended
12. "___ is born unto trouble" (Job 5:7)
13. Preposition
15. A stone's throw
17. What Peter cut off
18. Article
19. Carry out instructions
20. Desire
21. Whether
24. Used to connect oxen
26. Missouri, for one
27. Threatening
28. _____ bone
30. In particular
31. Not they
32. Ripen
33. "as the _____ of a great rock in a weary land" (Isaiah 32:2)
34. Crown component
37. Linking verb
39. Used to catch fish

40. West. state
43. "Or if he shall ask an _____, will
     he offer him a scorpion?"
     (Luke 11:12)
44. _____and Magog
47. Alert
48. Continent (abbr.)
49. Prominent word in young
     vocabulary

by
JoAnn Horn

ACROSS

1. "Hallowed be thy _____"
   (Matthew 6:9)
5. Crazy
7. "And he [Jesus] took the blind
   man...and... __ on his eyes"
   (Mark 8:23)
11. Tarry
13. Common contraction
14. Not well
15. To bring low in spirit
18. What the herd of swine did
    (Matthew 8:32)
19. "He was _____ as a sheep to the
    slaughter" (Acts 8:32)
20. Already sold
21. Finish
23. Vote cast
25. "I will pull down my _____ and
    build greater" (Luke 12:18)
28. Sound of suffering
31. What Moses held to "do signs"
32. "Saul, Saul, ___ persecutest thou
    me?" (Acts 22:7)
33. Conjunction
34. Apportioned
35. We should pray for this person
36. Linking verb
39. "_____ out!"
42. "They have _____ upon me with
    their mouth" (Job 16:10)
44. Son of Noah
47. Am
48. Was led astray
49. Good for a point
50. Clever
52. Godly person
54. _____ and Sidon (Luke 10:13)

55. "If _____ of you lack wisdom, let
    him ask of God" (James 1:5)
56. "Behold, I am a dry ____"
    (Isaiah 56:3)

DOWN

1. What held Jesus to the cross
2. "the ...word, which is ___ to save
   your souls" (James 1:21)
3. Gentle
4. Masculine nickname
6. "_____ to righteousness, and sin
   not" (1 Corinthians 15:34)
7. "God __ loved the world"
   (John 3:16)
8. Undefiled
9. Asian country
10. Take care of
12. "Take, ___; this is my body"
    (Matthew 26:26)
13. Japanese currency
16. "spreading himself like a green
    ___ tree" (Psalm 37:35)
17. Galilee, for one
22. "And on the seventh day God
    ___ his work" (Genesis 2:2)
24. "is not this a _____ plucked out
    of the fire?" (Zechariah 3:2)
26. Linking verb
27. Decay
29. "joy shall be in heaven over ___
    sinner that repenteth"
    (Luke 15:7)
30. Nav. officer
36. "scatter thou the people that
    delight in ___" (Psalm 68:30)
37. _____ strings
38. Espy
39. Author Howard
40. Military force
41. Bring a child to maturity

42. Obtain
43. One who deals with crowns and
    bridges (abbr.)
44. ____piece
45. Skin affliction
46. "For with the same measure that
    ye _____ withal it shall be mea-
    sured" (Luke 6:38)
51. Again (prefix)
53. Preposition

by
JoAnn Horn

ACROSS

1. Carved gem
6. Tree leftovers
12. Son of Chislon (Numbers 34:21)
14. Doorway
15. Preposition
16. "And upon a set day Herod...made an___ unto them" (Acts 12:21)
18. Biblical exclamation
19. "The trees of the Lord are full of ___" (Psalm 104:16)
21. Conceited smile
22. Cathodes (abbr.)
23. "these are the sons of Shuthelah: of ___" (Numbers 26:36)
25. French military leader Michel
26. ____ number
27. "Thou shalt prepare thee a way...that every___ may flee" (Deuteronomy 19:3)
29. "they shall plant vineyards, but not drink the___" (Zephaniah 1:13)
30. Hitched
31. "they cast their garments upon the___" (Luke 19:35)
32. What William Wallace wore
33. Outlaw
35. Felines
36. Fire
37. Fabric edge
39. Summer drink
40. Its capital is Tripoli
42. Collection of anecdotes
43. Second tone of diatonic scale
44. "he shall bring his offering...of young___" (Leviticus 1:14)

46. Member of AMA
47. "and the men of Hamath made___" (2 Kings 17:30)
49. "Now when this was___ abroad" (Acts 2:6)
51. Zara of___ (Matthew 1:3)
52. Self-named Mara

DOWN

1. "Stop this minute!"
2. "The sin of Judah...is graven upon...the horns of your____" (Jeremiah 17:1)
3. Third tone of diatonic scale
4. People living in Benin region of Nigeria
5. Rows
6. Curled
7. Grabbed
8. Pedestaled vase
9. 1,000 kilograms (abbr.)
10. "If she be a wall, we will build upon her a ____ of silver" (Song of Solomon 8:9)
11. To agitate
13. "That they all might be____ who believed not the truth" (2 Thessalonians 2:12)
17. Row of seats
20. Helez the_____ (2 Samuel 23:26)
22. South of the border gathering place
24. Builder's need (pl.)
26. Having a soft, pleasant flavor
28. Still
29. Was the victor
31. The Grand ____
32. "the border shall be even from Tamar unto the waters of strife in___" (Ezekiel 48:28)
33. ___ in the woods

34. One behind another
35. Precious stone measure
36. Burns's trademark
38. Verily, indeed
40. Bean variety
41. Immediately (arch.)
44. Two-thirds of a shekel
45. "the children of ___" (var.)
   (Ezra 2:44)
48. Laugh sound
50. Therefore

by
Derrick Randle

PUZZLE 116

ACROSS

1. "Jesus ...saw his [Peter's] wife's mother laid, and sick of a ___" (Matthew 8:14)
6. One ruling a country or colony
8. Mideast metropolis
10. Network of blood vessels
11. "Jesus cried with a loud voice saying,___" (Mark 15:34)
13. "take thee a sharp knife, ...a barber's ____" (Ezekiel 5:1) (var.)
14. Muscle contraction
16. Unit; sound (comb. form)
17. Part of a cry
18. Little twigs
19. Off ____
20. A piece (abbr.)
22. "And the priest shall put of the oil...upon the great___" (Leviticus 14:28)
23. To rub (comb. form)
27. Playing for____
29. Home _____
30. "Canst thou put an hook into his___?" (Job 41:2)
31. Bones
34. Heretofore (arch.)
35. Elizabeth _____ (Roman Catholic leader)

DOWN

1. One subjected to criticism
2. Silver crown (seventeenth century)
3. "Go thy way: for he is a chosen____ unto me" (Acts 9:15)
4. Period of time
5. Parts
6. To forbid or prohibit
7. To cry out sharply
8. A son of Naphtali (Genesis 46:24)
9. Word used to describe Ruth
10. Defense or bulwark
12. One of two or more atoms with same number of neutrons
13. Button found in bowling alley
15. He would not set foot in the Promised Land
21. "And saying,____ ye: for the kingdom...is at hand" (Matthew 3:2)
24. Common suffix (pl.)
25. To sunbathe
26. "on the sixth day they gathered twice as much bread, two ___" (Exodus 16:22)
27. "for there is nothing covered...and hid, that shall not be____" (Matthew 10:26)
28. Thousands of years
32. Sheltered place
33. As well

by
Derrick Randle

234

ACROSS

1. "Cursed be...that trusteth in___, and maketh flesh his arm" (Jeremiah 17:5)
4. Head cover
7. Isaac's mother (var.)
8. Honest men?
10. Flat, round cap
11. "for love is strong as___" (Song of Solomon 8:6)
13. "I will___ in thy truth" (Psalm 86:11)
14. Son of Nathan (2 Samuel 23:36)
16. Serving of summer vegetable
18. Copper, for one
19. Preposition
20. Hardy cabbage
21. "what persecutions I ____" (2 Timothy 3:11)
23. Ape
24. Flammable fluid
25. Tribe of Israel
26. Hesitate
29. In a harsh manner
33. Removable part of a trunk
34. "Wherefore it is lawful to do___ on the sabbath days" (Matthew 12:12)
35. To row
36. Patriotic org.
37. Except
38. What the English call the Thames, west of Oxford
39. "The___ went out, being hastened by the king's command-ment" (Esther 3:15)
41. Joined together
43. In clean and good order
44. "and the sons of____" (1 Chronicles 7:39)
45. Before (poet.)
46. Sheltered place

DOWN

1. "Take____ and bring him with thee"(2 Timothy 4:11)
2. Linking verb
3. Permanent residents of a country
4. "And Baalhanan the son of Achbor died, and___ reigned" (Genesis 36:39)
5. Eve's second son
6. Biscuit or bag
7. One of the sons of Nadab (1 Chronicles 2:30)
9. Roller or boat
10. "Consider the ravens:...which neither have storehouse nor___" (Luke 12:24)
12. Border of children of Asher (Joshua 19:25)
13. Affliction
15. H.S. diploma equivalent
17. Room or hall
19. ____ exam
20. Chess piece
22. Designated duckling
23. Heavy hammer
25. "and their houses shall be full of ___ creatures" (Isaiah 13:21)
26. Reg.
27. Sand ____
28. Moses' mouthpiece
29. To accelerate
30. Minor prophet
31. ____ back
32. Pts. of a century
34. "And I will lay it[Jehovah's vineyard]___" (Isaiah 5:6)

37. "And I will give him the morning
    ____" (Revelation 2:28)
38. ____ of Man
40. Note
42. Suffix meaning "little"

by
Derrick Randle

ACROSS

1. Ruth's kinsman-redeemer
5. "The Lord hath made ____ His holy arm" (Isaiah 52:10)
9. A son of Jacob
12. "half of the people followed Tibni...to make him king...and half followed ____" (1 Kings 16:21)
13. "____in me" (John 15:4)
15. Chem. element
16. "_____not; she is not dead" (Luke 8:52)
17. Monastery
18. Belonging to me
19. The grain of mustard seed, the pearl, et al.
23. Israeli folk dance
24. Inspiring awe
26. ____of the covenant
27. Soul or spirit (Gr.)
28. _____, Nehemiah, Esther
30. Roman official
32. Jacob's wife
33. Legal abbr.
34. "a ___caught in a thicket" (Genesis 22:13)
35. Sect widespread in Japan
36. Peevish moods
38. "My ____I give unto you" (John 14:27)
39. Bird's appendage
41. Memo abbr.
42. Continent (abbr.)
44. "And _____, and the city of Salt" (Joshua 15:62)
47. "strong bulls of _____ have beset me round" (Psalm 22:12)
48. "let us...love ...in _____and in truth" (1 John 3:18)

DOWN

1. What God set in the cloud (Genesis 9:13)
2. Unit of measurement for manna (Exodus 16:33)
3. Linking verb
4. Moses' wife
5. Wife of Shaharaim (1 Chronicles 8:8)
6. "whereby we cry,_____, Father" (Romans 8:15)
7. "...the borders a _____of blue" (Numbers 15:38)
8. Mountain flower
10. "Thou hast a mighty ____" (Psalm 89:13)
11. Forty ____ and forty nights
14. Striking person or thing (colloq.)
20. Docked on Mt. Ararat?
21. Ancient region in lower valley of the Euphrates
22. Satan
23. Lot's father (Genesis 11:31)
25. Musical syllable
27. Biblical bird
29. Province of The Netherlands (abbr.)
30. High priest to whom Jesus was brought
31. "the people ____ a vain thing" (Psalm 2:1)
36. Galilee, for one
37. Lukewarm
39. "A ____ son maketh a glad father" (Proverbs 10:1)
40. "a colt the foal of an ____" (Matthew 21:5)
43. Exclamation

45. "_____ye therefore perfect"
    (Matthew 5:48)
46. Made to withstand great strain
    (abbr.)

by
Janet Lee Friesorger

ACROSS

1. Besides
5. Prohibits
9. "I do set my ____ in the cloud" (Genesis 9:13)
12. "fear him which is able to destroy both ___ and body (Matthew 10:28)
13. Prepare for publication
14. Her name means "life"
15. "and ___ the lintel and the two side posts" (Exodus 12:22)
17. To annoy
19. At all
20. "For ___ your treasure is, there" (Matthew 6:21)
21. "in the days when the judges ___" (Ruth 1:1)
23. "so that a bow of __ is broken by mine arms" (2 Samuel 22:35)
25. "If ____ man have ears to hear" (Mark 4:23)
26. Qualified
28. "And Israel...spread his tent beyond the tower of ____" (Genesis 35:21)
31. Eur. country (abbr.)
32. Monetary units of Iran
34. "____ still. And the wind ceased" (Mark 4:39)
35. "and ____ begat Shem, Ham, and Japheth" (Genesis 5:32)
38. Thin slab of baked clay
39. _____ francaise
40. Spoken for
42. Challenged
44. "who hast set thy glory ____ the heavens" (Psalm 8:1)

46. "of Heber, which was the son of ____" (Luke 3:35)
47. Superficial appearance
49. Vigor
52. "for there is ____ God" (Mark 12:32)
53. "serpent, and set it upon a ____" (Numbers 21:8)
55. Temple (archaic)
56. Unite
57. "we have seen his ____ in the east" (Matthew 2:2)
58. Astound

DOWN

1. Member of Equus genus
2. "And Terah took Abram his son, and ____" (Genesis 11:31)
3. " ____ goodness and mercy shall" (Psalm 23:6)
4. "These are the two ____ trees" (Revelation 11:4)
5. ____ Elim, the "well of heroes"
6. ____ loc.
7. Penpoint
8. Harriet Beecher ____
9. "he ____ the city, and wept over it" (Luke 19:41)
10. Preposition
11. Common contraction
16. "Woe is me...that I dwell in the tents of ____!" (Psalm 120:5)
18. Biblical pronoun
21. "and the ____ from heaven was restrained" (Genesis 8:2)
22. Until
23. "Worthy is the Lamb that was ____" (Revelation 5:12)
24. "charged him to ____ no man" (Luke 5:14)

27. "But if ye _____ and devour one another, take heed" (Galatians 5:15)
29. "but who is _____ to stand before envy?" (Proverbs 27:4)
30. To understand one's character
33. Automobile
36. Reconciled
37. Possess
39. "upon the mountains of _____" (Genesis 8:4)
41. Retains possession of
43. First letter of Hebrew alphabet (pl., var.)

44. To declare openly
45. Nota _____
46. "a Prophet was beforetime called a _____" (1 Samuel 9:9)
48. "the name of the wicked shall _____" (Proverbs 10:7)
50. Large antelope
51. To yearn
54. ... _____ ti do

by
Audrey Steele

PUZZLE 120

ACROSS

1. "two doors were of ____ tree (1 Kings 6:34)
4. Cheerless
8. Cash amounts
12. Lyric poem
13. "run with patience the ____" (Hebrews 12:1)
14. "given the children of ____ all the tenth in Israel" (Numbers 18:21)
15. Proclamation or edict
16. Survive, with "out"
17. Euphrates, for example
18. "Jacob gave ____ bread and pottage" (Genesis 25:34)
20. Hiding place
21. Pledged
23. "give me neither ____ nor riches" (Proverbs 30:8)
26. Altar end of a church
27. "But the tongue can no man ____" (James 3:8)
28. Prefix meaning "again"
29. Greek letter
30. "Come up...unto mount Sinai, and ____ thyself there" (Exodus 34:2)
33. Apiece (abbr.)
34. Preposition
35. "The ____ are a people not strong" (Proverbs 30:25)
36. Superior (comb. form)
38. Arbitrator
41. "in the habitation of dragons...shall be____with reeds" (Isaiah 35:7)
42. To encourage and support

43. "that I may ____ the pillars" (Judges 16:26)
44. Embellishment
46. OT bk .
47. "the days of her purification according to the ____ of Moses" (Luke 2:22)
50. "say ____ at thy giving of thanks" (1 Corinthians 14:16)
51. Nation
52. "Ezbon, ____, and Arodi" (Genesis 46:16)
53. Occupied
54. Large pitcher
55. Until

DOWN

1. Watch chain
2. Highest mountain in Crete
3. Causes to exist again
4. "Fear and ____ shall fall upon them" (Exodus 15:16)
5. Rough earthenware
6. Pro
7. Linking verb
8. "thou, being a wild ____ tree" (Romans 11:17)
9. "fire that ____ shall be quenched" (Mark 9:43)
10. "Adam knew ____ his wife" (Genesis 4:1)
11. "saying ____, we would see Jesus" (John 12:21)
17. Poe subject
19. Ooze
20. Divides, with "between"
21. Visibly floating moisture
22. Express orally
23. Adhesive
24. "fruit of the ____ of the garden" (Genesis 3:2)

242

25. Tropical and solar, to name two
27. Doctrine held to be true
31. Less seldom found
32. Severed violently
37. "____ of the shadow of death" (Psalm 23:4)
39. "Moses and Aaron fell on their ____ before all" (Numbers 14:5)
40. "horns of ivory and ____" (Ezekiel 27:15)
41. ____ , son of Uri (1 Kings 4:19)
43. ____ lift
44. Pat
45. Large Australian bird

46. Turn left
48. Linking verb
49. "we do you to ____ of the grace of God" (2 Corinthians 8:1)
51. Concerning

by
Audrey Steele

ACROSS

1. "certain householder...went into a ____ country" (Matthew 21:33)
4. "Thou also ____ with Jesus" (Matthew 26:69)
8. Balak, the king of ____ (Numbers 23:7)
12. Before (poet.)
13. "Aholibamah the daughter of ____" (Genesis 36:2)
14. "him that is ____ to keep you from falling" (Jude 1:24)
15. "And he [Herod] ____ to see him" (Luke 9:9)
17. "Provide neither... silver, nor ____ in your purses" (Matthew 10:9)
18. Preposition
19. "only Rahab the ____ shall live" (Joshua 6:17)
20. Flowering plant
22. "except ye utter...words ____ to be understood" (1 Corinthians 14:9)
23. Distinction
24. Certain vessels
25. "No man can serve ____ masters" (Matthew 6:24)
28. ____ Augustus
30. "children of ____ are these; Uz, and Aran" (Genesis 36:28)
32. "the harvest is the ____ of the world" (Matthew 13:39)
33. Digits
35. ____ men
36. Farm animals
37. "two side ____ and on the upper door" (Exodus 12:7)
38. "Peter, Get thee ____ me" (Matthew 16:23)
41. Kind
42. "went the high priest ____ once every year" (Hebrews 9:7)
43. "and when both they and their father saw the ____ of money" (Genesis 42:35)
46. "____ unto me, all ye that labour" (Matthew 11:28)
47. "In the beginning was the ____" (John 1:1)
48. " of ____, the family of the Erites" (Numbers 26:16)
49. "I never ____ you: depart from me" (Matthew 7:23)
50. Farm animals
51. "God ____ them in the firmament" (Genesis 1:17)

DOWN

1. Satisfied
2. "Blessed ____ they that mourn" (Matthew 5:4)
3. "and all the multitude ____ unto him, and he taught them" (Mark 2:13)
4. Belongings
5. "of Eshcol, and brother of ____" (Genesis 14:13)
6. "be not, as the hypocrites, of a ____ countenance" (Matthew 6:16)
7. Day of the wk. (abbr.)
8. "Whosoever shall put away his wife, and ____ another" (Mark 10:11)
9. "And ____, and Abimael, and Sheba" (Genesis 10:28)
10. Too
11. "Bring forth the ____ robe and put it on him" (Luke 15:22)
16. Climbing vines
17. Operatic parts (Ital.)
19. "in their [angels'] ____ they shall bear thee up" (Matthew 4:6)
20. At some time
21. Horse
22. Apiece (abbr.)
24. Multitude
25. "Thorns also and ____ shall it bring forth" (Genesis 3:18)

26. Biblical verb

27. "their great ____ exercise authority" (Mark 10:42)

29. Make reparation

31. "Yea, a ____ shall pierce through thy own soul" (Luke 2:35)

34. Einsteinium (abbr.)

36. "the children of Israel eat not of the ___ which shrank" (Genesis 32:32)

37. Fish pads?

38. "rolled ____ the stone from the door" (Matthew 28:2)

39. "Adah the daughter of ____" (Genesis 36:2)

40. ____ team

41. "Command... that the sepulchre be made ____ until the third" (Matthew 27:64)

43. "every knee shall ____" (Isaiah 45:23)

44. Before (poet.)

45. Elated entertainer's command to audience

47. Not they

by
Audrey Steele

ACROSS

1. Extinct, flightless birds
5. Pronoun
8. "what he had promised, he was ____ also to perform (Romans 4:21)
12. Pulpit in an early Christian church
13. Clue
14. Cripple
15. Liability
16. "he planted an ____, and the rain doth nourish it" (Isaiah 44:14)
17. Vases
18. One whom Joshua saved (Joshua 6:25)
20. Rent again
22. Feel under the weather
23. Permit access (poet.)
24. Alert, with "on"
27. He anointed Solomon as king
31. Linking verb
32. "Lord, the Holy ____ of Israel" (Isaiah 45:11)
33. "Canst thou fill his skin with ____ irons?" (Job 41:7)
37. "let not your ____ faint" (Deuteronomy 20:3)
40. Gold for the golden years? (abbr.)
41. Capital of Eritrea (abbr.)
42. Wax candle
44. Meadows (poet., var.)
47. "the ____ to walk, and the blind" (Matthew 15:31)
48. Small amount
50. Area distinguished from adjacent areas
52. Made a living, barely, with "out"
53. Before (poet.)
54. "But whoso hearkeneth unto me...shall be quiet from fear of ____" (Proverbs 1:33)
55. Lions' lairs
56. Uproar
57. Puts in a particular position

DOWN

1. "Surely oppression maketh a wise man ____" (Ecclesiastes 7:7)
2. The tenth part of an ephah
3. "And he said, ____, Father, all things" (Mark 14:36)
4. With the purpose
5. Balanced
6. Towel marking
7. "____ the Hittite answered Abraham" (Genesis 23:10)
8. Charm
9. Reveal
10. Cotton fiber
11. Printer's measures
19. Vowel trio
21. Govt. agency
24. Restaurant bill
25. Gershwin
26. By means of
28. Biblical mount (Numbers 20)
29. "Go to the ____ thou sluggard" (Proverbs 6:6)
30. Manual abbr.
34. Twofooted animals
35. Before (poet.)
36. Moved suddenly or swiftly
37. Suburb of New Haven, Connecticut
38. Dir.
39. Overwhelms
42. "____ not thy holy spirit from me" (Psalm 51:11)

43. "And the four beasts said, ____"
    (Revelation 5:14)
45. " the Spirit like a ____ descend-
    ing" (Mark 1:10)
46. State of agitation
47. "I have ____ thee in right paths"
    (Proverbs 4:11)
49. Greek nickname
51. These loop the Loop

by
Audrey Steele

ACROSS

1. One cubit equals two ____
6. "Laban went into ____ tent...but he found them not (Genesis 31:33)
12. "the mariners, and all the ____ of the sea, shall come" (Ezekiel 27:29)
14. Mount in present-day Turkey
15. ____ EloheIsrael
16. Cricket player
18. Dublin dad
19. ___wife
21. "faith as a ____ of mustard seed (Matthew 17:20)
22." ____ your affection on things above" (Colossians 3:2)
23. Speed
25. "no room for them in the ____" (Luke 2:7)
26. "ye shall ____ up early" (Genesis 19:2)
27. "Them that sin ____ before all" (1 Timothy 5:20)
29. "formed man of the ____ of the ground" (Genesis 2:7)
30. "I am the ____ of Sharon" (Song of Solomon 2:1)
31. Handle for a weapon
32. Prophetess, the daughter of Phanuel
33. "might ____ us from all iniquity" (Titus 2:14)
35. "____ without ceasing" (1 Thessalonians 5:17)
36. Serpent
37. "My doctrine shall ____ as the rain" (Deuteronomy 32:2)

39. Afflict
40. "the ____ is in thine own people" (Exodus 5:16)
42. "saying, ____, we would see Jesus" (John 12:21)
43. Linking verb
44. "and after will I send for many ____" (Jeremiah 16:16)
46. Chemical element (abbr.)
47. Pea or bean, for example
49. Courses
51. Nighttime noises
52. To harass in a petty way

DOWN

1. "was there a shield or ____ seen among forty thousand" (Judges 5:8)
2. "she became a ____ of salt" (Genesis 19:26)
3. Div. of Orioles but not Cardinals
4. "____, the city of the priests" (1 Samuel 22:19)
5. Fullgrown male deer
6. "Jemuel, and ____, and Ohad" (Exodus 6:15)
7. "sons of Dishan; Uz, and ____" (1 Chronicles 1:42)
8. "My punishment is greater than I ____ bear" (Genesis 4:13)
9. Conjunction
10. "And Jacob said...I have done according as thou ____ me" (Genesis 27:19)
11. Avow
13. "take of the blood, and ____ it on the two side posts" (Exodus 12:7)
17. Mentally sound
20. "shall I do, that I may have ____ life?" (Matthew 19:16)
22. Women of the same race (colloq.)

24. "horns of ivory and ____"
(Ezekiel 27:15)
26. "days when the judges ____"
(Ruth 1:1)
28. Team ____
29. Performed
31. "I will not be an ____; for in my
house is neither bread"
(Isaiah 3:7)
32. Originated
33. Defeat handily
34. Fabrics with wavy patterns
35. Buckets
36. Nemeses

38. Variety of chalcedony
40. Odorous smoke or vapor
41. Gait
44. "Aaron and ____ stayed up his
hands" (Exodus 17:12)
45. "if any man will ____ thee at the
law" (Matthew 5:40)
48. "____ ye into all the world"
(Mark 16:15)
50. Grad student's position (abbr.)

by
Audrey Steele

ACROSS

1. "And the Lord God called...Where ____ thou?" (Genesis 3:9)
4. "king of ____, which is Zoar" (Genesis 14:2)
8. Dead and Red
12. "And I ____ a new heaven" (Revelation 21:1)
13. Bashemath, daughter of ____ (Genesis 26:34)
14. Soft mixture
15. "How ____ thou that Saul...be dead?" (2 Samuel 1:5)
17. Not as good
18. Linking verb
19. ____ put
20. "____, the family of the Arelites" (Numbers 26:17)
23. "canst not tell whence it cometh, and ____ it goeth" (John 3:8)
26. Red ____, NJ
27. Biblical verb
28. "Let ___ pull out the mote out of thine eye" (Matthew 7:4)
29. Vanquish
30. Unclean bird not to be eaten (Deuteronomy 14)
32. "Hast thou considered my servant ____" (Job 1:8)
33. "____ the hart panteth" (Psalm 42:1)
34. ____ code
35. Silent
36. "What ____ thou by all this drove which I met?" (Genesis 33:8)
38. Carnivorous mammal of India
39. Old Testament offering (Leviticus 3)
40. Congeal
41. Deserve
43. Ropes used to hold animals
47. Kiln
48. To seep
49. "But woe unto you, Pharisees! for ye tithe mint and ____" (Luke 11:42)
50. "prepare to ____ thy God, O Israel" (Amos 4:12)
51. "make a mercy ____ of pure gold" (Exodus 25:17)
52. Greek letter

DOWN

1. "____, and it shall be given you" (Matthew 7:7)
2. What the herd of swine did (Mark 5)
3. "God made ____ great lights" (Genesis 1:16)
4. Hosea, son of ____ (Hosea 1:1)
5. Word contained in threat
6. "____ sat in the gate of Sodom" (Genesis 19:1)
7. "behold, ____ angel of the Lord" (Matthew 2:19)
8. "rough ways shall be made ____" (Luke 3:5)
9. ____ling
10. "find an ____ tied, and a colt" (Matthew 21:2)
11. QEII pronoun
16. Option for a batter
17. "thou canst not make one hair ____ or black" (Matthew 5:36)
19. Saltwater fish
20. "Terah begat ____" (Genesis 11:27)
21. "God is able of these stones to ____ up children" (Matthew 3:9)
22. Omega
23. "gather the ____ into his garner" (Luke 3:17)
24. To express emotion in an exaggerated manner

25. "Only _____ not ye against the Lord" (Numbers 14:9)
30. "_____ is our Lord...his understanding is infinite" (Psalm 147:5)
31. "beware _____ thou forget" (Deuteronomy 6:12)
32. To protrude
34. "thou shalt _____ it, to sanctify it" (Exodus 29:36)
35. Germinated grain
37. "if two of you shall _____ on earth as touching any thing" (Matthew 18:19)
38. Rent again

40. Where Samson would grind in the prison house
41. Pop's cohort
42. "Adam was first formed, then _____"(1 Timothy 2:13)
43. Gardening tool
44. Before (poet.)
45. Settled habit
46. Galilee, for one
48. Bone

by
Audrey Steele

PUZZLE **125**

ACROSS

1. Protective gear
5. Samuel's mother
10. Male wild hog
11. "And Manoah said unto the angel...Let us ____ thee (Judges 13:15)
12. Gennesaret, for example
13. Unclean because it chews the cud (Leviticus 11)
14. "but the end is ____ yet" (Matthew 24:6)
16. Adam's abode
17. Of a time past
18. "____ begat Enos" (Genesis 5:6)
19. Oafs
21. Exclamation of surprise
22. Unable to reproduce (arch.)
25. Shows affection
28. ____Christian religion
29. "thou art also taken, O Babylon, and thou wast not ____" (Jeremiah 50:24)
30. Not them
31. "And there were ____ at Jerusalem Jews, devout men" (Acts 2:5)
32. "Isaac was old, his eyes were ____" (Genesis 27:1)
34. Mature
37. Straightway (arch.)
39. Move fast
42. Hindrance
43. Psalm expression
45. To recover or heal
48. Juda's descendant (Luke 3:26)

50. "built an house upon the earth;...and the ____ of that house was great" (Luke 6:49)
51. "Herod, when he had...called the wise men, ____ of them" (Matthew 2:7)

DOWN

1. "And being fully persuaded...he was ____ also to perform" (Romans 4:21)
2. Way
3. Create
4. Son of Jerahmeel (1 Chronicles 2:25)
5. King in Judea (Matthew 2)
6. Ingested
7. Sodium (abbr.)
8. Number
9. "Art thou he...or do we look for ____?" (Matthew 11:3)
11. Philistine god
13. Healthy
15. Not these
19. Emblem of glory
20. "The Son of man must suffer many things...and be ____" (Luke 9:22)
22. "wist ye not that I must be about my Father's ____?" (Luke 2:49)
23. Announcement
24. Actor Buttons
26. To possess
27. Aimless wanderer
28. One of Christ's apostles
33. Small mammal
35. Fish
36. City in Shinar (Genesis 10:10)
38. Title
40. Terah's home
41. Ancestor of Christ (Luke 3:27)

44. Domestic fowl
46. Big _____, CA
47. "Bind them continually upon thine heart and _____ them"
   (Proverbs 6:21)
49. Measure of mind (abbr.)

by
Barbel Goertz

ACROSS

1. He received a coat of many colors
6. "Wherefore ____ thou thy face, and holdest me for thine enemy?"(Job 13:24)
11. Mount that was cursed (Deuteronomy 11:29)
12. Standard, basic quantity
14. Summer vegetable serving
15. Son of Zephaniah (Zechariah 6:14)
16. "remember, brethren, our labour and ____"(1 Thessalonians 2:9)
18. Cow characteristic
19. To lean or incline
20. "God ____ love" (1 John 4:8)
21. "how pleasant it is for brethren to dwell together in ____" (Psalm 133:1)
23. "the sucking child shall play on the hole of the ____"(Isaiah 11:8)
24. "____ things work together for good" (Romans 8:28)
26. Projecting lower edge of a roof
27. Festival; celebration
28. "Cain ____ up against Abel" (Genesis 4:8)
30. To exist
31. Monetary unit of Italy (pl.)
32. State that borders NJ (abbr.)
33. Meadow
35. Puts on
36. A city of the tribe of the children of Benjamin (Joshua 18:23)
38. "Thus saith the Lord...____ your ways" (Jeremiah 7:3)
40. Where Daniel was cast

42. "Is any thing ____ hard for the Lord?" (Genesis 18:14)
44. What the devil sets for us (2 Timothy 2)
47. Masculine name
51. High places were set up for this "god" (Numbers 22)
52. Verb in the Great Commission
53. "____ ye therefore, and be converted" (Acts 3:19)
54. Where Jesus sits with the Father (Revelation 3:21)

DOWN

1. Prophet who is son of Hanani (1 Kings 16:7)
2. Son of Boaz and Ruth
3. "the angel said unto him [Peter],...bind on thy ____" (Acts 12:8)
4. ___ Shaddai
5. Helped Aaron hold up Moses' hands
6. "Shechem the son of Hamor the ____"(Genesis 34:2)
7. Where Paul spent his final days
8. Long, snakelike fish
9. Continent (abbr.)
10. "And if he ____ against thee seven times in a day" (Luke 17:4)
13. "weep..for him...for he shall return no more, nor see his ____ country" (Jeremiah 22:10)
16. "how ye turned...to serve the living and ____ God" (1 Thessalonians 1:9)
17. Pronoun
20. Melita, for example
22. Abigail's husband (1 Samuel 25)
23. Moses' brother

24. "Concerning Damascus. Hamath is confounded, and ____" (Jeremiah 49:23)
25. "There is a lad here, which hath five barley ____" (John 6:9)
27. He "laid out the fleece"
29. Kind of tree
34. Where Lot sat in Sodom (Genesis 19)
37. Where there was no room (Luke 2)
39. Abram passed through this plain (Genesis 12)

41. Husk of grains of wheat, etc., separated from the flour
43. Preposition
45. Honest man
46. "Take no thought...what ye shall ____" (Matthew 6:25)
48. Conceit
49. Jesus, the ____ of God
50. "I would thou wert cold ____ hot" (Revelation 3:15)

by
Teresa Zook

ACROSS

1. Azariah was given this name
   (Daniel 1)
8. A son of Jacob and Zilpah
   (Genesis 30)
11. Philistine stronghold
12. "Ethiopia and Egypt were her
    strength...Put and ____ were thy
    helpers" (Nahum 3:9)
14. One of the thirteen original states
    (abbr.)
15. The field of blood (Acts 1)
17. Receipt abbr.
18. "Pharaoh was wroth...against the
    chief of the ____" (Genesis 40:2)
19. City of Lycaonia (Acts 14)
22. "I will tread them in mine
    anger...and I will ____ all my
    raiment" (Isaiah 63:3)
24. Part of the head where there may
    be holes
26. "which is ___ for many for the
    remission of sins"
    (Matthew 26:28)
28. Enoch's son (Genesis 4)
29. Abijam's son (1 Kings 15)
30. Masculine nickname
31. Sport of the Stanley Cup
33. Yr. in H.S.
34. Linking verb
35. Reading, for one (abbr.)
36. Tree under which Deborah was
    buried
38. Siamese sigh
41. Preposition
44. Kind of drum
46. "For he knoweth our ____"
    (Psalm 103:14)

48. Salathiel's father (Luke 3)
50. "In Damascus the governor under
    ____ the king"
    (2 Corinthians 11:32)
52. Palm fruit
54. Greek letter
55. Where the Egyptians camped by
    the Red Sea, with Pi (Exodus 14)
56. What Samson saw in a lion's
    carcass

DOWN

1. Prophet from Judea who took
   Paul's girdle
2. "Who passing through the valley
   of ____ make it a well"
   (Psalm 84:6)
3. Son of Buzi (Ezekiel 1:3)
4. Valley
5. Flexible
6. Firm flesh surrounding the teeth
7. Minor prophet
9. "For he said, I will ____
   him...peradventure he will accept
   of me"(Genesis 32:20)
10. Mom's main man
13. "ye shall make images...of your
    mice that ____ the land"
    (1 Samuel 6:5)
16. Sts.
20. "a woman that hath a familiar
    spirit at____" (1 Samuel 28:7)
21. Certain nose?
23. Linking verb
25. Actor Aldo
27. Son of Terah (Genesis 11)
31. Meshillemith's father
    (1 Chronicles 9:12)
32. "For this is an heinous ____"
    (Job 31:11)
33. Mary's husband

37. "The border went out from Tappuah westward unto the river _____" (Joshua 16:8)
39. Preposition
40. "and were by nature the children of _____"(Ephesians 2:3)
42. "Cast the _____ on the right side" (John 21:6)
43. Fertile place in the desert
45. Second tone of the diatonic scale
47. Linking verb
49. Words that have a certain ring?

51. Animal brought by the navy of Tharshish (1 Kings 10)
53. By

by
Teresa Zook

PUZZLE **128**

ACROSS

1. Jephunneh's son (Numbers 13)
5. Biblical pronoun
7. Another name for King Azariah
10. Adam's second son
11. Symptom of Peter's mother-in-law (Matthew 8)
13. Preposition
14. Number of ungrateful lepers (Luke 17)
15. Eliasaph's father (Numbers 3)
16. Pronouncements
17. "___ thy daughter in law hath played the harlot (Genesis 38:24)
19. Mount Moses ascended to view Canaan (Deuteronomy 34)
21. Not too bright
22. Home of the Hawkeyes and the Cyclones (abbr.)
23. Masculine nickname
25. Container
27. ____ of Eden, Steinbeck classic
29. "And the children of Israel set forward, and pitched in ____"(Numbers 21:10)
31. "____ humbug"
32. Father of Hophni and Phinehas (1 Samuel 1)
34. Jesus wore a purple ____
35. Samuel's second son (1 Samuel 8)
36. Linking verb
37. "Take away the ____from the silver"(Proverbs 25:4)
39. Sped
40. Stadium sound

41. "they came to the threshingfloor of ____, which is beyond Jordan (Genesis 50:10)
43. Dancer/actress Ellen
44. Relatively small
47. Styles
48. Honor
49. Greeting
51. "and, behold, it was ____ good" (Genesis 1:31)
52. "God with us"

DOWN

1. Where Jesus performed His first miracle
2. Hezekiah's mother (2 Kings 18)
3. "I [Hannah] have ____ him to the Lord" (1 Samuel 1:28)
4. Slain because he came to take away cattle (1 Chronicles 7)
5. Jesus' parents went to Jerusalem every ____
6. Christmas ___
7. Abram's "hometown"
8. Ahitub's son (2 Samuel 8)
9. Possessive
11. "His eyes were as a ____ of fire" (Revelation 19:12)
12. Nehushta's father (2 Kings 24)
16. "____ in me, and I in you" (John 15:4)
18. State admitted to the U.S. in 1837 (abbr.)
20. "Come unto me, all ye that ____"(Matthew 11:28, Amer. sp.)
22. "____ the prophet the son of Amoz" (2 Kings 19:2)
24. On whom Elijah cast his mantle
25. Where John baptized
26. Solomon's son (Matthew 1)
28. et al. or etc., e.g.

30. Witness
33. These shall have their part in the lake of fire (Revelation 21)
38. Rational
40. Into this sea the Lord cast the locusts (Exodus 10)
42. Fruit of a palm
43. "Favour is deceitful, and beauty is ____" (Proverbs 31:30)
45. The Lord took ____ of Adam's ribs
46. Moon walker (abbr.)
47. Gov't. agcy.
50. ____ Shaddai

by
Teresa Zook

PUZZLE 129

ACROSS

1. "The just shall live by ____"
   (Romans 1:17)
3. Simon Peter's "weapon"
   (John 18)
8. Abraham set up housekeeping
   near this place (Genesis 20)
10. Outdoor task
12. King Saul's "hatchet man"
    (1 Samuel 22)
14. Item to lend
15. Sarai's spouse
17. "____ humbug!"
18. Politicians thrive on this (abbr.)
19. Gov't agcy.
20. "My beloved is like a ____"
    (Song of Solomon 2:9)
22. Ave.
23. Brother of Ulam
    (1 Chronicles 7)
24. "All my ___ shall Tychicus
    declare unto you"
    (Colossians 4:7)
25. First name of U.N. fame
27. Govt. committee
28. Cushion
31. Each of the twenty-four elders
    had one (Revelation 5)
33. Chinese measure of distance
35. God used this to destroy Egypt's
    vines (Psalm 78)
36. Ref. bk.
37. "there is a great ____ fixed"
    (Luke 16:26)
41. The devil
42. Abimelech was king here
    (Genesis 20)

DOWN

1. "But there were ____
   ____...who... shall bring in
   damnable heresies" (2 Peter 2:1)
2. Abram built an altar west of here
   (Genesis 12)
3. David's relationship to Jesse
4. "when he saw her, that he rent his
   clothes, and said, Alas, my ___"
   (Judges 11:35)
5. "I am the ___: by me if any man
   enter in" (John 10:9)
6. Grandfather of Bezaleel
   (Exodus 31)
7. ____ Hill (San Francisco area)
9. Reubenites were exiled here
   (1 Chronicles 5)
10. Grad. degree
11. "And there was ____ in heaven"
    (Revelation 12:7)
13. "breakest the ships of Tarshish
    with an ____ wind" (Psalm 48:7)
15. Shinab was king here
    (Genesis 14)
16. Brother of Miriam
19. Satisfied
21. Yaddayaddayadda (abbr.)
26. Tribe of Israel
27. Mimic
29. Twelve-step group
30. "to ____ is gain"
    (Philippians 1:21)
32. Elijah commanded there be no
    ____
33. Former name of Bethel
    (Judges 1)
34. State bordered by IA, among
    others (abbr.)
38. Expect alarm
39. Tribe of Israel
40. Ezekiel prophesied against this
    place

PUZZLE 130

Note: All clues preceded by * are from the Passion account as told in John's Gospel, chapters 18 and 19.

ACROSS

1. Dir.
*2. Burial spice
5. Characteristic of (suffix)
7. Exclamation
8. Before CD (abbr.)
10. "___ ___ forget thee, O Jerusalem" (Psalm 137:5)
12. What a horse "saith among the trumpets" (Job 39:25)
13. Preposition
15. Hebrew measure
*16. Place "over the brook Cedron"
*17. Roman who sentenced Jesus to death
18. To be busy
19. Power unit (abbr.)
20. Thick boards
24. God led Israel through this body of water
27. Not left (abbr.)
28. Take ____
*29. Jesus' words to Pilate: "To this ____ was I born"
30. Player on certain PGA tour (abbr.)
31. Toddler's first word?
32. Kind of engineer (abbr.)
33. Printer's measure
35. Time zone (abbr.)
36. Tumor (suffix)
38. ____ Thomas, USVI
39. Okay, to Jorge

40. Church denomination (abbr.)
41. Adam's ____ (Genesis 2:22)
42. Greek letter
43. Gridiron feat (abbr.)
44. Where a single guy used to crash
45. Feminine nickname
46. Early (prefix)
47. "The great dragon" of Revelation 12
49. American painter
51. "Behold the fowls of the air: for they ___ not" (Matthew 6:26)
52. Name of temple gate (2 Kings 11:6)

DOWN

*1 Pilate: "I find in him ___ ____ at all"
3. _____to
4. Kind of milk (abbr.)
*6. "took they the body of Jesus, and wound it in linen _____"
*7. "Then Simon Peter...smote the ____ _____ servant"
*9. "And it was the ____ of the passover"
11. Feminine name
12. Masculine pronoun
14. Musical syllable
15. Parts of trucks
21. Application abbr.
22. Biblical relative
23. Attacked (arch.)
*24. "And he [a soldier] saw it bare _____...that ye might believe"
25. Foes
26. Seminary degree (abbr.)
34. King of Greek mythology
35. Tree of the custardapple family

37. Namesakes of Adam's second son
*38. This weapon pierced Jesus' side
48. Preposition
50. College in Athens (abbr.)

Note: All clues preceded by * are from John's letters to the seven churches, as recorded in Revelation 1-3.

ACROSS

*1. "I John, who also am your... companion in ____"
11. Othello was one
*12. Fear ____ of those things which thou shalt suffer"
14. Conjunction
16. Head (colloq.)
17. Son of Leah
18. Unit of dry measure (abbr.)
*19. Message to Sardis: "strengthen the things which remain, that are ready to ____"
21. Electric current measurement (abbr.)
22. Interjection
*23. Number of days Smyrna believers would have tribulation
24. Tom, for one
26. Actress Benedaret
*27. Overcomers will sit on this
*28. This church was poor yet rich
*30. Antipas of Pergamos was one
*35. Message to Pergamos: "thou hast there them that hold the doctrine of ____"
*39. "____ of Man"
40. Adam lost this and gained Eve
41. Wish
42. Computer software company (abbr.)
43. Symbol for rubidium

45. Members include the Timberwolves and the Raptors (abbr.)
47. Apiece (abbr.)
48. Lest (poet.)
49. Political party founded around 1830 (abbr.)
51. Joshua dispatched a small force against this city
52. "So be it"
53. Son of Shem (Genesis 10)
*55. Son of man: "his ____ was as the sun shineth in his strength"

DOWN

2. Paper measure (abbr.)
3. Electrically charged atom
*4. "I will not blot out his name of the____ of life"
5. Paul's "helper in Christ" (Romans 16)
*6. What the seven stars represent from the seven churches
7. Kohathite (1 Chronicles 6:33, 34)
8. Midwest state (abbr.)
9. West Germanic language (abbr.)
*10. Paradise belongs to Him
13. Roof or deck
*15. What the Laodicean church claimed to be
18. Actor Orson
20. Phone or flap
23. Region before statehood (abbr.)
25. Preposition
26. Word on title page
27. Son of Eunice (abbr.)
29. Biblical symbol of strength
*31. John wrote to the seven churches of ____

*32. The overcomer will rule with this

33. Andrew Jackson's stomping ground (abbr.)

*34. Men must do this to escape God's wrath

35. Something you carry

36. List of seagoing vessels of all countries (abbr.)

37. Village inhabited by Simeon's descendants (1 Chronicles 4:32)

38. Name that means "Father"

*41. Where Jezebel will be cast

42. Small songbird

44. Actor Lugosi

46. Melody

48. Bird similar to the ostrich

*50. What God opens, this one can not close

52. Invoice abbr.

54. Like a ringmaster (abbr.)

ACROSS

1. "the Lord is upright: he is my ___" (Psalm 92:15)
5. Attribute of God
7. Article
9. European capital
10. Small deer
12. Good king of Israel
13. "Blessed ____", favorite hymn
15. "as unto a light that shineth in a dark place, until the day ____" (2 Peter 1:19)
17. Pretty mad
18. Long Island catch
20. "Tarshish was thy merchant...with silver, iron, ____, and lead" (Ezekiel 27:12)
22. Choir part
25. Pronoun
26. Continent (abbr.)
27. "____ on Me", popular song
28. Develop
32. Lie
33. "Jesus____" (John 11:35)
34. British noble
35. "Why ____ ye? rise and pray" (Luke 22:46)
37. To be wrong
38. Tabernacle
39. Hurt
41. Preposition
42. Part of R & R
43. Sandwich
44. Numeral
45. State of Hope (abbr.)
46. Directed
47. Sacred songs
48. Mediterranean sea

DOWN

1. "And Achish said, Whither have ye made a ___ to day?" (1 Samuel 27:10)
2. Mr. in Thessaly
3. Sharp nail
4. Pugilist's pursuit (abbr.)
5. Parable that ends "likewise joy shall be in heaven over one sinner that repenteth" (2 wds.)
6. Sin
7. Belief
8. Free gift to all believers
11. Dinghy adjunct
14. Employ
16. Day time
19. Limited employee?
21. Elected
22. Once popular TV show
23. Fish spears
24. Overturned in the temple
29. French conjunction
30. Wheat ____
31. "Give ye ____, and hear my voice" (Isaiah 28:23)
33. Suit or hen
36. Shows, that has (suffix)
37. Wear away
39. "a woman...came behind him, and touched the ___ of his garment" (Matthew 9:20)
40. ____ code
41. Preposition
42. Knock sharply
43. "____ Name Is Wonderful," favorite hymn
44. Metal
46. I ____(name of God)

by
Dan Stevens

ACROSS

1. Produced by skill
5. Entrusts for safekeeping
12. First created on earth
13. Blotted out
15. "and darkness was upon the face of the ____" (Genesis 1:2)
17. Hungarian-born nuclear physicist
18. Laziness
20. Iron (abbr.)
21. Kind of tree
24. Inflammation (suffix)
25. Twofold
27. Found at Bethesda
30. Mole's hole? (abbr.)
31. Pentateuch
32. Attribute of God
36. Middle Easterner
38. Pronoun
39. South American sight
40. Member of AMA
41. Serpent
43. Gateway of Shinto shrine
46. Atlanta inst.
47. Disregards intentionally
49. "it is a ____ thing that the king requireth" (Daniel 2:11)
51. Linking verb
52. "the passages are stopped, and the ____ they have burned with fire" (Jeremiah 51:32)
53. Capital of Shantung province

DOWN

2. In the year of our Lord (abbr.)
3. Progenitor (colloq.)
4. "The ____ of the Lord are in every place" (Proverbs 15:3)
5. Station
6. "____, Judah's firstborn, was wicked" (Genesis 38:7)
7. "in all your ways acknowledge him, and he will make your ____ ____"(Proverbs 3:6, NIV)
8. Full of (suffix)
9. Character of person
10. Avoiding effort
11. Abraham's wife (var.)
14. "and____ us not into temptation" (from the Lord's Prayer)
16. Samuel's mentor
19. Musical syllable
22. Goal of graduate
23. Piece or ball
26. "Eliasaph the son of ____" (Numbers 3:24)
27. Beseech
28. Row
29. "And the sons of Simeon; Jemuel, and Jamin, and ____" (Genesis 46:10)
33. Raised places for sacrifices
34. Part of Chinese philosophy
35. King of Israel following Zimri (1 Kings 16)
37. "every base had four ____ wheels, and plates of brass" (1 Kings 7:30)
38. Ishmael's mother
42. Chaste
44. Preposition
45. Formerly called Persia
48. Epoch
50. Classified

by
Dan Stevens

ACROSS

1. Only large flowing river in Palestine
5. Longest book in the Bible
10. Nice friend
11. Chamber or flower
12. Where living believers will meet Jesus
13. "____sharpeneth ____; so a man sharpeneth the countenance of his friend" (Proverbs 27:17; use word once)
14. What ears of corn grew on in Pharaoh's dream
15. Ceremonial form of prayer
18. Seventh tone of the diatonic musical scale
19. Greek letter
21. John the Baptist's was made of camel's hair
24. Baby's breechcloth
27. Used to express hesitation
28. Missile of warning from Jonathan
31. Not left (abbr.)
32. Items belonging to Joseph's brothers that were searched
35. Eleventh letter of the Hebrew alphabet
36. Exclamation of surprise
37. Where Jonah was sent by the Lord
39. Wisemen
40. Put off
41. Linking verb
42. Article
43. Firstborn of Isaac and Rebekkah
44. Comrade
45. How Joseph's brothers were first treated when they went to Egypt
48. Corn or pea
49. Abraham's father

DOWN

1. He was converted following an earthquake (Acts 16)
2. Sixth king of Israel (1 Kings 16)
3. Violent public disturbance
4. Common Roman coin during Jesus' time
5. "we are the clay, and thou our ____" (Isaiah 64:8)
6. To discolor
7. "These both were cast alive into a ____ of fire" (Revelation 19:20)
8. God's initial watering system
9. Yr. in HS
11. Missive abbr.
16. He was told by Elisha to wash himself seven times in the river Jordan
17. To yelp
20. Masculine nickname
22. Fruit of the Spirit
23. Where Noah's ark is believed to rest
25. Word on some boxes
26. Wise man of Solomon's time (1 Kings 4)
29. Cheer
30. Ezekiel saw this in a vision
31. Sixth book of the New Testament
33. October refresher
34. Word often found in Psalms
38. Burial chamber
41. "Who passing through the valley of ____ make it a well" (Psalm 84:6)

45. "_____ is a rewarder of them that diligently seek Him" (Hebrews 11:6)
46. Preposition
47. Biblical pronoun

by
Miya McKenney

ACROSS

1. Division of opposing parties
6. "____ thy way unto the Lord" (Psalm 37:5)
9. Exclamation of surprise
10. Ninth letter of the Greek alphabet
11. "____ my Father's house are many mansions" (John 14:2)
12. "Thy will be ____" (from Lord's Prayer)
13. Display of a stable with figures, as at Christmas
16. Exclamation of protest
17. Where Goliath was from
18. To look narrowly or searchingly
20. Conjunction
21. NT bk.
22. Isaiah's father
25. "Attention!"
27. Rachel's handmaid
28. "____ is a rewarder of them that diligently seek Him" (Hebrews 11:6)
29. Significant square on a board game
31. Legendary bird of prey (Arabian and Persian)
33. Wooden frame for joining together draft animals
34. Pasture paean
37. "Thy word have I ____ in mine heart" (Psalm 119:11)
39. Great hate or disgust; loathing
44. Small particle of dust
46. Where Job lived
47. High-ranking Turkish official
48. "he planted an ____, and the rain doth nourish it" (Isaiah 44:14)
49. He helped restore Saul's sight

DOWN

1. In NYC, the word for pop
2. Breed of dog, originally from China
3. Term of endearment
4. Yup, to Yolanda
5. Used for grinding
6. Secret stockpile
7. "What shall be the trespass offering...five golden ____" (1 Samuel 6:4)
8. Be innate
14. Hebrew unit of measure
15. Hesitation sound
17. Move along
19. To take property illegally
22. Tree Solomon requested from Lebanon (2 Chronicles 2)
23. City of David
24. Ring of light
26. She was married to Herod Antipas
30. Servant of Elisha
32. Pertaining to bodily appetites
35. Formal declaration or promise
36. "My meat is to ____ the will of him that sent me" (John 4:34)
38. Pronoun
40. "____ still, and know that I am God" (Psalm 46:10)
41. Day of the wk.
42. Joshua, the son of ____
43. King of Bashan
44. Pa's pal
45. Bone

by
Miya McKenney

ACROSS

1. "Ye are the ____ of the earth" (Matthew 5:13)
5. Man who Peter healed in Lydda
9. As compared with
10. "____, I am with you alway" (Matthew 28:20)
11. Og, king of Bashan's bedstead, was made of this
12. Dedicated to or set apart for worship
16. Masculine name
17. Within man's knowledge
18. "it shall return, and shall be eaten: as a ____ tree" (Isaiah 6:13)
20. Forget it, to Philippe
22. Dromedary
25. ____ hill
26. Noah's son
27. Man, Wight, et al.
30. Magistrate of ancient Rome
32. Case for holding small articles
33. Second tone of the diatonic musical scale
35. Doubled, a tot's infraction
36. "number our days, that we may ____ our hearts unto wisdom" (Psalm 90:12)
37. "I will ____ thee...in the way which thou shalt go" (Psalm 32:8)
40. Preposition
41. Nocturnal creature
42. Weight (abbr.)
43. "Is any sick among you? let him call for the ____" (James 5:14)
47. One that is antagonistic
49. Case or well
50. Pronoun
51. Distribute widely

DOWN

1. "that certain ____ which spake, How long shall be the vision" (Daniel 8:13)
2. "That if two of you shall ____ on earth" (Matthew 18:19)
3. One of the churches God asked John to send His Revelation
4. Silver-white metallic element
5. "we know that we are of the truth, and shall __our hearts before him" (1 John 3:19)
6. Where Samson dwelled after he burned the Philistines' cornfield (Judges 15)
7. Deserve
8. Natives of the place where Paul first met Aquila and Priscilla
13. Salary ____
14. ____ Shaddai
15. Succession of rulers from the same family
19. Express sorrow
21. Plugged in
23. Hardy shrub or tree of the olive family
24. Where "snowbirds" fly (abbr.)
26. Professional penmen learned in the Jewish law
28. Musical groups
29. Fish with no pelvic fins
31. Sullen, bad tempered
34. Father of Ahira (Numbers 1)
38. "And there shall come forth a rod out of the ____of Jesse" (Isaiah 11:1)
39. Lack of (prefix)
40. Either

44. ____ pool
45. What would happen to man if
    Adam ate of the forbidden fruit
46. Botch up
48. Kennebunkport locale (abbr.)
49. Island in New York Bay (abbr.)

by
Miya McKenny

ACROSS

1. "Be fruitful, and ____" (Genesis 1:22)
7. Where the foolish man built his house (Matthew 7)
10. To declare as king
11. U.S. state
12. The prodigal son almost ate their food
13. "____ not at all; neither by heaven; for it is God's throne" (Matthew 5:34)
16. Metal not burned by fire (Numbers 31)
17. Greek letter
19. Omega, put another way
20. Penn's bailiwick (abbr.)
21. To trap
23. "Every one that lappeth of the water with his tongue, as a ____" (Judges 7:5)
25. St.
26. Rough rock where the eagle dwells (Job 39)
28. "And ye shall hear of ___ and rumours of" (Matthew 24:6)
31. Member of the cat family
33. From (prefix)
34. Screen or worm
37. To allow the poor to follow the reapers and gather grain
39. "every ___ word that men shall speak, they shall give account" (Matthew 12:36)
40. At the age of (abbr.)
41. "That which hath been is ____ already" (Ecclesiastes 6:10)
44. Dir.
45. Direct the course of
46. Gideon hoped this would be wet then dry
48. Exclamation of surprise
49. Graduate degree (abbr.)
50. Not them
51. " ____ what!"
52. Tall pasture grass
54. Printer's measure
55. Levitical city in the hill country of Judah (Joshua 15)
56. Agrees

DOWN

1. Teacher
2. Take your shoes off
3. "Stand therefore, having your ___ girt about with truth" (Ephesians 6:14)
4. Memorable Baum character, with "man"
5. Not precise
6. Liquid measure (abbr.)
7. "Though I walk through the valley of the ____ of death" (Psalm 23:4)
8. Craft or brush
9. Only with God's help could Joseph interpret these
14. Not they
15. Jesus will be with us until then
18. To supply with water
22. "the fourth beast was like a flying ____" (Revelation 4:7)
24. Seventh son of Jacob
27. Letter of the English alphabet
29. Bought with a price
30. Everything
32. "to give his life a ____ for many" (Mark 10:45)
34. What every man or woman is, save Jesus

35. "Little children, keep yourselves
    from _____" (1 John 5:21)
36. City in the southern part of Judah
    conquered by Joshua (Joshua 12)
38. Prophet during the reigns of
    David and Solomon
42. Downeaster's state (abbr.)
43. Persian coin
47. Dove declaration
52. "Get out!"
53. Article

by
Miya McKenny

ACROSS

1. First priest to minister in the tabernacle
4. Those who form cloth
9. Carolina or Dakota (abbr.)
10. "If any man shall ____ unto these things, God shall" (Revelation 22:18)
11. Half of British goodbye
12. Preposition
13. ____ of the Chaldees
14. In the position of
16. Burnt offering
18. Aromatic substances used for anointing oils
21. Exclamation of disgust
22. Joseph was cast here by his brothers
24. "____ a child is known by his doings" (Proverbs 20:11)
26. To exercise control over
28. What was given to purify from sin
30. Color rams' skins were dyed for the tabernacle (Exodus 25)
31. Dined
32. "And the ____ shall stretch forth their wings on high" (Exodus 25:20)
37. Preposition
38. Middle school period (abbr.)
39. Fourteenth letter of the Greek alphabet
40. Dated
41. To make something seem more attractive
43. Offense

44. Where Joshua's men fought and lost after Jericho
45. Pronoun (colloq.)
46. Greatest Christian virtue
47. Fabric dyed blue, purple, and scarlet for the tabernacle
48. Samuel's mentor

DOWN

1. ____ of the Covenant
2. Semiprecious stone on which the names of the children of Israel were engraved
3. "____ man can serve two masters" (Matthew 6:24)
4. State of conflict
5. Masculine nickname
6. To make fit or suitable
7. French conjunction
8. "let us run with patience the ____ that is set before us" (Hebrews 12:1)
12. Bend forward
13. No or not (prefix)
15. Musical syllable
17. "the Lord shall reign for ever and ____" (Exodus 15:18)
18. Half of a prison's nickname
19. Uncovered space surrounded by walls (pl.)
20. Corn or money
22. To ink
23. He was chosen by God to deliver the Israelites
25. Competitor
27. Shelter from the wind
29. Richly embroidered outer vestment worn by Jewish priest
31. "of Zebaim, the children of ____" (Ezra 2:57)
33. Printer's measure

34. News agency (abbr.)
35. What Aaron wore so that he could be heard when he entered the Holy Place
36. Mountain where Moses talked with God
39. Greek letter
40. Used for anointing
41. Past tense of "to begin" (arch.)
42. "A ____ returneth to his vomit" (Proverbs 26:11)
43. Understand
45. Biblical pronoun

by
Miya McKenney

ACROSS

1. Rural fixture in Bible times
8. British 'bye
10. Result of Jesus' first miracle
11. Prophet who warned Paul of his arrest in Jerusalem
14. To set apart for an office of the Church
15. "wrestle not against flesh and blood...but...the ____ of...darkness" (Eph. 6:12)
16. To have a strong offensive smell
17. "an altar with this inscription, TO THE ____ GOD" (Acts 17:23)
19. This servant of God must be the husband of one wife, and not double tongued
20. " ____, and ye shall receive" (John 16:24)
23. Tower where Jacob camped on his way to Canaan (Genesis 35)
25. Be mortal
27. Poisonous snakes
29. "follow thou ____" (John 21:22)
30. Where Israel was held in bondage
31. ____ blond
33. ____ Sci. (FFA member's major?)
34. Servant of the high priest lost this body part momentarily
36. "____ your ways...and I will cause you to dwell in this place" (Jeremiah 7:3)
37. "Teaching them to ____ all things" (Matthew 28:20)
40. ____ and fro
41. Second tone of the diatonic musical scale
42. ____ instinct

43. He helped Moses speak
46. One who held up Moses' hands during battle
47. "draw near with a true heart in full ____ of faith" (Hebrews 10:22)

DOWN

1. The Word of God is sharper than this
2. "the labourer is worthy of his ____" (Luke 10:7)
3. Ceased
4. Reached a maximum
5. Men once employed as chamberlains by Asian potentates
6. Symbol of evil in Bible
7. Ring of light
8. Chances
9. Balaam rode this animal
12. "Annie Get Your ___", popular musical
13. "____ of false prophets, which come to you in sheep's clothing"(Matthew 7:15)
18. " ___ way!"
21. God's reign or rule
22. Sty denizen
24. "I ____ that I ____ " (Exodus 3:14) (one word)
25. Prophetess
26. Notices
27. Ancestor of a family of porters (Nehemiah 7)
28. "Children, obey your ____ in the Lord" (Ephesians 6:1)
32. "Is not my word like...a ____ that breaketh the rock" (Jeremiah 23:29)
33. Sluggards should learn from this insect

35. Region in Assyria from which Sargon brought men to populate devastated Samaria (2 Kings 17)
38. Boyfriend
39. Self
44. Reading, for one (abbr.)
45. Continent (abbr.)

by
Miya McKenney

PUZZLE **140**

ACROSS

1. Early Christian known for her works of charity
6. The day Jesus rose from the dead
10. Sixth Jewish month (Nehemiah 6)
11. "But Jesus gave him [Pilate] no _____" (John 19:9)
12. In the direction of
13. Use of derisive wit to attack folly
15. All _____
18. Exclamation of wonder
19. "What man...shall not see ____" (Psalm 89:48)
20. Bible vessel
22. "And I took the little book...and ___ it" (Revelation 10:10)
23. Attendee
26. First name of famous musical collaborator
27. Expressing gratitude
30. Ceremonial act
31. Part of plant that makes the food
32. On the ___
34. Up to now
35. Biblical term for length
38. "This is the ____ which the Lord hath made" (Psalm 118:24)
40. Absence or closure of bodily passage
43. To impart
45. With the Lord, we can ____ in green pastures
47. Remember your p's and q's
49. Exclamation of delight
50. "Now I ___ me down to sleep"
51. Musical notations
52. Pronoun

DOWN

1. From (prefix)
2. Chemical suffix
3. She married Naomi's son
4. Jesus ascended up to heaven in a ____
5. Weekly day of rest and worship
6. Kind of curve
7. From any given place
8. To gel
9. To falter
14. Son of Shelah and grandson of Shem (Genesis 10)
15. "the child Jesus ____ behind in Jerusalem" (Luke 2:43)
16. "The life is more than ___" (Luke 12:23)
17. "for everyone that ____ shall be cut off" (Zechariah 5:3)
18. Esau was, but Jacob wasn't
21. Town in Galilee given to Zebulun (Joshua 19:15)
23. What the wisemen brought to Jesus
24. Preposition
25. Good or bad (colloq.)
28. Draw ____ to God
29. Miriam died here
33. Amorite king of Bashan (Joshua 2:10)
36. Crosscountry and drag
37. "The mountains and the ____ shall break forth " (Isaiah 55:12)
39. Time period
41. Father of Rizpah, Saul's concubine (2 Samuel 3:7)
42. Gym exercise (abbr., sing.)
44. Blvd.
46. Ogle
48. M. ___ (NEA member's degree?)

49. Simile syntax

by
Miya McKenney

ACROSS

1. The _____ of the Fisherman, West novel
5. He oversaw King Solomon's household (1 Kings 4)
11. "The sorrows of ___ compassed me" (Psalm 18:5)
12. In the same degree
13. Poem part
14. Like a store window
17. Western state (abbr.)
18. Ms pts.
19. Exclamation of triumph
20. Einsteinium (abbr.)
21. Distinguished from amplitude modulation (abbr.)
23. Pugilist's peak
24. High priest who engineered defeat of Athaliah (2 Kings 11)
25. Arsenic (abbr.)
27. Work (abbr.)
28. Page pts.
29. Site of Lake Winnipesaukee (abbr.)
30. They loop the Loop
32. Paul was brought before this deputy by the Jews (Acts 18)
35. Nineteenth-century American poet
36. Poems
37. You'll need this to get a handle (abbr.)
38. "And now abideth..._____" (1 Corinthians 13:13)
39. As an alternative
40. Stone Mountain is here (abbr.)
41. Indefinite article
42. Acidity measurement of a solution

43. Chromium (abbr.)
44. Nourished
45. Sudden attacks
48. One of twelve officers Solomon placed over Israel (1 Kings 4)
50. Radium (abbr.)
51. Head or toe
52. One of King Solomon's princes, the son of Zadok the priest (1 Kings 4)
53. Nursemaid

DOWN

1. King Josiah sent this scribe to the house of the Lord (2 Kings 22)
2. Pronoun
3. Age or hand
4. Son of Shisha, he was a scribe for King Solomon (1 Kings 4)
5. Not with us
6. _____ League
7. Selenium (abbr.)
8. Govt. body
9. A king over Judah, he did right in God's eyes (1 Kings 15)
10. Son of Ulla (1 Chronicles 7:39)
12. News org.
15. "___ what!"
16. Tree with silver-gray bark
21. Something used to increase bulk
22. Shaded walks
24. Once governor of all Egypt (Genesis 42)
26. Scribe to King Hezekiah (2 Kings 18)
31. Complete circuits for electrical currents
32. "Gotta ___!"
33. He oversaw the tribute for King David (2 Samuel 20)

34. King Ahab set this man up as governor of his palace (1 Kings 18)
37. Coupe
40. Germanium (abbr.)
43. Projecting part on a shaft that gives motion to another part
44. To send work to a freelancer, with "out"
46. Part of savings plan (abbr.)
47. Patriotic group (abbr.)
48. Exclamation of contempt
49. Representative of teachers (abbr.)
51. "That's a good one!"

by
Mary Louise DeMott

ACROSS

1. A Persian official, he protested Nehemiah's rebuilding the walls of Jerusalem (Ezra 4)
6. Nephew to King David, he became David's commander-in-chief (1 Samuel 26)
9. Violent attack
11. Surgeon's pointed two-edged knife
13. One or only one (prefix)
15. Travelers, for one (abbr.)
16. Christian publishing org.
19. Unit of energy (abbr.)
20. Metric unit (abbr.)
21. He was King David's scribe, aka Seraiah (2 Samuel 8)
23. Outward movement of the tide
24. Pierced part
26. Owns
28. The first state (abbr.)
29. Prime minister for King Hezekiah (2 Kings 18)
30. ___ rem
31. Ocean touching western Africa (abbr.)
32. Smallest particle of a chemical element
33. Radio freq.
34. Long strip or track
37. Argon (abbr.)
39. Scale tipper (abbr.)
41. Pronoun
42. Mao ___ Tung
43. Kind of lettuce with long leaves
45. Stubborn
46. Flying machine

49. He succeeded Manasseh as king of Judah (2 Kings 21:18)
50. He was a superintendent of the levies of forced laborers during the reigns of David, Solomon, and Rehoboam (1 Kings 4:6)

DOWN

1. Not liquid or gas
2. Electrically charged particles
3. Conceive
4. Arsenic (abbr.)
5. Linking verb
6. TV's Mrs. Cleaver
7. Small oval fruits with hard stone and bitter pulp
8. Preposition
10. Gold (abbr.)
12. Opinion
14. Leader in the Jewish community who returned to Jerusalem with (Ezra 8, var.)
17. Chief bodyguard to King David and King Solomon (2 Samuel 8)
18. St. (var.)
21. Transfers ownership in exchange for money
22. He was one of King Solomon's secretaries (1 Kings 4:3)
25. Count on
27. Sum (abbr.)
28. Israel's most famous king
30. Stockpile
31. Labor conglomerate (abbr.)
35. Old English dial.
36. Allegro or andante
38. He returned with Zerubbabel to repopulate Jerusalem from the exile (Ezra 2)
40. Nee
42. Row or rank

44. Usually headed by a superinten-
    dent (abbr.)
46. Be
47. Exclamation of triumph
48. Part of the psyche

by
Mary Louise DeMott

ACROSS

1. Jonathan gave him a kiss of friendship
6. Leader or ruler
11. Do coif again
12. Moses' father-in-law (Exodus 18)
14. Electrical abbr.
15. Where the Hamptons are (abbr., part of NY)
17. Simile syntax
18. Iridium (abbr.)
19. Prince of Wales, for one
21. ____ talk
24. Capitol presence (abbr.)
25. Touch
27. Hat or style
28. She lived to see the Messiah
29. Mulberry, for one (abbr.)
30. Engineering major (abbr.)
32. Irish patriarch
33. Part of AL lineup
34. Judas, most prominently
35. Masculine nickname
37. Tantalum (abbr.)
38. "When I say ____..."
39. Part of lineup (abbr.)
41. Flying insect
43. Objective case of he
45. Father of Shem
47. Park or Madison (abbr.)
48. Mother-in-law of Orpah
50. Mlle's maman
51. Quadrant in Washington, D.C. (abbr.)
52. Am
53. Dogpatch doyenne?
55. Well-known safety gp.
56. These were used as a warning to David about Saul's intentions (1 Samuel 20)
59. Jacob married her sister first
61. Condition of the mind
62. To be foul

DOWN

1. Lies
2. Actinium (abbr.)
3. Latin version of the Bible (abbr.)
4. Showy flower
5. Metric measurement (abbr.)
6. Court officer (abbr.)
7. Mend
8. Possessive
9. Exclamation of inquiry
10. Jonathan, to David
11. ____keller, German restaurant
13. Naomi's daughter-in-law
16. "with the mouth confession is made unto ____" (Romans 10:10)
20. Article
22. The Show Me State (abbr.)
23. Netherlands dial.
24. ER presence
26. "As vinegar to the ____, and as smoke to the eyes" (Proverbs 10:26)
28. Moses' mouthpiece, at times
31. JFK info
32. Lair
35. "And Joab said to ___, Art thou in health, my brother" (2 Samuel 20:9)
36. David and Bathsheba, for example
39. He anointed Saul
40. Hard outer covering
42. Tellurium (abbr.)

43. Exclamation of surprise
44. Metric measurement (abbr.)
46. Brit. achievement
48. Small lizardlike creature
49. Moslem ruler
52. Stole
54. Court cyclone?
57. Not left (abbr.)
58. Dir.
59. Indian monetary unit (abbr.)
60. Brit. parliament div.

by
Mary Louise DeMott

ACROSS

1. Genesis, the First Book of _____
6. The church is called the _____ of Jesus
11. Jewish captive in Babylon
12. Heat again
14. Astatine (abbr.)
15. Not sing.
17. Unit of electricity (abbr.)
18. Third note of musical scale
19. Book of the OT
21. Lose by a natural falling off
24. Twitch
25. Tie
27. Diamonds (colloq.)
28. Prophetess
29. Biblical pronoun
30. Radium (abbr.)
32. In the same degree
33. Exclamation of doubt
34. OT writer who ministered during the reign of King Josiah
35. Court official (abbr.)
37. Contains twenty-seven bks.
38. One without a home (abbr.)
39. Instruction to typesetter (abbr.)
41. Propellers?
43. Vanquish
45. Perceive
47. Gov't. commission
48. God's loving mercy toward humankind
50. _____ wife
51. Exclamation of pain
52. Mr. Hirt
53. Lawrencium (abbr.)
55. Vessel (abbr.)
56. Heavy rope or cable used for mooring a ship
59. OT writer called the chief of the writing prophets
61. OT writer who was a contemporary of Amos, Isaiah, and Micah
62. OT writer who prophesied during the reign of King Hezekiah

DOWN

1. Age
2. With it
3. Leisurely lap lemonade?
4. Snakelike fish
5. Without place of publication (abbr.)
6. European (abbr.)
7. Kind of sleep (abbr.)
8. Labor org.
9. Dublin dad
10. Animal of the weasel family
11. Man paying excessive attention to his appearance
13. OT writer who was a prophet in Judah but wrote primarily about Samaria
16. OT writer who was a prophet to the remnant
20. Sandwich state (abbr.)
22. Kona state (abbr.)
23. First state (abbr.)
24. Wt.
26. Small brown songbirds
28. OT writer noted for prayers and words of praise
31. Appropriate
32. Help
35. OT writer who had a mind of his own, for a while
36. Outcast
39. Oily resin obtained from tree

40. Newly made
42. Disaster org.
43. Short Line, e.g.
44. Where you can ride the Metro (abbr.)
46. Apiece (abbr.)
48. Triumphant joy
49. Feminine name
52. What Balaam rode
54. Stadium sound
57. Trouble (arch., var.)
58. Radium (abbr.)
59. Preposition
60. Vowel duo

by
Mary Louise DeMott

ACROSS

1. Act of causing a division in the church
6. Paint or monkey
12. River where the Babylonian Jews gathered before going back to Jerusalem (Ezra 8)
14. River that was the boundary between Israel and Moab (Numbers 21)
15. Green Mountain state (abbr.)
16. Org. of Clippers and Celtics
18. Skill or ability
19. Part of modern weapons arsenal (abbr.)
20. Containers
22. Having three atoms (prefix)
23. Peachy place (abbr.)
24. Easily deceived person
26. Hosp. area
27. Formerly (arch.)
29. River that was turned to blood by Moses
31. River in the Garden of Eden
32. Part of a list
34. Large deer of Northern Europe and Asia
37. Nickel (abbr.)
38. Wading birds
43. Common abbr.
44. AKC members
46. Unwraps
47. TV cable channel abbr.
48. Anger
49. Unit of work or energy
50. Expression of surprise
51. David killed one
54. River in the Garden of Eden
56. Heaviest known metal of a blue-white color
57. To feel certain about, with "on"

DOWN

1. Wild and fierce
2. River where Ezekiel saw some of his visions
3. To injure or damage
4. Hospital abbr.
5. Continent (abbr.)
7. Radium (abbr.)
8. Unsure sound
9. First-year med course (abbr.)
10. Light reddish brown
11. Whole
13. One of two that flows through Damascus, and mentioned by Naaman when he derided the Jordan
16. Gov't. research facility
17. French greeting (var.)
20. U.S. enemy, once
21. Therefore
24. Tree vestige
25. Joints
28. Understand
30. Manhattan, for one (abbr.)
32. Plant of the legume family
33. River in the Garden of Eden
35. River where Deborah and Barak defeated Sisera
36. "Who's on _____?"
39. Biblical exclamation
40. Unveil (poet.)
41. Part of U.K.
42. Calcutta currency (abbr.)
45. Where two edges join
47. To give medicine
52. Nickel (abbr.)
53. Day of the wk.

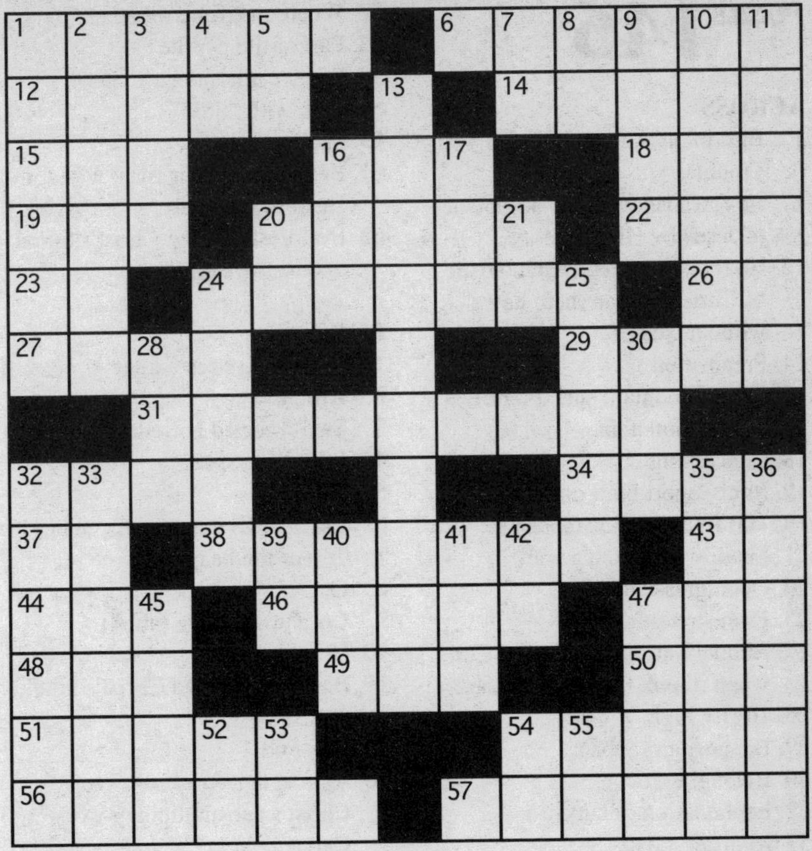

54. Ed.'s abbr.
55. Stat. for Stottlemyre

by
Mary Louise DeMott

ACROSS

1. Bird of strength and speed
6. Troubles
11. He foreshadowed the acceptance of Jesus by His Father
12. He foreshadowed characteristics of Christ, among them hated without cause
14. Preposition
15. Stone Mountain state (abbr.)
17. Application abbr.
18. Concerning
19. Eur. seaport built on more than 100 small islands (abbr.)
21. Shallow recess in a wall
24. Open grassland
25. Firm strength
27. Animal that foreshadowed Christ when it took the place of Isaac
28. To rise high
29. Dysposium (abbr.)
30. Belonging to
32. Exclamation of surprise
33. Minister's deg.
34. Those expressing others' thoughts
35. Pronoun
37. OT bk.
38. School uniforms may be required here (abbr.)
39. Famous TV palomino
41. Shouts of approval
43. Of the futon family
45. Wan
47. Wrongdoing
48. He foreshadowed the death of Jesus
50. Humble, for one
51. Einsteinium (abbr.)
52. Where one finds Obad.
53. Part of the psyche
55. Legal eagle's deg.
56. Lad, with "little"
59. Spa features
61. Belonging to this man, who foreshadowed Christ
62. He foreshadowed Christ's burial and Resurrection

DOWN

1. Inexpensive restaurant
2. Article
3. Two-wheeled horsedrawn carriage
4. Like Jack Sprat
5. Annex
6. Like Dr. Dentons (sing., abbr.)
7. Top of the heap
8. O.T. bk.
9. Cornhusker state (abbr.)
10. Unfold
11. He foreshadowed Christ's kingly ministry
13. Was told
16. Animal that foreshadowed Christ's substitutionary work on Calvary
20. Dir.
22. Iridium (abbr.)
23. Metric measurement of length (abbr.)
24. Alas
26. Slangy denials
28. Animal that foreshadowed Christ's redemptive work on Calvary
31. Wild animal of the dog family
32. Unit of electricity (abbr.)
35. He foreshadowed Christ's prophetical ministry

36. He foreshadowed Christ's miracles
39. Many thought John the Baptist was he
40. Property proofs
42. Printer's measure
43. Cesium (abbr.)
44. Grad student position
46. News agcy.
48. Article
49. Aloha, in Italia
52. Mature female egg cells
54. Ask persistently for payment of a debt

57. Not B.C.
58. Dough, in Delhi (abbr.)
59. Religious org.
60. Continent (abbr.)

by
Mary Louise DeMott

ACROSS

1. Animal used for plowing, the children of Israel were told it was good for food (2 words)
6. Jacob and his sons took these animals to Egypt
12. To decree
14. Shout of encouragement
15. Mil. officer
16. To stumble?
18. Former Mideast nation (abbr.)
19. Small mouthful
20. What sets the stage (pl.)
22. Fed. corp. organized in 1933
23. Common abbr.
24. Small wide antelope found in the mountains of Europe and Asia; Israel was told this animal was clean
26. One-half an em
27. Company character?
29. Female animal of the deer family, also listed as clean and edible
31. Full of short, amusing stories
32. Small burrowing animal, spoken of by Isaiah
34. College/university org.
37. Part of the psyche
38. Sales occurring during December
43. Apiece (abbr.)
44. Sixties student gp.
46. Animals that had a legion of demons come into them
47. NASA gear (abbr.)
48. Pronoun
49. Persuaded
50. Animal brought back to King Solomon from Trashish

51. To make expiation for sin
54. Name
56. Type of antelope deemed clean for the Israelites
57. Animals taken by Joseph in exchange for bread during the seven-year famine

DOWN

1. Small fierce animal listed as unclean for Israelites
2. Deep blue
3. God is a ____ unto our feet
4. You can walk the Mall here (abbr.)
5. Where you can find Neh.
7. Electrical abbr.
8. Thorium (abbr.)
9. Of the Germans (abbr.)
10. Yeast does this
11. Short trip with a purpose
13. Animals found in N. Africa to India, known for fast riding
16. Period of history
17. Reading mail? (abbr.)
20. Acidity measure
21. Silicon (abbr.)
24. Similar to a rabbit, this animal was listed as unclean for the Israelites
25. Potsherd
28. What Grandma might call herself?
30. Labor org.
32. Unfortunate accident
33. Unusual person or thing
35. Conical structure
36. Beasts of burden
39. Einsteinium (abbr.)
40. Small pointed tool for making holes

41. Extreme limit
42. Dir.
45. Polluted fog
47. Bailiwicks of beakers (abbr.)
52. Sodium (abbr.)
53. RN's milieu
54. See (arch.)
55. Argon (abbr.)

by
Mary Louise DeMott

ACROSS

2. Covering
11. Common contraction
13. One of seven original deacons chosen to minister by the early Christian community (Acts 6)
14. Union Pacific, e.g.
15. Metric measurement (abbr.)
16. Ben Casey, e.g.
17. Site of Taos (abbr.)
18. Greek letter
19. To bring legal proceedings against
20. Costa del ____
22. Riviera resort
24. Where you find flowers
26. Long loose garment
28. About (abbr.)
29. Belonging to a certain prophetess
31. College deg.
32. Cheerful
34. Indian, for one
37. Contains cliques and classes (abbr.)
38. High seas fighter
40. Okay, to Jorge
42. Pronoun
44. Agape, eros, or phileo
46. Ball or card
48. Crazy, to a cowboy
50. Anger
51. Friend
52. You might get sent to the showers after this (abbr.)
53. Hospital malady (abbr.)
58. Radium (abbr.)
59. Tradition says he was subsequently the Bishop of Nicodemia and a martyr of Antioch (Acts 6)

DOWN

1. Deacon who did his duties without fanfare (Acts 6)
3. To furnish with power to do a specific job
4. Terrible; dreadful
5. Hilton Head locale (abbr.)
6. Deacon who, tradition states, died a martyr at Philippi (Acts 6)
7. One who administers TLC
8. Centuries upon centuries
9. "Put on the whole ____ of God" (Ephesians 6:11, var.)
10. "____goeth before destruction" (Proverbs 16:18)
12. Metric measurement (abbr.)
14. Med. prescription
19. Lasting mark
21. Pierced part
23. Flavored summer coolers
24. Bank abbr.
25. Rep. of the state
27. Pasture pleas
29. Asian nurse
30. Make dirty
32. Belonging to deacon who was one of the first to speak to Greek-speaking Jews (Acts 6)
33. Unit of electrical power (abbr.)
35. Russian faction (abbr.)
36. Deacon who may have been the founder of the heretical sect of Nicolaitans (Acts 6)
39. Family turf, with "room"
41. First lady
43. Apex
45. Valuable mineral

47. Repetition of sounds
49. Edsel, for one
53. Elder (abbr.)
54. Preposition
55. Elec. (abbr.)
56. Measure of acidity
57. Thirteenth letter of the Greek
    alphabet

by
Mary Louise DeMott

ACROSS

1. Slave
5. "I am thy ____, and thy exceeding great reward" (Genesis 15:1)
7. "his goods shall flow away in the ____of his wrath" (Job 20:28)
8. Feminine name
10. Bug or board
11. "they should offer an oblation and sweet____unto him" (Daniel 2:46)
13. Anger
14. At any time
15. Linking verb
17. "he shall begin to ____ Israel out of the hand of the Philistines" (Judges 13:5)
19. Where you hang your hat
21. Apiece (abbr.)
22. Saul's uncle (1 Samuel 14)
23. 1051, in Rome
24. Job's homeland (Job 1)
25. One from Mongolia, for example
27. "A false ____ is abomination to the Lord" (Proverbs 11:1)
29. Yukon ___ (abbr.)
30. "because thou didst ____ on the Lord" (2 Chronicles 16:8)
31. Electric fish
32. Write hurriedly
34. Owns
35. Sound of laughter
36. Big ____, CA
37. "When the blood of thy ____ Stephen was shed" (Acts 22:20)
39. "Thou shalt not avenge, nor ____ any grudge" (Leviticus 19:18)

DOWN

1. Bashful
2. Islands of Indonesia (abbr.)
3. "I will ____ praises unto thee" (Psalm 56:12)
4. Stun
5. "her [Hannah's] countenance was no more ____" (1 Samuel 1:18)
6. Actress Joanne
7. Devil (Scot.)
9. "In the forest in ____ shall ye lodge" (Isaiah 21:13)
10. Plate or bone
11. Preposition
12. Theatre sign
13. Thought, opinion
14. "at ____ there was upon the tabernacle...the appearance of fire" (Numbers 9:15)
16. Works out from facts
18. Graft one plant to another
19. Associate
20. "come to the place...and shalt remain by the stone ____" (1 Samuel 20:19)
23. Pedestrian walkway lined with stores
26. Plural suffix
27. "Then ____ lest thou forget the Lord" (Deuteronomy 6:12)
28. Neighborlike
30. "And they went...into an harlot's house named ____" (Joshua 2:1)
33. "And he shall offer the ___ for a sacrifice" (Numbers 6:17)
34. Helped Aaron hold up Moses' hands (Exodus 17:12)
36. Mideast country (abbr.)
38. British 'bye

by
Janet W. Adkins

PUZZLE 150

ACROSS

1. "And I sought for a man...that should...stand in the ____ before me" (Ezekiel 22:30)
4. "So ____ took Ruth, and she was his wife" (Ruth 4:13)
8. Sr's counterpart, in Seville
11. Son of Jephunneh (1 Chronicles 4)
12. Son of Hosah, and chief among his sons (1 Chronicles 26)
13. "Aaron and ____ are with you" (Exodus 24:14)
14. Abner's father (2 Samuel 2)
15. Confederate soldier
16. Mr. Kringle
18. "And Balak brought Balaam unto the top of ____" (Numbers 23:28)
20. Having wings
21. NT bk.
22. "if any man have a ____ against any" (Colossians 3:13)
25. "ye shall in no___ enter into the kingdom of heaven" (Matthew 5:20)
26. "they come unto me; and I ____ between one and another" (Exodus 18:16)
27. Dir.
28. Vowel trio
29. Vowel trio, revisited!
30. Fruit drink
31. Simile syntax
32. Chop very finely
34. "a leper as white as ____" (2 Kings 5:27)
35. Cedars of _____
37. Noxious weed thought to be darnel (Matthew 13)
38. German river

39. "And all the people shall answer and say ____" (Deuteronomy 27:15)
41. Jewish philosopher of Alexandria during Jesus' time
43. "And ____ did that which was right" (1 Kings 15:11)
44. "____ ____[2 wds] thy shield and thy exceeding great reward"(Genesis 15:1)
47. Fish eggs
48. "For a bishop must be...but a ____ of hospitality" (Titus 1:7, 8)
50. In the manner of
51. Ever (poet.)
52. "In the thirteenth ____ they rebelled" (Genesis 14:4)
53. Like a fox

DOWN

1. "for a ____ and a snare to the inhabitants of Jerusalem" (Isaiah 8:14)
2. Linking verb
3. "I ____ to build an house unto the name of the Lord" (1 Kings 5:5)
4. "And king David himself followed the ____" (2 Samuel 3:31)
5. Govt. budget office
6. State of Hope (abbr.)
7. "David and his men were come to ____on the third day" (1 Samuel 30:1)
8. To bake eggs
9. Formerly part of USSR (abbr.)
10. "____ longa, vita brevis" (art is long, life is short)
12. Theatre sign
17. "And it is a ____ thing that the king requireth" (Daniel 2:11)
19. Crony (arch.)
20. Actor Murphy
21. "they shall ____ up the former desolations" (Isaiah 61:4)
22. Vashti or Esther

23. "There is a woman that hath a familiar spirit at ____" (1 Samuel 28:7)
24. One of Lerner's musical partners
25. Cookout necessity (sing.)
26. Panel member
30. "____,with Sapphira his wife, sold a possession"(Acts 5:1)
32. "Then Saul (who is also called ____)" (Acts 13:9)
33. "for sinners, for ___ and profane" (1 Timothy 1:9)
34. Jeanne d'Arc (abbr.)
36. "instead of the ____ shall come up the myrtle tree" (Isaiah 55:13)

39. Tribe of Anna the prophetess (Luke 2)
40. "images of your mice that ____the land" (1 Samuel 6:5)
41. Before (prefix)
42. Garden tool
43. Gardner of film
45. "____have sinned" (Romans 5:12)
46. "that the Lord's law ____ be in thy mouth" (Exodus 13:9)
49. English dialect (abbr.)

by
Janet W. Adkins

ACROSS

1. "And Ezbon, _____, and Arodi" (Genesis 46:16)
4. "And _____ said unto her two daughters-in-law" (Ruth 1:8)
8. "Ye _____ witnesses this day" (Ruth 4:9)
11. "And the name of the other _____" (Ruth 1:4)
13. "From going to and _____ in the earth" (Job 1:7)
14. "Teman, _____, Zepho, and Gatam" (Genesis 36:11)
15. "And when thou _____ up" (Deuteronomy 6:7)
16. "For I am _____" (Isaiah 6:5)
17. "And a row of _____ timber" (Ezra 6:4)
18. "Let thine _____ now be attentive" (Nehemiah 1:6)
20. Medical test (abbr.)
21. "_____ is confounded" (Jeremiah 50:2)
22. "Canst thou fill his skin with barbed _____?" (Job 41:7)
24. Military female (abbr.)
26. "Called the altar _____: _____ it shall be" (Joshua 22:34; 2 words)
28. Elevate
30. South (abbr.)
31. "Have they hid for me their _____ in a pit" (Psalm 35:7)
32. "Where thou diest, will I _____" (Ruth 1:17)
33. "For it grieveth me much for your _____" (Ruth 1:13)
37. "Even a tenth part of the _____" (Numbers 18:26)
40. "And _____ them about thy neck" (Proverbs 6:21)
41. "Shall not they _____ thee" (Job 8:10)
44. "As a _____ doth gather her brood" (Luke 13:34)
45. "_____ me now go to the field" (Ruth 2:2)
47. "I _____ no pleasant bread" (Daniel 10:3)
48. To be ill
49. "And to _____ the desolations thereof" (Ezra 9:9)
50. "It is the Moabitish _____" (Ruth 2:6)
52. New car option (abbr.)
53. Transportation company (abbr.)
55. "And a tabret, and a _____, and a harp" (1 Samuel 10:5)
56. Initials for 1960s vice president
57. "Howbeit _____ is a kinsman nearer than I" (Ruth 3:12)
58. "And Naomi took _____ child" (Ruth 4:16)

DOWN

1. "Do they not _____ that devise evil?" (Proverbs 14:22)
2. "For Jerusalem is _____" (Isaiah 3:8)
3. "That which dieth of _____" (Leviticus 22:8)
5. Later in time
6. Pacific Northwest state (abbr.)
7. Grieved
8. Frenzied
9. "Have her forth of the _____" (2 Chronicles 23:14)
10. "But _____ the messenger came to him" (2 Kings 6:32)
12. "And Hiram's builders did _____ them" (1 Kings 5:18)
14. Song
19. Verb tense (abbr.)
21. Teacher's degree (abbr.)
22. "Shall _____ not seek _____ for thee" (Ruth 3:1; 2 words)
23. "What _____ my lord unto his servant?" (Joshua 5:14)

25. "And the _____ said unto Naomi" (Ruth 4:14)
27. Sole
29. "And Shimei, and _____, and the mighty men" (1 Kings 1:8)
33. _____ Paul (abbr.)
34. "What _____ thee, Hagar?" (Genesis 21:17)
35. "Thou shalt _____ fast by my young men" (Ruth 2:21)
36. "And she _____ beside the reapers" (Ruth 2:14)
38. "Tarry _____ night, and _____ shall be in the morning" (Ruth 3:13; 2 words)

39. "And their coast was from _____" (Joshua 19:33)
42. "The Lord of all the _____" (Joshua 3:13)
43. "To bring _____ trees from Lebanon" (Ezra 3:7)
46. Metallic element symbol
48. Unit of electrical measurement
49. Shout of enthusiasm for your team
51. General Robert E. _____
54. "Surely _____ will return with thee" (Ruth 1:10)

by
Diana N. Rowland

ACROSS
1. Group (suffix)
3. "And all that handle the _____" (Ezekiel 27:29)
6. "But _____ for the promise of the Father" (Acts 1:4)
9. "And be _____, _____ the third day rise again" (Luke 24:7; 2 words)
14. "A pound of ointment of spikenard, very _____" (John 12:3)
15. "_____, and his sister, and Olympas" (Romans 16:15)
17. "What mean these seven _____ lambs" (Genesis 21:29)
18. "And John also was baptizing in _____ near to Salim" (John 3:23)
20. "Therefore _____ all the house of Israel know" (Acts 2:36)
21. "That the _____ of your faith" (1 Peter 1:7)
23. Universal signal for help
25. Famous section of London
28. "And _____ came upon every sou" (Acts 2:43)
31. Pain sound
32. "Ye _____ of Israel, hear these words" (Acts 2:22)
34. "Rise, Peter; kill and _____" (Acts 10:13)
35. Midwestern state (abbr.)
36. "And when _____ was dead" (1 Chronicles 1:44)
38. Two (prefix)
40. "And their _____ are dull of hearing" (Acts 28:27)
42. "Go to the _____" (Proverbs 6:6)
44. What is currently fashionable
47. State of Auburn University (abbr.)

49. "An _____ of a sweet smell" (Philippians 4:18)
52. "Then said _____, Now know _____ that" (Judges 17:13; 2 words)
55. "For I will _____ of thee" (Job 38:3)
58. "To be a witness with us of his _____" (Acts 1:22)
60. Dull noises
61. "And _____, Judah's firstborn" (Genesis 38:7)
62. Jolly sound
63. Chinook state (abbr.)

DOWN
1. _____ signum
2. "I _____ not" (Luke 17:9)
3. "They were children _____ fools, _____" (Job 30:8; 2 words)
4. "For _____ is spoiled" (Jeremiah 49:3)
5. Silver state city
6. "Which _____ against the soul" (1 Peter 2:11)
7. "Of new cloth on _____ old garment: _____ the new piece" (Mark 2:21; 2 words)
8. "Then _____ will give you rain in _____ season" (Leviticus 26:4; 2 words)
10. "For every one that _____ milk is unskilful" (Hebrews 5:13)
11. Nutmegger's home (abbr.)
12. "_____ the Ahohite" (1 Chronicles 11:29)
13. "And in _____ and caves of the earth" (Hebrews 11:38)
16. Roadway (abbr.)
19. Baseball organization (abbr.)
22. "Tell me, art thou a _____?" (Acts 22:27)
24. "For as _____ as ye eat this bread" (1 Corinthians 11:26)

26. "_____ no man any thing" (Romans 13:8)
27. Pronoun
29. "And fowls of the _____" (Acts 10:12)
30. Medical staff members (abbr.)
33. Fargo's state (abbr.)
37. Calif. city (abbr.)
39. Commerce group (abbr.)
41. "Shaphat the son of _____" (1 Chronicles 27:29)
43. "The son of Elihu, the son of _____" (1 Samuel 1:1)
45. "But though I be _____ in speech" (2 Corinthians 11:6)

46. "Babel, and _____, and Accad" (Genesis 10:10)
47. Morning (abbr.)
48. Italian currency
50. Dreadful
51. Woman's name
53. Mortar (abbr.)
54. "Which of you shall have an _____ or an ox fallen into a pit" (Luke 14:5)
56. WWII battle area (abbr.)
57. At this time
59. Iron horse (abbr.)

by Diana N. Rowland

ACROSS

1. "_____, a prisoner of Jesus Christ" (Philemon 1)
5. "Not reckoned of grace, but of _____" (Romans 4:4)
9. "I am a man which am a Jew of _____" (Acts 21:39)
11. "That we may _____ a quiet and peaceable life" (1 Timothy 2:2)
13. "Now they are ____ from thine eyes" (Luke 19:42)
14. "And _____ did that which was right in the eyes of the Lord" (1 Kings 15:11)
15. "And the _____ fell upon Matthias" (Acts 1:26)
17. "Or _____ be absent" (Philippians 1:27)
19. Volunteer state (abbr.)
20. "Maaz, and Jamin, and _____" (1 Chronicles 2:27)
21. "That we should _____ unto the heathen" (Galatians 2:9)
22. "_____, give unto your servants that which is just" (Colossians 4:1)
25. "But ye have not _____ learned Christ" (Ephesians 4:20)
26. "After these things were _____" (Acts 19:21)
28. "For he looked for _____ _____ which hath foundations" (Hebrew 11:10; 2 words)
30. Mouths
31. Deface
32. "And your old men shall _____ dreams" (Acts 2:17)
34. "Leadeth them up into an high mountain _____" (Mark 9:2)
37. "_____, thou that destroyest the temple" (Mark 15:29)
38. "I have _____ _____ foundation" (1 Corinthians 3:10; 2 words)
42. "And the king of _____ they took alive" (Joshua 8:23)

43. "And when this epistle is _____ among you" (Colossians 4:16)
45. Collegiate cheer
46. Stun
48. "He planteth an _____" (Isaiah 44:14)
49. "There was a place on the two _____ westward" (Ezekiel 46:19)
51. "And dwelt in the land of _____" (Genesis 4:16)
52. "And Rizpah the daughter of _____" (2 Samuel 21:10)
54. "And with a certain _____ named Tertullus" (Acts 24:1)
56. "____ thing thou lackest" (Mark 10:21)
57. "And after him _____" (Judges 12:11)

DOWN

1. Tablets
2. "Because I have given _____ unto the children" (Deuteronomy 2:9)
3. Its cap. is Washington, D.C.
4. "Deceived, serving divers _____" (Titus 3:3)
6. Aboveground transportation
7. "That ye may _____ counted worthy" (2 Thessalonians 1:5)
8. "How they might entangle him in his _____" (Matthew 22:15)
9. "Rinnah, Benhanan, and _____" (1 Chronicles 4:20)
10. _____ Domingo
12. "For thou that judgest _____ the same things" (Romans 2:1)
13. "The custody of _____ the king's chamberlain" (Esther 2:3)
16. City of Homer's Iliad
18. "In sight like unto an _____" (Revelation 4:3)
20. "And _____ his hands" (2 Corinthians 11:33)
23. "The first man _____ was made _____ living soul" (1 Corinthians 15:45; 2 words)
24. "A voice was heard in _____" (Jeremiah 31:15)

27. Deer

29. "_____ the son of Ikkesh the Tekoite" (1 Chronicles 11:28)

32. "And Calcol, and _____" (1 Chronicles 2:6)

33. "Was the son of Joanna, which was the son of _____" (Luke 3:27)

35. "Take thee a barber's _____" (Ezekiel 5:1)

36. "Ye shall find a colt _____" (Mark 11:2)

39. "And Jerimoth, and _____, five" (1 Chronicles 7:7)

40. Groove

41. "For _____ are many unruly and vain talkers" (Titus 1:10)

44. "And _____ went before the ark" (2 Samuel 6:4)

47. "And _____ with joy receiveth it" (Matthew 13:20)

49. "The wife see that _____ reverence her husband" (Ephesians 5:33)

50. My Gal _____

53. "Paul, _____ apostle of Jesus Christ" (1 Timothy 1:1)

55. "Submitting yourselves one _____ another in the fear of God" (Ephesians 5:21)

by
Diana N. Rowland

ACROSS

1. "Signified it by his angel unto his servant_____ " (Revelation 1:1)
5. "As it is also written in the second _____" (Acts 13:33)
9. "And _____, and Jachan" (1 Chronicles 5:13)
10. "For the statutes of _____ are kept" (Micah 6:16)
11. "Behold I have _____ before thee an open door" (Revelation 3:8)
12. Metallic symbol
13. Cheyenne is its cap. (abbr.)
14. "The beginning and the _____" (Revelation 22:13)
17. North American country
18. "And the mother of Jesus was _____" (John 2:1)
20. "The sons of Judah; _____, and Onan" (1 Chronicles 2:3)
21. "And will _____ with him" (Revelation 3:20)
23. "And hath raised up an _____ of salvation" (Luke 1:69)
24. "And the name of his city was _____" (Genesis 36:39)
25. "And of thy sons that shall _____ from thee" (Isaiah 39:7)
27. "That I will cause an _____ of war" (Jeremiah 49:2)
29. "Behold, I come _____ a thief" (Revelation 16:15)
30. "Come and _____" (Revelation 6:5)
32. "But _____ and Onan died in the land of Canaan" (Genesis 46:12)
33. "Their words seemed to them as idle _____" (Luke 24:11)
36. Cane

39. "And the archers _____ him" (1 Samuel 31:3)
40. A male person
42. _____ Paulo
43. "And there came _____ _____ to him" (Mark 1:40; 2 words)
45. "And Lot _____ in the gate of Sodom" (Genesis 19:1)
47. Hospital staff member (abbr.)
48. Roman emperor
49. Angered
50. "In all things ye are _____ superstitious" (Acts 17:22)
51. Unit of force
53. Fabric
55. Legal defender (abbr.)
56. "Put off thy _____ from thy feet" (Acts 7:33)

DOWN

1. "One _____ or one tittle shall in no wise pass from the law" (Matthew 5:18)
2. Surgeon's milieu (abbr.)
3. Owns
4. "The _____, a topaz" (Revelation 21:20)
5. "And I will give _____ unto my two witnesses" (Revelation 11:3)
6. "Unto the angel of the church in _____ write" (Revelation 2:8)
7. "Because I have given _____ unto the children of Lot" (Deuteronomy 2:9)
8. "And are not, but do _____" (Revelation 3:9)
9. "Amen. Even so, come, Lord _____" (Revelation 22:20)
11. "Gaddi the son of _____" (Numbers 13:11)
15. "Let us draw _____ with a true heart" (Hebrews 10:22)
16. Tympanum

19. "But he shall be free at _____ one year" (Deuteronomy 24:5)
22. "Awake, _____ and harp" (Psalm 108:2)
24. "The great city was divided into three _____" (Revelation 16:19)
26. "If a man _____ it lawfully" (1 Timothy 1:8)
28. Rent
31. Back-to-school item
33. "And the last to be more _____ the first" (Revelation 2:19)
34. "What _____ thee, O thou sea" (Psalm 114:5)
35. A female person

37. "And _____ rod that budded" (Hebrews 9:4)
38. Prohibited thing
41. "Of _____, the family of the Erites" (Numbers 26:16)
44. Puddle
46. "And _____ bare to Esau Eliphaz" (Genesis 36:4)
50. "And upon the great _____ of his right foot" (Leviticus 8:23)
52. Each (abbr.)
54. Attention getter

by
Diana N. Rowland

ACROSS

1. "He restoreth my _____"
   (Psalm 23:3)
4. "The _____ is my shepherd"
   (Psalm 23:1)
8. "The way he should ____"
   (Proverbs 22:6)
9. "Sing unto him a _____ song"
   (Psalm 33:3)
11. Eatery
12. "He fighting _____ oppresseth
    _____" (Psalm 56:1; 2 words)
14. "Even _____ beard"
    (Psalm 133:2)
17. "And he will lift up an _____ to
    the nations" (Isaiah 5:26)
20. "And _____ word was God"
    (John 1:1)
21. "He saith among the
    trumpets, ____" (Job 39:25)
23. "_____ would I give it"
    (Psalm 51:16)
24. "Now Barzillai was a very
    _____ man" (2 Samuel 19:32)
27. "Took a ____, and girded
    himself" (John 13:4)
30. Woman's name
31. "Know ye that the Lord _____ is
    God" (Psalm 100:3)
32. Beef cut
34. "The _____ which he placed
    among men" (Psalm 78:60)
37. Half a quart
38. "Thou rulest the raging of the
    _____" (Psalm 89:9)
40. Typeface style (abbr.)
42. Man's nickname
43. Printer's measures
44. "I have _____ astray like a lost
    sheep" (Psalm 119:176)
45. Poster

46. "And _____ the son of Jeroham"
    (1 Chronicles 9:8)
49. "Make a joyful noise unto God,
    all _____ lands" (Psalm 66:1)
50. "And the wine is _____"
    (Psalm 75:8)
51. Twenty-first president
54. "A bruised _____ shall he not
    break" (Isaiah 42:3)
55. Slender

DOWN

1. "The ungodly are not _____"
   (Psalm 1:4)
2. Untie
3. "He shall _____ upon his house"
   (Job 8:15)
4. Paint
5. "Neither wilt thou suffer thine
   Holy _____ to _____
   corruption" (Psalm 16:10;
   2 words)
6. Second tone of diatonic scale
7. Medical staff member (abbr.)
8. Indian stairway
10. "And put to shame that _____
    me evil" (Psalm 40:14)
11. Color
13. Solitary
15. "_____, our eye hath seen it"
    (Psalm 35:21)
16. "Afterwards I came into the
    _____ of Syria" (Galatians 1:21)
18. "But if it seem _____ _____
    thee to come" (Jeremiah 40:4;
    2 words)
19. Skiing event (abbr.)
22. Environmental measurement
    (abbr.)
25. Adapt
26. "For a voice declareth from
    _____" (Jeremiah 4:15)
28. Exclamation of surprise
29. Soggy

32. Songs
33. "____, tekel, upharsin" (Daniel 5:25)
35. "On the _____ day ye shall have a solemn assembly" (Numbers 29:35)
36. Ecru
37. Romp
38. "He shall _____ from heaven" (Psalm 57:3)
39. ____ Minor
41. Shakespeare's king
46. Anger
47. "When I remember thee upon my _____" (Psalm 63:6)

48. "Thou _____ near, O Lord" (Psalm 119:151)
52. Greeting
53. United Nations (abbr.)

by
Diana N. Rowland

ACROSS

1. "In the beginning was the
   _____" (John 1:1)
5. Assist
7. "Go to my servant _____, and
   offer up for yourselves a burnt
   offering" (Job 42:8)
10. "Upon the mountains of _____"
    (Genesis 8:4)
12. Beginning statement
15. Farewell
16. "_____ no man any thing"
    (Romans 13:8)
17. "And dwelt in the land of
    _____" (Judges 11:3)
19. "And he must _____ go through
    Samaria" (John 4:4)
22. Pale
24. "Duke Elah, duke _____"
    (Genesis 36:41)
26. "Libnah, and _____, and Ashan"
    (Joshua 15:42)
28. Northeast state (abbr.)
29. "_____ _____ Moses lifted up
    the serpent in the wilderness,
    even _____ must"
    (John 3:14; 3 words)
31. "Daughter of Poti-pherah priest
    of _____" (Genesis 41:45)
33. "And Ramoth with her suburbs,
    and _____" (1 Chronicles 6:73)
34. "They shoot out the _____, they
    shake the head" (Psalm 22:7)
35. "I am the _____ of Sharon"
    (Song of Solomon 2:1)
36. Compass point
37. "Till I make thine _____ thy
    footstool" (Luke 20:43)
40. Medical assistance site (abbr.)
41. "He measured it by the four
    _____" (Ezekiel 42:20)
43. Man's name

45. Legal beagle (abbr.)
46. "One man _____ one day above
    another" (Romans 14:5)
49. "To this _____ was I born"
    (John 18:37)
51. Adrift
52. "I _____ on the work of thy
    hands" (Psalm 143:5)
54. Coined
56. Back talk
57. Ballads
58. Entitlement prog.

DOWN

1. "Thou _____ altogether born in
   sins" (John 9:34)
2. Surgeon's site (abbr.)
3. "They said unto him, _____"
   (John 1:38)
4. "He walketh through _____
   places" (Luke 11:24)
5. Symbol for radioactive halogen
6. "This _____, and thou shalt live"
   (Luke 10:28)
7. "Am I a _____?" (John 18:35)
8. "That they may be _____, as
   _____ are" (John 17:11;
   2 words)
9. "Ahasuerus commanded Vashti
   the queen to _____ brought"
   (Esther 1:17)
11. "And John also was baptizing in
    _____" (John 3:23)
13. "And the letters were sent by
    _____" (Esther 3:13)
14. "The water _____ round about the
    altar" (1 Kings 18:35)
18. "Thou _____ thine hand"
    (Psalm 145:16)
20. "To fables and _____
    genealogies" (1 Timothy 1:4)
21. "Let no man therefore _____
    him" (1 Corinthians 16:11)
23. "There _____ up a new king over
    Egypt" (Ex. 1:8)

25. "And one of them, _____ Caiaphas" (John 11:49)
27. "The _____ lifteth up both the bright sword and the glittering spear" (Nahum 3:3)
28. "_____ goeth forth to his labour" (Psalm 104:23)
30. Target
32. "Abner, the son of _____, Saul's uncle" (1 Samuel 14:50)
38. "That Christ must _____ have suffered" (Acts 17:3)
39. "The serpent beguiled _____" (2 Corinthians 11:3)
42. Entries

44. Aeries
45. "Who can utter the mighty _____ of the Lord?" (Psalm 106:2)
47. Golfer's needs
48. Belonged to
50. Greek letters
53. "From the south even to Beth-_____" (Genesis 13:3)
54. A fraction of an aeon (abbr.)
55. Exists

by Diana N. Rowland

ACROSS

1. "A _____ man will hear" (Proverbs 1:5)
5. "Glory, _____ in the cross" (Galatians 6:14)
9. "And _____ with joy receiveth it" (Matthew 13:20)
10. Footnote term
11. "He that is greedy of _____ troubleth his own house" (Proverbs 15:27)
13. "And a word spoken in _____ season" (Proverbs 15:23)
14. "_____ the son of Joseph" (Numbers 13:7)
18. "Go to the _____, thou sluggard" (Proverbs 6:6)
19. Fuse
21. "How long will it be _____ ye make" (Job 18:2)
22. "Through knowledge shall the just _____ delivered" (Proverbs 11:9)
23. "Who hath _____ of eyes?" (Proverbs 23:29)
25. College degree (abbr.)
26. "And thy want as an _____ man" (Proverbs 6:11)
28. "That _____ to the sound of the viol" (Amos 6:5)
30. "And Jehiel, and _____, and Jeremoth" (Ezra 10:26)
31. "Elah, and _____" (1 Chronicles 4:15)
32. Group of jurors
34. "The way of the righteous is made _____" (Proverbs 15:19)
37. Member of military (abbr.)
38. "I have _____ thee in right paths" (Proverbs 4:11)
40. "And I will punish _____ in Babylon" (Jeremiah 51:44)
41. French article
42. Sharp knock
44. Like some rooves
46. "I _____, and considered it well" (Proverbs 24:32)
48. "_____ saith the Lord God of hosts" (Jeremiah 5:14)
49. "Or is there any taste in the white of an _____?" (Job 6:6)
50. Greetings
51. Bosc
53. Take apart
56. Leans
57. "And the wringing of the _____" (Proverbs 30:33)

DOWN

1. "She also lieth in _____ as a prey" (Proverbs 23:28)
2. "When we came to the _____" (Genesis 43:21)
3. "For as he thinketh in his heart, _____ is he" (Proverbs 23:7)
4. "Until they have _____ all my harvest" (Ruth 2:21)
5. "Draw thee waters for the ___" (Nahum 3:14)
6. Canadian province (abbr.)
7. Nero's seven
8. "And he do not whet the ____" (Eccles. 10:10)
11. "The men of Ramah and _____" (Nehemiah 7:30)
12. "_____ with her suburbs" (1 Chronicles 6:70)
14. Samovar
16. "The sons of Dishan; Uz, and _____" (1 Chronicles 1:42)
17. "_____ thou come to poverty" (Proverbs 20:13)
19. "Before it be _____ with" (Proverbs 17:14)
20. "Ye that have _____ the sword" (Jeremiah 51:50)

23. "But if ye refuse and _____"
    (Isaiah 1:20)
24. "And he _____ direct thy paths"
    (Proverbs 3:6)
27. "A _____ hath joy by the answer
    of his mouth" (Proverbs 15:23)
29. MD's group
32. "And shall have _____ of the
    inheritance" (Proverbs 17:2)
33. "And the children of _____ were
    these" (Genesis 36:25)
35. "_____ the Ahohite"
    (1 Chronicles 11:29)
36. "So is good _____ from a far
    country" (Proverbs 25:25)

39. "But be ye _____ of the word"
    (James 1:22)
40. Started
43. Whelps
46. "Over Edom will I cast out my
    _____" (Psalm 60:8)
48. "The way of a ship in the midst
    of the _____" (Proverbs 30:19)
52. Relating to farming (abbr.)
54. "Where _____ counsel is"
    (Proverbs 11:14)
55. Odontist's degree (abbr.)

by
Diana N. Rowland

ACROSS

1. Lincoln's nickname
4. "That it _____ be fulfilled which was spoken" (Matthew 1:22)
7. Early
10. "In the days of _____ the king" (Matthew 2:1)
12. "How _____ would I have gathered thy children" (Matthew 23:37)
14. Deserve
15. Very fast (slang)
17. "And came into the _____ of Israel" (Matthew 2:21)
18. Iron horse (abbr.)
19. _____-de-France
20. "As thou _____ to do unto those" (Psalm 119:132)
21. "I will cut off the multitude of _____" (Ezekiel 30:15)
22. "Barley and the _____ in their place?" (Isaiah 28:25)
23. Highway (abbr.)
25. "The son of _____, which was the son of Seth" (Luke 3:38)
27. Famous London district
30. "And they did so at the going up to _____" (2 Kings 9:27)
32. Erodes
33. Pair
34. Sent one (abbr.)
35. "Arose a great tempest in the _____" (Matthew 8:24)
36. Earth
38. "I can _____ all things through Christ" (Philippians 4:13)
40. "I _____ doing a great work" (Nehemiah 6:3)
41. Where Kennebec County is (abbr.)

42. Chauffeur
45. Landing prognosis (abbr.)
47. Before
48. Gusset
50. Pursues
51. Pools
52. Year (abbr.)
53. Becomes bored
54. Group

DOWN

1. "Ir, and Hushim, the sons of _____" (1 Chronicles 7:12)
2. "Slew both the lion and the _____" (1 Samuel 17:36)
3. Transgress
4. Doctor
5. "Which being interpreted is, _____ with us" (Matthew 1:23)
6. Message-sending place (abbr.)
7. Greek letters
8. Lets
9. "But he that endureth to the _____" (Matthew 10:22)
11. Pungent vegetable
13. "And they twain shall be one _____" (Mark 10:8)
15. Mind changer
16. Hunt
21. "Abner the son of _____ came to the king" (2 Samuel 3:23)
24. "And it came to pass in _____ days" (Luke 2:1)
26. Metal source
28. Orifaces
29. Strange
30. Girl
31. "But there went _____ a mist" (Genesis 2:6)
35. "Salute every _____ in Christ Jesus" (Philippians 4:21)
37. "I am Alpha and _____" (Revelation 1:8)

39. Northwest state (abbr.)
41. French river
42. Glum
43. Nickname for fortieth president
44. Weskit
46. Hills
47. Coy
49. Superlative suffix
51. Engineer's measurement (abbr.)

by
Diana N. Rowland

ACROSS

1. "And _____ saith unto them" (Mark 14:27)
6. "Of ____, the family of the Jesuites" (Numbers 26:44)
11. "And the chambers and the _____" (Ezekiel 40:38)
14. Convenes
15. "Even _____, Father" (Matthew 11:26)
16. Belonging to the Gem state
18. Wing
19. "And if any man will _____ thee at the law" (Matthew 5:40)
21. "Of Eri, the family of the _____" (Numbers 26:16)
23. That is (abbr.)
24. "As the partridge sitteth on _____" (Jeremiah 17:11)
26. Chemically saturate (prefix)
27. Seeks information
28. "For Herod _____ laid hold on John" (Matthew 14:3)
30. Norm (abbr.)
31. "Woven from the _____ throughout" (John 19:23)
32. "But _____ up for yourselves treasures in heaven" (Matthew 6:20)
34. "For ye _____ up the kingdom of heaven" (Matthew 23:13)
35. Microscopic water plants
37. "Hath lifted up his _____ against me" (John 13:18)
38. "And touched the _____ of his garment"(Matthew 9:20)
40. "Of _____, the family of the Eranites" (Numbers 26:36)
41. Salem's its cap. (abbr.)
42. "And your old men shall dream _____" (Acts 2:17)
45. Sagebrush state (abbr.)

46. "And from _____, and from Hamath" (2 Kings 17:24)
48. "They _____ the _____ are they which when they hear" (Luke 8:13; 2 words)
50. Radioactive element symbol
52. "And the sons of Jahdai: ____, and Jotham" (1 Chronicles 2:47)
54. "As a _____ which melteth" (Psalm 58:8)
56. Sun
57. "And _____ is the way" (Matthew 7:13)

DOWN

1. "There shall be a root of _____" (Romans 15:12)
2. "It is _____ for the disciple that he be as his master" (Matthew 10:25)
3. Artery (abbr.)
4. "And Bezaleel the son of _____" (Exodus 38:22)
5. "Some seeds fell by the way" _____ (Matthew 13:4)
6. San ____
7. Related chemical entity (prefix)
8. "____ the salvation of the Lord" (Exodus 14:13)
9. Dissimilar
10. "And upon the _____ of the sea" (Esther 10:1)
12. "Which is neither _____ nor sown" (Deuteronomy 21:4)
13. Part of leg
17. Ear (comb. form)
20. Middle Eastern country (abbr.)
22. Feral
25. "What wilt thou that I _____ do unto thee?" (Mark 10:51)
29. "Given to hospitality, _____ to teach" (1 Timothy 3:2)
30. "_____ things are delivered unto me of my Father" (Matthew 11:27)

31. Definite article
33. "Merchants received the linen _____ at a price" (1 Kings 10:28)
34. Waits on
35. "And the chief of the children of _____" (Daniel 11:41)
36. Roof part
37. "And even to _____ hairs will I carry you" (Isaiah 46:4)
38. "Even as a _____ gathereth her chickens" (Matthew 23:37)
39. "He that hath _____ to hear" (Matthew 11:15)
43. Gypsies (abbr.)
44. "The priest shall pronounce him clean; it is but a _____" (Leviticus 13:6)
47. "Hast thou not heard long _____" (Isaiah 37:26)
49. "In the night _____ of Moab is laid waste" (Isaiah 15:1)
51. "Of a _____ countenance" (Matthew 6:16)
53. Aboveground transportation
55. "_____, we have left all, and followed thee" (Luke 18:28)

by
Diana N. Rowland

ACROSS

1. "The Lord _____ is my strength" (Habakkuk 3:19)
4. "Your young men shall _____ visions" (Joel 2:28)
7. "The men that _____ at peace with thee" (Obadiah 7)
8. "I will shake mine _____ upon them" (Zechariah 2:9)
10. "And I _____ Esau" (Malachi 1:3)
11. "Jesher, and Shobab, and _____" (1 Chronicles 2:18)
13. "Make bare the _____" (Isaiah 47:2)
14. "And the other I called _____" (Zechariah 11:7)
16. "And upon the new wine, and upon the _____" (Haggai 1:11)
18. Domain
20. "And as it was in the days of _____" (Luke 17:26)
21. Universally (comb. form)
22. "His sides east and _____; a portion" (Ezekiel 48:1)
23. Beginning
24. Tawny
26. Midweek (abbr.)
27. "And all the glory of _____ shall fail" (Isaiah 21:16)
31. "And Phares begat _____" (Matthew 1:3)
35. "_____, lama sabachthani?" (Mark 15:34)
36. "But I will remove _____ off from you" (Joel 2:20)
38. Monetary option (abbr.)
39. Dampen
40. "And John also was baptizing in _____" (John 3:23)

42. "Though thou _____ thy nest among the stars" (Obadiah 4)
43. "Shall be _____ the son of Enan" (Numbers 2:29)
45. "_____; Thy kingdom is divided" (Daniel 5:28)
47. "_____ are counted as stubble" (Job 41:29)
48. "Of _____, the family of the Eranites" (Numbers 26:36)
49. "A bird that wandereth from her _____" (Proverbs 27:8)
50. "Neither was I a prophet's _____" (Amos 7:14)

DOWN

1. "Come, _____ you down" (Joel 3:13)
2. "Make their nobles like _____" (Psalm 83:11)
3. "The men of _____ were thy" merchants (Ezekiel 27:15)
4. "The Lord is thy _____ upon thy right hand" (Psalm 121:5)
5. "Their _____ shall be deaf" (Micah 7:16)
6. "He will make an utter _____ of the place" (Nahum 1:8)
7. "And he that earneth _____" (Haggai 1:6)
9. Condemns
10. "Yea, gray hairs are _____ and there upon him" (Hosea 7:9)
12. "Three thousand _____ hundred and thirty" (Nehemiah 7:38)
13. "The _____ of truth was in his mouth" (Malachi 2:6)
15. "Art thou better than populous _____" (Nahum 3:8)
17. Began burning
19. "And she bare him _____" (1 Chronicles 2:35)

21. "despise not one of these little
    _____;" (Matthew 18:10)
23. "_____ no man any thing"
    (Romans 13:8)
25. "The Moabites which dwell in
    ____" (Deuteronomy 2:29)
27. Australian city
28. "And Ezer, and _____"
    (1 Chronicles 7:21)
29. "I heard them say, Let us go to
    ____" (Genesis 37:17)
30. "Thy god, O _____, liveth"
    (Amos 8:14)
32. "My people is _____ up as an
    enemy" (Micah 2:8)

33. Metal sources
34. Rug
36. "I despise your _____ days"
    (Amos 5:21)
37. "If they bind me fast with new
    ____" (Judges 16:11)
40. Skills
41. Roman emperor
44. Anger
46. "And _____ unto him in the fury
    of his power" (Daniel 8:6)

by Diana N. Rowland

ACROSS

1. "_____ thee out" (Luke 13:31)
4. "And when _____ had cried with a loud voice" (Luke 23:46)
8. Basin
11. "There was darkness _____ all the land" (Matthew 27:45)
13. To tear up
14. Prohibit
15. "I have found no cause of _____ in him" (Luke 23:22)
17. "I will _____ things" (Matthew 13:35)
18. Tar Heel state (abbr.)
19. "Sitting in sackcloth and _____" (Luke 10:13)
22. Ozark state (abbr.)
23. Inert gas symbol
25. Indian tribe of New Mexico
26. Columbus discovery (abbr.)
27. Man's nickname
29. Chemist's environment
31. Scandinavian
35. Uncovered
36. Two (prefix)
37. Org. Booths founded (abbr.)
38. Canadian province (abbr.)
39. Gear
41. "If any man shall _____ unto these things" (Revelation 22:18)
42. Goodman (arch. abbr.)
43. Climate (abbr.)
44. Ever (poet)
46. "The sons of Judah; _____, and Onan" (1 Chronicles 2:3)
48. "And, lo, I _____ with you alway" (Matthew 28:20)
49. "A broken spirit drieth the _____" (Proverbs 17:22)
51. "Lo, he that betrayeth me _____ at hand" (Mark 14:42)
53. "The _____ that sowed them is the devil" (Matthew 13:39)
55. "For I mean not that other men be _____" (2 Corinthians 8:13)
58. "There is _____ other name under heaven" (Acts 4:12)
59. "Behold, two _____ stood by them" (Luke 24:4)
61. Roman emperor
62. "Thy dominion to the _____ of the earth" (Daniel 4:22)
63. "And when _____ saw Jesus" (Luke 23:8)
64. "Thou knowest Abner the son of _____" (2 Samuel 3:25)

DOWN

1. "Truly this was the Son of _____" (Matthew 27:54)
2. "_____ unto the end of the world" (Matthew 28:20)
3. "For the Holy Ghost shall _____ you" (Luke 12:12)
5. "And he called his name _____" (Genesis 38:3)
6. "And he vanished out of their _____" (Luke 24:31)
7. "And they rose _____ the same hour" (Luke 24:33)
8. Firework
9. "The children of _____ of Hezekiah" (Nehemiah 7:21)
10. 31-Across country (abbr.)
12. Highway (abbr.)
14. Lake Champlain's state (abbr.)
16. "He saith among the trumpets, _____" (Job 39:25)
17. "while he opened to _____ the scriptures?" (Luke 24:32)
20. Replacement (abbr.)
21. Even (poet.)
24. "They shall deceive the very _____" (Matthew 24:24)
26. "This shall they have for their _____" (Zeph. 2:10)
27. Inky
28. "_____ is a lion's whelp" (Deuteronomy 33:22)

30. "Why make ye this _____"
(Mark 5:39)
32. "Wherewith the _____ number of them" (Numbers 3:48)
33. Theory
34. Auto
40. Earth (comb. form)
41. "_____ ye come out as against a thief" (Matthew 26:55)
43. "When he began to _____"
(John 4:52)
45. "Lest ye _____ into temptation"
(Mark 14:38)
47. "The Lord is _____ indeed"
(Luke 24:34)
48. "And _____ with joy receiveth it" (Matthew 13:20)

49. Farewell
50. Compass point
52. Very dry
53. Carbon compound (suffix)
54. "All power is given unto _____"
(Matthew 28:18)
56. "_____ honourable counsellor"
(Luke 15:43)
57. "The king of _____ in the coast of Dor" (Joshua 12:23)
59. Pinetree state (abbr.)
60. "I find _____ fault in this man"
(Luke 23:4)

by
Diana N. Rowland

ACROSS

1. "_____ the king of Bashan" (Numbers 21:33)
3. "Are they ____? so am I" (2 Corinthians 11:22)
8. Notice
10. "Shall say to his brother, _____" (Matthew 5:22)
11. "And if the _____ shall say" (1 Corinthians 12:16)
12. "I will put my laws _____ their mind" (Hebrews 8:10)
13. Aboveground transportation
14. "For I _____ in the law of God" (Romans 7:22)
17. "Measure of braininess" (abbr.)
18. "_____ than the least of all saints" (Ephesians 3:8)
20. "The son of _____, the son of Zerah" (1 Chronicles 6:41)
22. "And from thy _____ shall he pull _____ down" (Isaiah 22:19; 2 words)
25. Type of bran
27. Hoosier state (abbr.)
28. Watering places
30. "The son of _____, which was the son of Nachor" (Luke 3:34)
32. Displayed
34. "Seeing thou _____ instruction" (Psalm 50:17)
36. Nuclear (abbr.)
37. Wages
38. Leak
40. "The mote that is in thy brother's ____" (Luke 6:41)
41. "Blessed art thou, ____ Bar-Jona" (Matthew 16:17)
44. Abe Lincoln's son

46. "_____ thyself also in the Lord" (Psalm 37:4)
48. "For the _____ of mine apostle-ship are ye" (1 Corinthians 9:2)
50. Columbia River state (abbr.)
51. "Grace be with you all _____" (Hebrews 13:25)
54. Toronto's province (abbr.)
55. "Acknowledge _____ to the _____" (2 Corinthians 1:13; 2 words)
56. "They _____ alway err in their heart" (Hebrews 3:10)

DOWN

1. Iron source
2. "Their grapes are grapes of ____" (Deuteronomy 32:32)
3. "Neither _____ pleasure therein" (Hebrews 10:8)
4. "And I will punish _____ in Babylon" (Jeremiah 51:44)
5. "God was able to _____ him up" (Hebrews 11:19)
6. Physicist's work unit
7. "Where Christ _____ on the right hand of God" (Colossians 3:1)
8. "God, who _____ sundry times and _____ divers manners" (Hebrews 1:1; 2 words)
9. Column style
15. "In his chariot read _____ the prophet" (Acts 8:28; 2 words)
16. "_____ that _____ to be rich" (Proverbs 28:22; 2 words)
19. "And I will settle you after your old _____" (Ezekiel 36:11)
21. "_____ _____ also that money should have been given him" (Acts 24:26; 2 words)
23. Volunteer state (abbr.)

24. Lung disease (abbr.)
25. "There is none _____ God but one"
    (1 Corinthians 8:4)
26. "Because thou saidst, _____"
    (Ezekiel 25:3)
29. Tilt
31. Concerning (abbr.)
33. Flock of pheasants
35. "And fashioned it with a graving _____" (Exodus 32:4)
36. Colorado River state (abbr.)
39. Pungent vegetable
42. "And withal they learn to be _____" (1 Timothy 5:13)

43. NE state (abbr.)
45. "And they came to the threshing floor of _____" (Genesis 50:10)
47. Higher ed. exam (abbr.)
48. "If we neglect _____ great salvation" (Hebrews 2:3)
49. Printer's measure
52. Schooling (abbr.)
53. "There is _____ more offering for sin" (Hebrews 10:18)

by
Diana N. Rowland

PUZZLE 163

ACROSS

1. "Then the Lord was with the _____" (Judges 2:18)
5. "The son of _____, king of Gath" (1 Samuel 27:2)
10. "No mention shall be made of _____" (Job 28:18)
11. "To _____ the pride of all glory" (Isaiah 23:9)
13. Yr. (abbr.)
14. "And Adithaim, and _____, and Gederothaim" (Joshua 15:36)
16. "And, _____, a cake of barley bread tumbled" (Judges 7:13)
17. "The king of _____, one; the king of Hazor, one" (Joshua 12:19)
19. "And to loose the _____ thereof?" (Revelation 5:2)
21. "_____ my _____ Absalom" (2 Samuel 18:33; 2 words)
22. "And Joshua _____ up twelve stones" (Joshua 4:9)
24. "_____ thou, and fall upon us" (Judges 8:21)
25. Loses strength
27. "_____, lama sabachthani?" (Mark 15:34)
28. "And a poor man is better than a _____" (Proverbs 19:22)
29. "Thy right hand offend thee, cut it _____" (Matthew 5:30)
31. "And served _____ gods" (Judges 10:13)
33. Interjection of agreement
35. Longstanding quarrel
37. Pork
38. "The daughter of Phanuel, of the tribe of _____" (Luke 2:36)
40. "In thee are men that carry _____" (Ezekiel 22:9)

42. "And _____ answered the king" (2 Samuel 15:21)
43. "And the sons of Judah; _____, and Onan" (Genesis 46:12)
44. "Azrikam, _____, and Ishmael" (1 Chronicles 8:38)
45. Score (abbr.)
46. "Where the birds make their _____" (Psalm 104:17)
48. Spy inits.
50. "As I _____, _____ shall ye do" (Judges 7:17; 2 words)
51. "Come _____, I pray thee" (Genesis 27:21)

DOWN

1. "_____ was a sign unto the Ninevites" (Luke 11:30)
2. "They went forth with them from _____ of the Chaldees" (Genesis 11:31)
3. "To offer a great sacrifice unto _____ their god" (Judges 16:23)
4. Valley
6. "Nevertheless _____ heart was perfect" (1 Kings 15:14)
7. "Which were on the _____ side Jordan" (Joshua 17:5)
8. Azusa's state (abbr.)
9. "Joshua smote all the country of the _____" (Joshua 10:40)
10. "And Jair died, and was buried in _____" (Judges 10:5)
12. "I will put my hook in thy _____" (2 Kings 19:28)
15. "From Dan _____ to Beersheba" (Judges 20:1)
18. "Lament with a _____ lamentation" (Micah 2:4)
20. "Neither the birds of the _____ to _____ on them" (2 Samuel 21:10; 2 words)
22. "Thus _____ the Lord God of Israel" (Judges 6:8)

23. "Ziph, and _____, and Bealoth" (Joshua 15:24)
25. Court
26. "And said, O _____, we came" (Genesis 43:20)
29. "He that being _____ reproved hardeneth his neck" (Proverbs 29:1)
30. "He that _____ the word of the Lord" (Exodus 9:20)
32. Supper item
34. Fever
36. "And forgive us our _____" (Matthew 6:12)

38. "_____ the head of the two ways, to _____ divination" (Ezekiel 21:21; 2 words)
39. Free
41. Mediocre
42. "And vessels of brass and _____" (Joshua 6:19)
47. "And God did _____ that night" (Judges 6:40)
49. Brazil's cont. (abbr.)

by
Diana N. Rowland

PUZZLE 164

ACROSS

1. "And he spake a _____ unto them" (Luke 6:39)
7. "They look and _____ upon me" (Psalm 22:17)
9. "And a cake of _____ bread" (Leviticus 8:26)
12. "Though it be _____ with fire" (1 Peter 1:7)
13. "The Lord was _____ to save me" (Isaiah 38:20)
14. "It is like a grain of mustard" _____ (Mark 4:31)
15. Sweet drink (suffix)
17. "Neither be ye of doubtful _____" (Luke 12:29)
19. "And Pispah, and _____" (1 Chronicles 7:38)
20. "Dwelt in the land of _____" (Genesis 4:6)
21. Service charge
22. "I _____ have baptized you with water" (Mark 1:8)
25. Farewell
26. Radioactive halogen symbol
27. "Peace _____ unto you" (Luke 24:36)
28. Like a copy (abbr.)
31. "Is a _____ brought to be put under a bushel" (Mark 4:21)
34. Scandinavian country (abbr.)
35. "The _____ ran violently down a steep place" (Mark 5:13)
37. Rodent
38. "Consider the lilies how they _____" (Luke 12:27)
40. "_____, and Arodi, and Areli" (Genesis 46:16)
41. Decorative belt
42. City in Oklahoma

44. "We _____ the seventh year? behold, _____ shall not sow" (Leviticus 25:20; 2 words)
46. "The blood of Abner the son of _____" (2 Samuel 3:28)
48. "Great is _____ of the Ephesians" (Acts 19:28)
49. Mote
50. Unacceptable (abbr.)

DOWN

1. "Till thou hast _____ the very last mite" (Luke 12:59)
2. "Those by the way side _____ they that hear" (Luke 8:12)
3. "For the sky is _____ _____ lowring" (Matthew 16:3; 2 words)
4. Drilled
5. "When he speaketh a _____" (John 8:44)
6. "And I will set my throne in _____" (Jeremiah 49:38)
7. "They cast four anchors out of the _____" (Acts 27:29)
8. "I give unto you power to _____ on serpents" (Luke 10:19)
10. "And things wherewith one may _____ another" (Romans 14:19)
11. Force unit
14. "And when _____ was now dangerous" (Acts 27:9)
16. "This _____, and thou shalt live" (Luke 10:28)
18. "But he that _____ me before men" (Luke 12:9)
23. "And he did _____ locusts and wild honey" (Mark 1:6)
24. Science fiction movie character
25. Nickname for son of Jacob
27. "But cast the _____ away" (Matthew 13:48)

29. "Now the serpent was ____
    subtil" (Genesis 3:1)
30. "And for ____ I will bring
    silver" (Isaiah 60:17)
31. "Ye ____ to me, and I delivered
    you" (Judges 10:12)
32. "The sword, the sword is ____"
    (Ezekiel 21:28)
33. "Nigh whereunto was the city of
    ____" (Acts 27:8)
35. Pronoun
36. "And he called his name ____"
    (Genesis 38:3)

39. "The one ____ of the cherub"
    (1 Kings 6:24)
41. Male deer
43. God (Lat.)
45. "____ with her suburbs, and
    Juttah" (Joshua 21:16)
47. Route (abbr.)

by
Diana N. Rowland

ACROSS

1. "And ____ his son, and Tahath his son" (1 Chronicles 7:20)
6. "And Husham of the land of ____ reigned" (Genesis 36:34)
12. "And ____ went up unto God" (Exodus 19:3)
13. "____ days shall ye eat unleavened bread" (Exodus 12:15)
14. ____ choy
15. Hasp
19. Bureau of federal gov't. (abbr.)
20. "Because the Hebrew women are not ____ the Egyptian women" (Exodus 1:19)
21. "And they shall be ____ boards" (Exodus 26:25)
22. Hebrew letter
23. "Behold, Saul ____ upon his spear" (2 Samuel 1:6)
26. Aquatic mammal
29. "They have ____ upon me with their mouth" (Job 16:10)
31. "Until the day that ____ entered into the ark" (Matthew 24:38)
32. ____ Paulo
33. "____ let not the Lord be angry" (Genesis 18:30)
35. Electrode (abbr.)
36. "____ am hath sent ____ unto you" (Exodus 3:14; 2 words)
38. "____; Thou art weighed in the balances" (Daniel 5:27)
40. English architect Jones
42. "And gave the ____" (Nehemiah 8:8)
44. Boulevard (abbr.)
45. "Ten asses ____ with the good things" (Genesis 45:23)
47. "____, I see four men loose, walking" (Daniel 3:25)
49. "I ____ no pleasant bread" (Daniel 10:3)
51. "Eri, and ____, and Areli" (Genesis 46:16)
52. Help
53. "Call me not ____" (Ruth 1:20)
55. "And the ____ of it was like wafers made with honey" (Exodus 16:31)
57. "For these men shall ____ with ____ at noon" (Genesis 43:16; 2 words)
58. Anesthetic

DOWN

1. "The physicians to ____ his father" (Genesis 50:2)
2. "Naphtali is a hind let ____" (Genesis 49:21)
3. "____ me never so much dowry" (Genesis 34:12)
4. Its cap. is Dover (abbr.)
5. "For he was fast ____ and weary" (Judges 4:21)
7. "And ____ begat Beth-rapha" (1 Chronicles 4:12)
8. Pinetree state (abbr.)
9. "And from ____, and from Hamath" (2 Kings 17:24)
10. "And let his ____ that ____ hath hid" (Psalm 35:8; 2 words)
11. Deduce
16. Assistant
17. English lang. study (abbr.)
18. Clan leader (abbr.)
24. "Go ____, and buy us a little food" (Genesis 44:25)
25. "And ____ took the child" (Ruth 4:16)
27. "And this shall be a ____ unto thee" (Exodus 3:12)

28. Freshwater ducks
30. Feminine nickname
34. "The son of _____, in Aruboth" (1 Kings 4:10)
37. "The howling thereof unto _____" (Isaiah 15:8)
39. "And the children of the _____" (Judges 1:16)
40. "And _____ answered the king" (2 Samuel 15:21)
41. "And all that handle the _____" (Ezekiel 27:29)
43. Cream of the crop
44. "And hid him in the _____" (Exodus 2:12)

46. "Why _____ ye not rather take wrong?" (1 Corinthians 6:7)
48. Czech river
50. Very long time period
52. "He planteth an _____" (Isaiah 44:14)
54. "They will not believe _____" (Exodus 4:1)
56. New car option (abbr.)

by
Diana N. Rowland

333

ACROSS

1. "Then said _____ unto the angel" (Luke 1:34)
5. Await
9. "Until _____ the prophet" (Acts 13:20)
11. "Is not this Jesus, the son of _____" (John 6:42)
13. "And the king of _____ they took alive" (Joshua 8:23)
14. "Where thou hast _____ him, _____ I will take him" (John 20:15; 2 words)
15. Howdy
16. Loiterers
18. "They _____ not to teach and preach Jesus" (Acts 5:42)
20. "A certain centurion's servant, who was _____ unto him" (Luke 7:2)
21. "Ye are _____ superstitious" (Acts 17:22)
22. "And it is a _____ thing" (Daniel 2:11)
23. "And birds of the air have _____" (Luke 9:58)
25. "For it might have _____ sold for more" (Mark 14:5)
27. Oglethorpe founded it (abbr.)
29. "Son of _____, which was the son of Nathan" (Luke 3:31)
34. "The churches of _____ salute you" (1 Corinthians 16:19)
36. "And Aaron's _____ that budded" (Hebrews 9:4)
37. "And ye _____ shall bear witness" (John 15:27)
40. "To depart unto the other _____" (Matthew 8:18)
42. "And _____, and Aridai, and Vajezatha" (Esther 9:9)
44. Letter's afterthought
46. "Behold, this _____ cometh" (Genesis 37:19)
47. Baseball org. (abbr.)
48. Creative thought
50. "And he called the name of the well _____" (Genesis 26:20)
52. "Friend, I do thee no _____" (Matthew 20:13)
53. "Being raised from sleep _____ as the angel" (Matthew 1:24)

DOWN

1. "And the mother of the _____" (Luke 8:51)
2. "I _____ Gabriel" (Luke 1:19)
3. "Ye _____ of the people" (Acts 4:8)
4. "Went the high priest alone once every _____" (Hebrews 9:7)
5. "This is now _____ of my bones" (Genesis 2:23)
6. "None _____ so fierce that _____ stir him up" (Job 41:10; 2 words)
7. Dover's state (abbr.)
8. "Ephah, and _____, and Henoch" (1 Chronicles 1:33)
9. "Then _____ the lord of the vineyard" (Luke 20:13)
10. Itemizes
11. "Art thou greater than our father _____" (John 4:12)
12. "And did _____ himself from them" (John 12:36)
17. "Shall be Eliasaph the son of _____" (Numbers 3:24)
19. "But be shod with _____" (Mark 6:9)
24. Breakfast beverage
26. "I have meat to _____ that ye know not of" (John 4:32)
27. Puff
28. Undergraduate deg. (abbr.)
29. "Then thus came every _____ unto the king" (Esther 2:13)

30. "Every _____ which bringeth not forth" (Matthew 3:10)
31. Message-sending spot (abbr.)
32. "For as in _____ all die" (1 Corinthians 15:22)
33. "And even to hoar _____ will _____ carry you" (Isaiah 46:4; 2 words)
35. "Which _____ the sea of Tiberias" (John 6:1)
38. "They _____ into the bottom as a stone" (Exodus 15:5)
39. "My head with _____ thou didst not anoint" (Luke 7:46)

41. "And gather them in their _____" (Habakkuk 1:15)
43. "A bruised _____ shall he not break" (Matthew 12:20)
45. "Saying, _____, we would see Jesus" (John 12:21)
49. "If any man will _____ his will" (John 7:17)
51. "The children of Gad called the altar _____" (Joshua 22:34)

by
Diana N. Rowland

ACROSS

1. "It is ____ the Tishbite"
(2 Kings 1:8)
6. "What ____ thee?"
(2 Kings 6:28)
11. "____ it rest on the head of
Joab" (2 Samuel 3:29)
12. "Assuredly Solomon thy son
shall ____" (1 Kings 1:13)
13. "But as the days of ____ were"
(Matthew 24:37)
14. "And Shimron, and ____, and
Bethlehem" (Joshua 19:15)
16. "John and ____ asked him
privately" (Mark 13:3)
18. "For, ____, he hath caught hold
on the horns" (1 Kings 1:51)
19. "Come home with me, and ____
bread" (1 Kings 13:15)
21. Business (abbr.)
22. "The ____ appeareth"
(Proverbs 27:25)
24. "The son of ____, in Aruboth"
(1 Kings 4:10)
26. Symbol for element used in
semiconductors
28. "I have given ____ unto the
children of Lot"
(Deuteronomy 2:9)
29. "Have I need of ____ men"
(1 Samuel 21:15)
30. "In ____ also is his tabernacle"
(Psalm 76:2)
32. "And unto Enoch was born
____" (Genesis 4:18)
34. "He maketh the storm a ____"
(Psalm 107:29)
35. "And gave the ____"
(Nehemiah 8:8)
37. Churchman's deg. (abbr.)
38. Environmental reading (abbr.)
40. "Down from Lebanon unto the
____" (1 Kings 5:9)
41. "Melech, and ____, and Ahaz"
(1 Chronicles 8:35)
43. "____ will thy servant do"
(1 Kings 2:38)
45. "And take away all thy ____"
(Isaiah 1:25)
46. "He saith among the trumpets,
____, ____" (Job 39:25;
2 words)
49. "Because three days ____ I fell
sick" (1 Samuel 30:13)
52. Garden insect
53. Style
54. "Turn thee aside to thy ____
hand" (2 Samuel 2:21)
57. "The ____ of Tahpenes the
queen" (1 Kings 11:19)
58. Drippy

DOWN

1. "The spirit of Elijah doth rest on
____" (2 Kings 2:15)
2. "But he ____ them to Samaria"
(2 Kings 6:19)
3. "They of ____ salute you"
(Hebrews 13:24)
4. "And Pispah, and ____"
(1 Chronicles 7:38)
5. "Yea, ____ gave good ____"
(Eccles. 12:9; 2 words)
6. "And I will make thy windows
of ____" (Isaiah 54:12)
7. "When we came to the ____"
(Genesis 43:21)
8. "Jonathan and Ahimaaz stayed
by ____" (2 Samuel 17:17)
9. "And upon the great ____ of his
right foot" (Leviticus 8:23)
10. Chop
15. "____, ye see the man is mad"
(1 Samuel 21:14)
17. Electrical voltage designation
(abbr.)
20. Pago Pago is its cap. (abbr.)
23. "And I will ____ and pursue
after David" (2 Samuel 17:1)
24. "Unless thou ____ spoken"
(2 Samuel 2:27)

25. Russian country house
27. Jane Austen novel
29. "But the poor ____ had nothing" (2 Samuel 12:3)
31. Boy
33. "I gave ear to your ____" (Job 32:11)
36. "Give the people, that they may ____" (2 Kings 4:43)
37. "And David sent out ____ young men" (1 Samuel 25:5)
39. "They did ____ me, and ceased not" (Psalm 35:15)
40. "And draw you before the judgment ____?" (James 2:6)
42. Roger Williams founded it (abbr.)

44. Canadian province (abbr.)
46. "____, every one that thirsteth" (Isaiah 55:1)
47. "The children of Dishan are these; Uz, and ____" (Genesis 36:28)
48. Hebrew letter
50. Gentile (var.)
51. "And ____ the lamp of God went out" (1 Samuel 3:3)
52. Energy measurement (abbr.)
55. "And Huppim, the children of ____" (1 Chronicles 7:12)
56. Sixty minutes (abbr.)

by Diana N. Rowland

ACROSS

1. "Behold the Lamb of ____" (John 1:29)
4. "Out of whose womb came the ____?" (Job 38:29)
6. "Is the young man Absalom ____?" (2 Samuel 18:29)
10. "The sons of ____, and Ithmah the Moabite" (1 Chronicles 11:46)
12. "The people ____ received him" (Luke 8:40)
14. "But, ____, he speaketh boldly" (John 7:26)
15. Businessman's deg. (abbr.)
16. Taxus
17. That is (abbr.)
18. "____ the son of Ikkesh the Tekoite" (1 Chronicles 11:28)
20. "Out of ____ have I called my son" (Matthew 2:15)
21. "When I remember thee upon my ____" (Psalm 63:6)
22. "And brought him to an ____" (Luke 10:34)
24. Pronoun
25. "____ me cometh a man" (John 1:30)
27. "____, Elah, and Naam" (1 Chronicles 4:15)
29. Meridian (abbr.)
31. Farewell
32. "For God ____ loved the world" (John 3:16)
33. "Sir, come down ____ my child die" (John 4:49)
35. "The children of ____ of Hezekiah" (Ezra 2:16)
37. "And Poratha, and ____" (Esther 9:8)
39. Rome is its cap. (abbr.)
40. "____ ____ the light of the world" (John 8:12; 2 words)
41. "I and my Father are ____" (John 10:30)
42. "The valley of ____, unto this day" (Joshua 7:26)

44. "Now is the Son of ____ glorified" (John 13:31)
46. Sioux state (abbr.)
47. "Hast thou not heard long ____" (Isaiah 37:26)
48. "For ye tithe mint and ____" (Luke 11:42)
50. "And ____ into Judaea" (John 7:3)
51. "On ____ side one, and Jesus in the midst" (John 19:18)
53. "For the Jews had ____ already" (John 9:22)
55. "Through faith also ____ herself received strength" (Hebrews 11:11)
56. "How is the gold become ____!" (Lamentations 4:1)
57. Fed. tax office (abbr.)

DOWN

1. "Father, ____ thy name" (John 12:28)
2. "And ___, the son of Peleth" (Numbers 16:1)
3. "Seven days it shall be with his ____" (Exodus 22:30)
4. "A graven ____ and a molten image" (Judges 17:4)
5. "Inhabitants of ____ shall know that ____ am the Lord" (Ezekiel 29:6; 2 words)
6. "Abraham... ____ my day" (John 8:56)
7. Year of our Lord (abbr.)
8. Leaflets
9. "Leah was tender ____" (Genesis 29:17)
10. "Samuel feared to shew ____ the vision" (1 Samuel 3:15)
11. Pres. Lincoln
13. "____ not your heart be troubled" (John 14:1)
19. "Go to the ____, thou sluggard" (Proverbs 6:6)
21. To ____ or not to be
23. "As an eagle stirreth up her ____" (Deuteronomy 32:11)
24. "____ of the brooks of Gaash" (1 Chronicles 11:32)
25. "His mother's name also was ____, the daughter of Zachariah"

	1	2	3		4		5		6	7	8	9
10				11			12	13				
14			15				16				17	
18		19		20						21		
	22		23						24			
25				26			27	28			29	30
31			32				33		34			
		35			36		37				38	
	39								40			
41				42				43		44		45
46			47				48		49		50	
51		52					53			54		
55					56			57				

(2 Kings 18:2)

26. "Deliver thyself as a _____ from the hand" (Proverbs 6:5)

28. "For the sky is _____" (Matthew 16:2)

30. Mouths

34. "Behold, I will break the bow of _____" (Jeremiah 49:35)

35. "I _____ no pleasant bread" (Daniel 10:3)

36. "And this is the _____ of John" (John 1:19)

37. "And _____ was over the tribute" (2 Samuel 20:24)

38. "The graven _____ also will I cut off" (Micah 5:13)

39. "From _____ even unto Ethiopia" (Esther 1:1)

41. "Ye despise not one of these little _____" (Matthew 18:10)

42. "He is of _____; ask him" (John 9:23)

43. Mat

45. "And dwelt in the land of _____" (Genesis 4:16)

47. "Because thou saidst, ___" (Ezekiel 25:3)

49. "And Ezbon, _____, and Arodi" (Genesis 46:16)

52. Twenty-sixth US pres. (initials)

54. "_____, and Onan, and Shelah" (1 Chronicles 2:3)

by

Diana N. Rowland

ACROSS

1. "And the Lord was with ____ " (Genesis 39:2)
6. "____ was twenty and two years old" (2 Kings 21:19)
10. "And pitched together at the waters of ____ " (Joshua 11:5)
11. "Give me children, or ____ I ____ " (Genesis 30:1; 2 words)
14. "____ , our eye hath seen it" (Psalm 35:21)
15. "Micaiah the son of ____ " (1 Kings 22:8)
17. "When Moses had made an ____ of writing" (Deuteronomy 31:24)
18. "And ____ shall be rent asunder" (Ezekiel 30:16)
19. "Then I will be an enemy unto thine ____ " (Exodus 23:22)
21. "The sons of Judah were ____ and Onan" (Numbers 26:19)
22. "How long will it be ____ ____ make an end of words?" (Job 18:2; 2 words)
24. "I will ____ water for thy camels also" (Genesis 24:19)
26. "And he shall make ____ for the harm" (Leviticus 5:16)
29. "Gilalai, ____ , Nethaneel" (Nehemiah 12:36)
31. Comedian Berle
32. "He destroyed their vines with ____ " (Psalm 78:47)
33. Do, Re, ____ , Fa, So, La, Ti, Do
34. Alarms
35. "Every man in ____ tent ____ " (Exodus 33:10; 2 words)
38. Buffalo
40. "Surely the Lord ____ in this place" (Genesis 28:16)
41. "The Syrians to ____ ____ noise" (2 Kings 7:6; 2 words)
43. "____ God created man in his own image" (Genesis 1:27)
44. Macon's state (abbr.)
45. "____ not to cry unto the Lord our God" (1 Samuel 7:8)
46. "Peradventure ____ shall be found there" (Genesis 18:32)
47. "Heard that I ____ builded the ____ " (Nehemiah 6:1; 2 words)
50. "____ thou tillest the ground" (Genesis 4:12)
52. "And he made him a ____ of many colours" (Genesis 37:3)
53. Tied tightly

DOWN

1. "And ____ his son reigned in his stead" (1 Kings 22:50)
2. Mouths
3. "If it be ____ , why am I thus?" (Genesis 25:22)
4. "Thou hast also built unto thee an ____ place" (Ezekiel 16:24)
5. "Are they turned about with a very small ____ " (James 3:4)
6. "And she called his name ____ " (Genesis 30:13)
7. Saco River's state (abbr.)
8. Lyric
9. "When Abram was ninety years old and ____ " (Genesis 17:1)
10. Tresses description
12. "The men ____ hold upon his hand" (Genesis 19:16)
13. "Which reigned in Ashtaroth and in ____ " (Joshua 13:12)
16. Publisher's staff member (abbr.)
19. "And let thine ____ look straight before thee" (Proverbs 4:25)
20. "And there was a sore famine in ____ " (1 Kings 18:2)
23. "But the Moabites call them ____ " (Deuteronomy 2:11)
25. Stays

27. "I ____ set my bow in the cloud" (Genesis 9:13)
28. "For as a ____ shall it come on ____ them that dwell" (Luke 21:35; 2 words)
30. "I will ____ ____ wild beasts among you" (Leviticus 26:22; 2 words)
32. "The Lord God of the ____ hath sent me" (Exodus 7:16)
35. "It is ____, I cannot attain unto it" (Psalm 139:6)
36. "And thou shalt call his name ____" (Genesis 17:19)

37. "And Hashubah, and ____" (1 Chronicles 3:20)
39. "____ his son, Jehoshuah his son" (1 Chronicles 7:27)
42. "____ it is in heaven" (Matthew 6:10)
45. Feline
46. A peg for golf
48. "This ____, and live; for I fear God" (Genesis 42:18)
50. Cascades Range state (abbr.)
51. LBJ's vice president (initials)

by
Diana N. Rowland

341

PUZZLE 170

ACROSS

1. "And Adam called his wife's name ____" (Genesis 3:20)
4. "And the darkness he called ____" (Genesis 1:5)
8. "____ shall be a serpent by the way" (Genesis 49:17)
11. "They that sow in tears shall ____ in joy" (Psalm 126:5)
13. "And the waters shall ____ more become ____ flood" (Genesis 9:15; 2 words)
14. "Whosoever shall compel thee to go a ____" (Matthew 5:41)
15. Painter
17. "Why ____ thou, She is my sister?" (Genesis 12:19)
19. "Let there ____ light" (Genesis 1:3)
20. "And Jacob was a plain man, dwelling in ___" (Genesis 25:27)
22. "But Sarai was barren; she had ____ child" (Genesis 11:30)
24. "And it was ____" (Genesis 1:7)
26. Born
27. "I ____ set my bow in the cloud" (Genesis 9:13)
29. "That were ____ to the war ____ to battle" (1 Chronicles 7:40; 2 words)
32. Block
34. Tramway (abbr.)
35. Boxing term (abbr.)
36. Yr. (abbr.)
37. Niantic Indian state (abbr.)
38. "Sent many letters unto ____" (Nehemiah 6:17)
41. "And thorns of the wilderness and ____" (Judges 8:16)
43. "These are the sons of Seir the Horite, who ____ the land" (Genesis 36:20)
45. Environmental measure (abbr.)
46. Boy

47. "As a ____ lappeth" (Judges 7:5)
49. "____ am the ____ in my father's house" (Judges 6:15; 2 words)
51. "I will not ____ it" (Genesis 18:30)
52. "Lo, ye see the man is ____" (1 Samuel 21:14)
54. Rodents
55. "What mean these seven ____ lambs" (Genesis 21:29)
57. "Rehoboam, ____ his son" (1 Chronicles 3:10)
58. "He planteth an ____" (Isaiah 44:14)
59. "Ye have made it a ____ of thieves" (Luke 19:46)
60. "The ____ of all flesh is come before me" (Genesis 6:13)

DOWN

1. Epoch
2. Part of speech
3. "For in the day that thou ____ thereof" (Genesis 2:17)
5. "Did not ____ to go up against them in battle" (Joshua 22:33)
6. "____ forth of the ark" (Gen 8:16)
7. "Make ____ to shed blood" (Proverbs 1:16)
8. "And they ____ ____ pursue after the sons of Jacob" (Genesis 35:5; 2 words)
9. "He made the stars ____" (Genesis 1:16)
10. "He shall pluck my feet out of the ____" (Psalm 25:15)
12. Greek letter
14. Do, Re, ____, Fa, So, La, Ti, Do
16. Roadway (abbr.)
18. Pago Pago's land (abbr.)
21. Compass point
23. "In the beginning God created the heaven and the ____" (Genesis 1:1)
25. "And sat under an ____ which was ____ Ophrah" (Judges 6:11; 2 words)

27. "Then Sarah ____, saying, I laughed not" (Genesis 18:15)
28. "____, take thy wife, and thy two daughters" (Genesis 19:15)
30. Expert
31. "____ walked with God" (Genesis 6:9)
32. Leap
33. "Do they not ____ that devise evil?" (Proverbs 14:22)
39. "That ____ the horse heels" (Genesis 49:17)
40. "And he ____ upon his thigh" (Genesis 32:31)
41. "Among them that were ____" (1 Samuel 9:22)

42. "Then the dukes of ____ shall ____ amazed" (Exodus 15:15; 2 words)
44. Undergraduate degree (abbr.)
45. "____, my lord, I beseech thee" (Numbers 12:11)
48. "They took no ____ of money" (Judges 5:19)
49. "____ the son of Ikkesh the Tekoite" (2 Samuel 23:26)
50. "____ it is in heaven" (Matthew 6:10)
53. Father
56. Midweek

by Diana N. Rowland

ACROSS

1. "When he had privily called the ____ men" (Matthew 2:7)
5. "O ____ your hands" (Psalm 47:1)
9. "When ____ the king had heard these things" (Matthew 2:3)
10. "Are there not twelve ____ in the day?" (John 11:9)
12. "And when ____ was dead" (1 Chronicles 1:44)
13. "Believe ye that ____ am able to ____ this?" (Matthew 9:28; 2 words)
15. "And thou Bethlehem, in the ____ of Juda" (Matthew 2:6)
17. "____ these things will I give thee" (Matthew 4:9)
18. "____ he that was escaped came" (Ezekiel 33:22)
20. Overly
21. "That it might ____ fulfilled which was spoken of the Lord" (Matthew 1:22)
22. "Thou ____ up mighty rivers" (Psalm 74:15)
24. "God is able of these stones to raise ____ children unto Abraham" (Matthew 3:9)
25. "Published throughout all his ____" (Esther 1:20)
27. "And they came with ____" (Luke 2:16)
29. "And ____ us not into temptation" (Matthew 6:13)
30. "Let not ____ widow be taken into ____ number" (1 Timothy 5:9; 2 words)
31. "And their camels shall be a ____" (Jeremiah 49:32)
33. "And of king ____ a thousand men" (2 Samuel 10:6)
36. Toronto's province (abbr.)
37. "Howl, O ____" (Jeremiah 49:3)
40. Pinetree state (abbr.)
41. "But the wheat and the ____ were not smitten" (Exodus 9:32)
43. "And they ____ make a covenant with the Assyrians, and ____ is carried" (Hosea 12:1; 2 words)
44. Pronoun
45. "But found ____" (Matthew 26:60)
47. "She hath also conceived a son in her old ____" (Luke 1:36)
48. "____, tekel, upharsin" (Daniel 5:25)
49. "And Abram and ____ took them wives" (Genesis 11:29)
51. "That which is ____ in the scripture of truth" (Daniel 10:21)
53. "Lord, shall we ____ with the sword?" (Luke 22:49)
54. Man's nickname

DOWN

1. "This is my beloved Son, in whom I am ____ pleased" (Matthew 3:17)
2. "____ the son of Ikkesh the Tekoite" (1 Chronicles 11:28)
3. "Suffer it to be ____ now" (Matthew 3:15)
4. "And were ____; and walking in the fear of the Lord" (Acts 9:31)
5. Triad
6. "and, ____, the star, which they saw in the east" (Matthew 2:9)
7. "Then thou shalt take an ____" (Deuteronomy 15:17)
8. Trick
9. "And the crowns shall be to ____" (Zechariah 6:14)
11. "As a jewel of gold in a swine's ____" (Proverbs 11:22)
12. "Ye shall find the ____ wrapped in swaddling clothes" (Luke 2:12)
14. Female deer
16. Goon
18. "Even Solomon in all his glory was not ____" (Matthew 6:29)
19. "Out of Zorah and out of ____"

(Judges 18:11)

22. "And no man _____ to himself" (Romans 14:7)
23. "And Telah his son, and _____ his son" (1 Chronicles 7:25)
26. Radical Middle Eastern group (abbr.)
28. Part of a minute (abbr.)
30. Background
31. "Now when Jesus was _____ in Bethlehem of Judaea" (Matthew 2:1)
32. "And the leeks, and the _____" (Numbers 11:5)
34. Alters
35. "We have _____ but five loaves" (Matthew 14:17)

38. "_____ then they _____ no more twain" (Mark 10:8; 2 words)
39. Swine
42. "Tappuah, and _____" (Joshua 15:34)
44. "Take _____ and beware of the leaven of the Pharisees" (Matthew 16:6)
46. "And Naaman, _____, and Rosh" (Genesis 46:21)
48. Manhattan transportation group (abbr.)
50. Extended game (abbr.)
52. "_____ that I might have my request" (Job 6:8)

by Diana N. Rowland

ACROSS

1. "____ God, what wilt thou give me" (Genesis 15:2)
4. "I am the Almighty ____" (Genesis 17:1)
6. "There shall the vultures be gathered, every one with her ____" (Isaiah 34:15)
10. "For these men shall ____ with me at noon" (Genesis 43:16)
12. "And the day following unto ____" (Acts 21:1)
14. "Sarai Abram's wife bare him ____ children" (Genesis 16:1)
16. "Which ____ his daughters" (Genesis 19:14)
18. Mother
19. "____ shall judge his people" (Genesis 49:16)
21. "It is ____; for they wist not what it was" (Exodus 16:15)
22. Computer part (abbr.)
23. "He made him ____ over all the land of Egypt" (Genesis 41:43)
25. Hot dog topper
27. "The water on the other side ____ ____ as blood" (2 Kings 3:22; 2 words)
28. Curt
30. Engineer's measurement (abbr.)
31. Bismarck is its cap. (abbr.)
32. "Whether there be any ____ in you" (Genesis 42:16)
34. "Said unto Balak, ____ not ____ thee" (Numbers 23:26; 2 words)
35. "And I will cause it to ____ upon the earth" (Genesis 7:4)
37. "And Jacob was yet scarce ____ out" (Genesis 27:30)
38. "I ____ no pleasant bread" (Daniel 10:3)
40. Citrus fruit
42. "And the ____ sitting upon the young" (Deuteronomy 22:6)

45. "What profit shall this birthright ____ to me?" (Genesis 25:32)
46. "And were come to the ____ of Sinai" (Exodus 19:2)
47. Jefferson City is its cap.
48. "And thou shalt ____ it, to sanctify it" (Exodus 29:36)
50. Eras
53. "And he said, ____ am I, my son" (Genesis 22:7)
54. Dirt
55. "The Spirit of God came upon Azariah the son of ____" (2 Chronicles 15:1)

DOWN

1. "Unto thy seed have I given this ____" (Genesis 15:18)
2. Artery (abbr.)
3. "And his eyes were ____" (Genesis 27:1)
4. "And Isaac dwelt in ____" (Genesis 26:6)
5. "And she shall say, ____" (Genesis 24:14)
6. Recent (abbr.)
7. Poster
8. Entices
9. "Then Jacob gave ____ bread and pottage" (Genesis 25:34)
11. "Is not he rightly ____ Jacob?" (Genesis 27:36)
13. "Before I had done speaking in mine ____" (Genesis 24:45)
15. "Wherein shall go no galley with ____" (Isaiah 33:21)
17. Nurse (abbr.)
20. "But bring them up in the ____ and admonition of the Lord" (Ephesians 6:4)
22. "And ____ me like cheese?" (Job 10:10)
24. "____ it be for ____ snare in the midst of thee" (Exodus 34:12; 2 words)
26. "And John also was baptizing in ____" (John 3:23)

27. "And bring to pass his ____" (Isaiah 28:21)
29. "And ____ blessed Elkanah and his wife" (1 Samuel 2:20)
33. "And ____ with her suburbs, Debir" (1 Chronicles 6:58)
34. The Lone Ranger's sidekick
36. "Where the birds make their ____" (Psalm 104:17)
37. Pierced
38. "And ____ bare to Esau Eliphaz" (Genesis 36:4)
39. Accent
41. Portland's state (abbr.)
43. "I ____ a stranger and a sojourner with you" (Genesis 23:4)
44. Form
46. "Give me children, or else I ____" (Genesis 30:1)
49. Mt. Hood's state (abbr.)
51. "We are true men; we are ____ spies" (Genesis 42:31)
52. Mt. Rushmore's state (abbr.)

by
Diana N. Rowland

ACROSS

1. "The beginning of the gospel of ____ Christ, the Son of God" (Mark 1:1)
5. "____ ye the way of the Lord" (Mark 1:3)
12. "To maintain good works for necessary ____" (Titus 3:14)
13. "____ the wife of Machir bare ____ son" (1 Chronicles 7:16; 2 words)
14. "Thy god, O ____, liveth" (Amos 8:14)
15. "See thou ____ nothing ____ any man" (Mark 1:44; 2 words)
16. "But the name of the wicked shall ____" (Proverbs 10:7)
17. "And from ____ to Jotbath" (Deuteronomy 10:7)
19. Massachusetts Cape
20. "They gave money also unto the ____" (Ezra 3:7)
21. "____ as ____ nurse cherisheth her children" (1 Thessalonians 2:7; 2 words)
22. "The son of ____, which was the son of Seth" (Luke 3:38)
23. "And all that handle the ____" (Ezekiel 27:29)
24. Undergraduate deg. (abbr.)
25. Flickertail state (abbr.)
26. Afternoon (abbr.)
27. "And the rent ____ made worse" (Mark 2:21)
28. Kokomo's state (abbr.)
30. Pronoun
31. "And they departed from ____" (Numbers 33:45)
33. "____ the new wine doth burst the bottles" (Mark 2:22)
35. "And the sons of Nadab; ____, and Appaim" (1 Chronicles 2:30)
36. "Jesus came ____ Galilee" (Mark 1:14)

38. "____ the Ahohite" (1 Chronicles 11:29)
39. "Er the father of ____, ____ Laadah" (1 Chronicles 4:21; 2 words)
42. "And I will punish ____ in Babylon" (Jeremiah 51:44)
43. "And ____ their sister" (Genesis 46:17)
44. "When thou vowest a ____ unto God" (Ecclesiastes 5:4)
45. "Jeshua, Nehemiah, Seraiah, ____" (Ezra 2:2)
47. Change (prefix)
48. "When Simon Peter saw ____, he fell ____ at Jesus' knees" (Luke 5:8; 2 words)
49. "What did ____ command you?" (Mark 10:3)

DOWN

1. "In the day of ____, than for that city" (Mark 6:11)
2. "Then Jacob gave ____ bread ____ pottage of lentiles" (Genesis 25:34; 2 words)
3. "Him therefore I hope to ____ presently, ____ soon as I shall see" (Philippians 2:23; 2 words)
4. Western hemisphere country (abbr.)
5. "Or else thou shalt ____ ____ talent of silver" (1 Kings 20:39; 2 words)
6. "But ____ grew worse" (Mark 5:26)
7. Habitat (comb. form)
8. Alkalinity measurement
9. "And it shall be upon ____ forehead" (Exodus 28:38)
10. "A damsel came to hearken, named ____" (Acts 12:13)
11. "And their word will ____ as doth a canker" (2 Timothy 2:17)
13. "Thou art ____. But she constantly affirmed that it was even ____" (Acts 12:15; 2 words)

15. "Thou art my beloved ____"
    (Mark 1:11)
18. "I declare unto you the ____
    which ____ preached"
    (1 Corinthians 15:1; 2 words)
19. "This man ____ not to speak"
    (Acts 6:13)
28. "Master, it ____ good for us to
    be here" (Mark 9:5)
29. "What further ____ ____ there
    that another priest"
    (Hebrews 7:11; 2 words)
30. "For he had ____ many"
    (Mark 3:10)
31. "And saw others standing ____
    ____ the marketplace"
    (Matthew 20:3; 2 words)

32. "The word of the Lord that came
    to ____" (Micah 1:1)
34. "How many ____ have ye?"
    (Mark 6:38)
35. Frozen precipitation
37. Slang negative
38. "And Zaccur, and ____"
    (1 Chronicles 24:27)
40. Period in history
41. C Major
43. "He ____ the heavens opened"
    (Mark 1:10)
46. "____, we have left all"
    (Mark 10:28)
47. Yr. part (abbr.)

by Diana N. Rowland

ACROSS

1. "The children of Israel murmured ____ Moses" (Exodus 16:2)
7. "Now ____ kept the flock of Jethro" (Exodus 3:1)
9. "Thy ____ and thy she goats" (Genesis 31:38)
11. "Hamath is confounded, and ____" (Jeremiah 49:23)
12. "In one house shall it be ____" (Exodus 12:46)
14. Cedar River state (abbr.)
15. "And he made ____ his chariot" (Exodus 14:6)
17. "For the barley was in the ____" (Exodus 9:31)
19. "Your little ____, which ye said should be a prey" (Deuteronomy 1:39)
21. Assist
22. "If thy father ____ all miss ____" (1 Samuel 20:6; 2 words)
23. "For a wave offering before the Lord: and it shall be thy ____" (Exodus 29:26)
24. "And thou shalt make ____ of gold" (Exodus 28:13)
26. Nuclear (abbr.)
28. Acidity measurement
29. Lunch stop
34. "Kish the son of ____" (2 Chronicles 29:12)
37. "Behold, Gaal the son of ____" (Judges 9:31)
38. Scull
40. Orderly
41. "So Daniel was taken up out of the ____" (Daniel 6:23)
42. "God smote him there for his ____" (2 Samuel 6:7)
44. "And Moses was fourscore ____ old" (Exodus 7:7)
46. "Bigvai, ____, Baanah" (Nehemiah 7:7)
49. "We came to ____, a city of Lycia" (Acts 27:5)
50. "Let the wicked fall into their own ____" (Psalm 141:10)
51. "In making brick both ____ and to day" (Exodus 5:14)

DOWN

1. "Shall play on the hole of the ___" (Isaiah 11:8)
2. Tackle
3. "Let her not be ____ one ____" (Numbers 12:12; 2 words)
4. "And ____ so require, let him ____ what he will" (1 Corinthians 7:36; 2 words)
5. Swing
6. Vietnam War offensive
7. "Called the name thereof ____: and it was like coriander seed" (Exodus 16:31)
8. "Aaron and his sons shall ____ it" (Exodus 27:21)
10. "When he ____ thee, he will be glad" (Exodus 4:14)
13. "Yet thou hast said, I know thee by ____" (Exodus 33:12)
16. "And the king of ____ they took alive" (Joshua 8:23)
18. "But when Pharaoh saw that there was ____" (Exodus 8:15)
19. "Therefore they took a key, and ____ them" (Judges 3:25)
20. "And thou shalt ____ by the river's brink" (Exodus 7:15)

22. "And Joshua said unto ____" (Joshua 7:19)
25. "And Moses went ____ unto God" (Exodus 19:3)
27. Titanium
30. "If ye will ____ my voice indeed" (Exodus 19:5)
31. "Hast thou found me, ____ mine ____?" (1 Kings 21:20; 2 words)
32. "____ rejoiced; I ____ alone" (Jeremiah 15:17; 2 words)
33. Snook
35. "For glory and for ____" (Exodus 28:2)
36. Gov't. legal counsel (abbr.)
39. Reagan nickname
42. Makes a mistake
43. "Neither ____ your clothes" (Leviticus 10:6)
45. Yes
47. "That ____ was ____ goodly child" (Exodus 2:2; 2 words)
48. Codex (abbr.)

by

Diana N. Rowland

ACROSS

1. "Then he called his ____ disciples together" (Luke 9:1)
6. "Thou art ____ the Son of God" (Luke 4:41)
11. "____, Eloi, lama sabachthani?" (Mark 15:34)
13. "And there was one ____, a prophetess" (Luke 2:36)
14. "And Jerimoth, and ____, five" (1 Chronicles 7:7)
15. "We pray you in Christ's ____" (2 Corinthians 5:20)
18. Pen point
20. Diamond state (abbr.)
21. "And he spake a ____ unto them to this end" (Luke 18:1)
23. Message-sending place
24. "That ye might receive ____ by us in nothing" (2 Corinthians 7:9)
26. "It is ____, saith the buyer" (Proverbs 20:14)
28. Space
29. "____ Kleine Nachtmusik"
30. President Eisenhower
31. "And Hur begat ____" (1 Chronicles 2:20)
32. "The hill is not ____ for us" (Joshua 17:16)
34. Lake Tahoe state (abbr.)
36. "And when the blood of thy ____ Stephen was shed" (Acts 22:20)
38. "and ____, and Cheran" (1 Chronicles 1:41)
41. "Son of Elmodam, which was the son of ____" (Luke 3:28)
42. "____ they may see, and not perceive" (Mark 4:12)
44. "Peace ____ to this house" (Luke 10:5)
45. Oslo is its cap. (abbr.)
47. "As ye walk, and are ____?" (Luke 24:17)
48. Russian space station
49. Bless
52. Blended
55. Teacher
56. "That ye, being ____ and grounded in love" (Ephesians 3:17)

DOWN

2. "It ____ better for him that ____ millstone" (Luke 17:2; 2 words)
3. "And ____ blessed Elkanah and his wife" (1 Samuel 2:20)
4. "And, ____, a spirit taketh him" (Luke 9:39)
5. "Their ____ is blacker than a coal" (Lamentations 4:8)
7. "And Amasa the son of ____" (2 Chronicles 28:12)
8. Medical staff member (abbr.)
9. "And brought him to an ____" (Luke 10:34)
10. "And he ____, Master, say on" (Luke 7:40)
12. "And from the ____ coast of Tyre and Sidon" (Luke 6:17)
14. "____ the son of Zechariah" (1 Chronicles 27:21)
16. "But lay up for yourselves ____ in heaven" (Matthew 6:20)
17. "Wherefore ____ with the ____ end of the spear" (2 Samuel 2:23; 2 words)
19. "Shall they not ____ fall into the ditch?" (Luke 6:39)
21. "And her ____ were astonished" (Luke 8:56)
22. "The ____ said, See, here is water" (Acts 8:36)
25. "For Israel hath forgotten his ____" (Hosea 8:14)

1	2	3	4	5		6	7	8	9	10	
	11					12		13			
14				15	16		17			18		19
20			21						22		23	
24		25					26			27		
		28					29					
	30								31			
		32		33					34			35
36	37						38	39			40	
41			42			43					44	
45		46			47				48			
	49		50	51		52		53	54			
55						56						

27. "And Isaac dwelt in ____"
    (Genesis 26:6)
33. "____ ____ of little faith?"
    (Luke 12:28; 2 words)
35. "of Manasseh; ____ with her
    suburbs" (1 Chronicles 6:70)
36. "Make you to become fishers of
    ____" (Mark 1:17)
37. "Then he ____, and rebuked the
    wind" (Luke 8:24)
39. English lang. study (abbr.)
40. "For to day I must ____ at thy
    house" (Luke 19:5)
43. "Whom say the people that ____
    ____?" (Luke 9:18; 2 words)

46. "And ____ unto the sepulchre"
    (Luke 24:12)
48. "There ____ him ten men that
    were lepers" (Luke 17:12)
50. Etna's country (abbr.)
51. "But ____ man laid hands on
    him" (John 7:30)
53. "____ here! or, lo there!"
    (Luke 17:21)
54. "____ good to them which hate
    you" (Luke 6:27)

by
Diana N. Rowland

PUZZLE 176

55. Old Testament money
56. Subdued

ACROSS

1. Overseer of the Nethinims (Nehemiah 11:21)
6. "Fine linen, and ____" (Ezekiel 27:16)
11. "____ cried aloud" (Daniel 3:4)
12. David's wife (2 Samuel 3:4)
14. Buckeye state (abbr.)
15. Longed for
17. City near Bethel
18. Capetown's country (abbr.)
19. Improve
20. Same (abbr.)
21. Author of Nehemiah
22. Fuss
23. Cooking vessel
24. City in Gad (Numbers 32:3)
28. "Another board for his two ____" (Exodus 36:24)
31. Blade
32. Pronoun
33. Development
36. Ring
39. Absent
40. Solomon's great-grandson (1 Kings 15:8)
42. Aaron's grave (Numbers 20:23)
43. Symbol for weed-killer element
44. Race of giants (Deuteronomy 2)
46. Eugene's state (abbr.)
47. Weekday (abbr.)
48. Amashai's father (Nehemiah 11:13)
50. "man be ____ with wife" (Matthew 19:10)
51. "From ____ a great light" (Acts 22:6)
53. Killer

DOWN

1. Elisha's servant
2. Erin (abbr.)
3. Speak
4. Claim
5. City in Naphtali (Joshua 19:36)
6. "Ye ____ do the things that ye would" (Galatians 5:17)
7. Jesse's father (Ruth 4:22)
8. Free
9. Radioactive halogen's symbol
10. Descendant of Gershon (1 Chronicles 23:7)
11. "Were bound in their coats, their ____" (Daniel 3:21)
13. Kings of the jungle
16. Color of blood
23. Vestibule
25. Debatable
26. Uncooked
27. ____ nouveau
29. Son of Benjamin (Genesis 46:21)
30. Saul's grandfather (1 Chronicles 8:33)
33. "Shall compass about to ____" (Jeremiah 31:39)
34. Hurried
35. "They hanged ____ ten sons" (Esther 9:14)
36. "Rabbi, when ____ thou hither?" (John 6:25)
37. Set free
38. Mistake
41. "____, I perceive that thou art a prophet" (John 4:19)
44. "At Bilhah, and at ____" (1 Chronicles 4:29)

45. "Land from _____ to the wilderness" (Isaiah 16:1)
48. "From Babylon, and from Cuthah, and from _____" (2 Kings 17:24)
49. Scram
52. City of Moab (Deuteronomy 2:9)
54. "_____ are spies" (Genesis 42:9)

by
N. Teri Grottke

ACROSS

1. Purify
6. Adah's son (Genesis 4:20)
11. "____ is love, not that we loved" (1 John 4:10)
12. "Heard him read the prophet ____" (Acts 8:30)
14. Multnomah Falls state (abbr.)
15. Hurt
17. Same (abbr.)
18. NA country
19. More painful
20. Judah's firstborn (Genesis 46:12)
21. Knight's title
23. Hebrew campsite (Numbers 33:45)
24. Dined
25. City in Judah (Joshua 15:52)
28. Young people
31. Hear
32. Rope web
33. Resurrection day
36. "Numbered them in ____" (1 Samuel 15:4)
39. "Jephunneh, and Pispah, and ____" (1 Chronicles 7:38)
40. Solomon's great-grandson (1 Kings 15:8)
42. Isaiah (abbr.)
43. Titanium (abbr.)
44. Wickednesses
46. Metric measurement (abbr.)
47. Altar name (Joshua 22:34)
48. Amorite village (Isaiah 15:4)
50. Sicily's country (abbr.)
51. City in Ephraim (1 Chronicles 7:28)
53. Son of Shaphan (Jeremiah 29:3)
55. Things
56. City in Benjamin (Joshua 18:25)

DOWN

1. Roman Christian
2. Abraham's birthplace
3. "Nathan the prophet, and Shimei, and ____" (1 Kings 1:8)
4. Traps
5. Command
6. Prophet's name (Latin)
7. "Of the tribe of ____ were sealed" (Revelation 7:6)
8. Wicked
9. City near Bethel
10. "____ himself with thick clay!" (Habakkuk 2:6)
11. Dwelling
13. Skin eruptions
16. "Shallum, and Telem, and ____" (Ezra 10:24)
22. Son of Zorobabel (Luke 3:27)
24. Abijah's brother (2 Chronicles 11:20)
26. Consume
27. "These ____ the generations of Noah" (Genesis 6:9)
29. Single
30. Married a foreign wife in exile (Ezra 10:34)
33. "Hast thou ____ of the tree" (Genesis 3:11)
34. Son of Haman
35. They fed Elijah
36. Higher
37. Son of Izrahiah (1 Chronicles 7:3)
38. Nagge's father (Luke 3:25-26)
41. "Of Keros, the children of ____" (Nehemiah 7:47)

44. "In the province of ____"
(Daniel 8:2)
45. "Land from ____ to the wilderness" (Isaiah 16:1)
48. Before
49. Son of Noah
52. Symbol for radioactive halogen
54. Johannesburg's country (abbr.)

by
N. Teri Grottke

PUZZLE 178

ACROSS

1. Destroys
6. Son of Ishmael (Genesis 25:14)
11. Encampment after Libnah (Numbers 33:21)
12. "Heard him read the prophet ____" (Acts 8:30)
14. Noble gas (suffix)
15. Repaid
17. Symbol for element used in coatings
18. "Forasmuch as ____ excellent spirit" (Daniel 5:12)
19. "A thousand ____ as one day" (2 Peter 3:8)
20. Judah's firstborn (Genesis 46:12)
21. Tree juice
23. "God created ____ heaven" (Genesis 1:1)
24. "____ did that which was right" (1 Kings 15:11)
25. Doubting disciple
28. "Because he ____ not of faith" (Romans 14:23)
31. Canon
32. Can
33. Small grain
36. Reputation
39. Rome is its cap.
40. Indebted
42. Governor of Jerusalem (abbr.)
43. Place of worship (abbr.)
44. "Upon the rocks of the wild ____" (1 Samuel 24:2)
46. "For, ____, the winter is past" (Song of Solomon 2:11)
47. Morning (abbr.)
48. Doors
50. Symbol for metallic element
51. Tikvath's father (2 Chronicles 34:22)
53. Jacob's firstborn
55. Stags
56. Made a mistake

DOWN

1. Son of Shimon
2. Guam is one of its territories (abbr.)
3. Name meaning "Yahweh is salvation" (abbr.)
4. Sea defenders
5. Bedclothes
6. Temperature measurement
7. "Good works for necessary ____" (Titus 3:14)
8. Insane
9. City near Bethel
10. "Thou ____ all workers of iniquity" (Psalm 5:5)
11. Cook
13. Well near Hebron
16. No (slang)
22. Head
24. Baptismal site of John the Baptist (John 3:23)
26. Bad (prefix)
27. Reverence
29. "Out of the angel's hand, and ____ it up" (Revelation 10:10)
30. End
33. Minor prophet
34. Valiant man (1 Chronicles 11:46)
35. "Shall let him go free for his ____ sake" (Exodus 21:27)
36. Step down
37. Counted on
38. Rose hazard
41. Battles

44. Winged insect
45. Prophet
48. Fail
49. Temple gate
52. Guiana's cont.
54. "I might _____ much bold in
    Christ" (Philemon 8)

by
N. Teri Grottke

ACROSS

1. Harassed
6. Hodiah's brother
11. Son of Midian (Genesis 25:4)
12. "Philip was found at ____" (Acts 8:40)
14. "Reel ____ and fro" (Isaiah 24:20)
15. "And make men go over ____" (Isaiah 11:15)
17. Midi (abbr.)
18. "____, come forth, and flee" (Zechariah 2:6)
19. "From ____, which is before Egypt" (Joshua 13:3)
20. British Isle (abbr.)
21. Fuss
23. Saul's grandfather (1 Chronicles 8:33)
24. Picnic insect
25. "That stood among the ____ trees" (Zechariah 1:11)
28. Throws
31. Hawaiian food
32. Noah's vessel
33. Remained
36. Eliphaz's son
39. No (slang)
40. Slow speed measurement (abbr.)
42. Father of Hophni
43. Symbol for semiconductor element
44. Wrong
46. Small land mass (abbr.)
47. Coliseum's country (abbr.)
48. "Which ____ and catcheth any beast" (Leviticus 17:13)
50. Repeat (abbr.)

51. Head of a family of exiles (Nehemiah 7:48)
53. Leper healed by Elisha
55. Deepness
56. Put forth effort

DOWN

1. Gory
2. Altar (Joshua 22:34)
3. Unhappy
4. Hearing appendages
5. "And all ____ wood" (Revelation 18:12)
6. "The name of ____ wife, Milcah" (Gen 11:29)
7. Sadoc's father (Matthew 1:14)
8. Son of Zophah (1 Chronicles 7:37)
9. Nuclear (abbr.)
10. Pondering
11. Encampment after Succoth
13. Kinds
16. "For ____ was fair to look on" (Esther 1:11)
22. Ruth's sister-in-law
24. Hock
26. Doll
27. Untruth
29. Thrash
30. "And ____ also the Jairite" (2 Samuel 20:26)
33. "As a ____ which melteth" (Psalm 58:8)
34. Savored
35. Levitical city (Joshua 21:35)
36. Agreement
37. Chislon's son (Numbers 34:21)
38. Brook (Psalm 83:9)
41. "Cast him into the bottomless ____" (Revelation 20:3)
44. Mother's sister

45. "The ____, which they saw in the east" (Matthew 2:9)
48. "Her ____ was to light on a part of the field" (Ruth 2:3)
49. "Between Bethel and ____" (Genesis 13:3)
52. "Blessed ___ the Lord my strength" (Psalm 144:1)
54. Northeast state (abbr.)

by
N. Teri Grottke

ACROSS

1. Chelub's son (1 Chronicles 4:11)
6. Tent
11. City in Reuben (Numbers 21:30)
12. Major prophet
14. "____, Lord God! behold" (Jeremiah 1:6)
15. Noisy fighter
17. Opposite of no.
18. Kings (abbr.)
19. Idol
20. Metric measurement (abbr.)
21. Stir
23. Jether's son
24. Pronoun
25. "_____, and at Jarmuth" (Nehemiah 11:29)
28. Villainy
31. "____, but set a king over us" (1 Samuel 10:19)
32. Son of Benjamin
33. Trapped
36. Option
39. "Without the word be ____ by" (1 Peter 3:1)
40. Pauline letter (abbr.)
42. Son of Jacob
43. Judah's firstborn (Genesis 46:12)
44. Daughter of Asher
46. "____ shall be rent asunder" (Ezekiel 30:16)
47. Lighting measurement (abbr.)
48. Taken from power
50. Undergrad's deg.
51. Lip related
53. Prophet confronting Jezebel
55. Like friable soil
56. City in Moab (Isaiah 15:9)

DOWN

1. "The children of ____, the children of Harsha" (Ezra 2:52)
2. Altar (Joshua 22:34)
3. NT book
4. "And Zaccur, and ____" (1 Chronicles 24:27)
5. Son of Cush
6. Priest with Nehemiah
7. "As he saith also in ____" (Romans 9:25)
8. Paddle
9. Symbol for alloy element
10. "The sons of ____ the Gizonite" (1 Chronicles 11:34)
11. Town of Judah (1 Kings 4:9)
13. "The ____ frost of heaven" (Job 38:29)
16. Fight
22. "The threshingfloor of ____" (1 Chronicles 21:15)
24. City of Benjamin (Ezra 2:33)
26. Hearing
27. Yes
29. No (slang)
30. From
33. Inflame
34. Common
35. Profoundly
36. Pursued
37. "Into the land of ____" (Leviticus 14:34)
38. Son of Seth
41. Favoring
44. Meeting of cloth
45. Jesus' grandfather (Luke 3:23)
48. Width (abbr.)
49. Unclear
52. Purchaser's choice (abbr.)
54. Dear (Scot.)

by
N. Teri Grottke

ACROSS

1. "What ____ thee, O thou sea" (Psalm 114:5)
6. "His hand took hold on ____ heel" (Genesis 25:26)
11. Brawl
12. Father of Ziza (1 Chronicles 4:37)
14. Weekday (abbr.)
15. More than
17. Radioactive element's symbol
18. Titanium symbol
19. Lucifer
20. Kittery's state (abbr.)
21. Grub
23. Became acquainted
24. Unclear
25. "Following unto ____" (Acts 21:1)
28. Gourmets
31. Bad (prefix)
32. "Of Keros, the children of ____" (Nehemiah 7:47)
33. Defer
36. Pippin
39. Ft. parts
40. Tear
42. Pose
43. Metallic element's symbol
44. Water creature
45. "Reel ____ and fro" (Isaiah 24:20)
46. Business (abbr.)
47. Levitical city (Joshua 21:28)
50. Partial salary (abbr.)
51. "Count them happy which ____" (James 5:11)

53. "____, shine; for thy light is come" (Isaiah 60:1)
55. Footwear
56. "And ____ reigned in his stead" (Genesis 36:39)

DOWN

1. Ancestor of Saul (1 Samuel 9:1)
2. Symbol for metallic element
3. Timber
4. Hearing appendages
5. Desires
6. Possessions
7. "Set it between Mizpeh and ____" (1 Samuel 7:12)
8. "To meet the Lord in the ____" (1 Thessalonians 4:17)
9. "Why did I not give ____ the ghost" (Job 3:11)
10. Son of Michah (1 Chronicles 24:24)
11. Complete
13. Things
16. Devoured
22. Above-ground graves
24. Business transactions
26. Water barrier
27. Father of Hophni
29. Snake
30. End
33. "____ thou wast precious in my sight" (Isaiah 43:4)
34. Joinings
35. Families
36. "In the house of ____ roll thyself in the dust" (Micah 1:10)
37. "Nothing ____ great or small" (1 Samuel 20:2)
38. Halt
41. Prophet during Uzziah's reign (abbr.)

44. Fee
47. Two
48. Environmental agency (abbr.)
49. Stowed
52. Batter (abbr.)
54. Venezuela's cont. (abbr.)

by
N. Teri Grottke

PUZZLE **182**

ACROSS

1. "Thy seed as the ____ of the heavens" (Genesis 22:17)
6. Chelub's son (1 Chronicles 4:11)
11. Dig
12. Jerahmeel's wife
14. 2.47 acres (abbr.)
15. Woman brought to David
17. Symbol for artificial radioactive element
18. City of Moab (Deuteronomy 2:9)
19. Shemida's son
20. Capetown's its cap.
21. Child's favorite seat
23. Girl (slang)
24. Flat (abbr.)
25. Easter flowers
28. Villainy
31. Solomon's great-grandson (1 Kings 15:8)
32. "The Oznites: of ____" (Numbers 26:16)
33. Possessions
36. "Separated with ____" (Hosea 4:14)
39. Untruth
40. Ember
42. Sir (abbr.)
43. Wabash's state (abbr.)
44. Greek philosophy
46. Symbol for platinum ore element
47. "Forasmuch as ____" (Daniel 5:12)
48. Basement
50. Kitchener prov.
51. Arabian mountain (Genesis 10:30)
54. Amorite king (Numbers 21:21)
56. Horse control
57. Highway (abbr.)

DOWN

1. Son of Bani
2. "Reel ____ and fro" (Isaiah 24:20)
3. "And from Cuthah, and from ____" (2 Kings 17:24)
4. Midianite king
5. "And ____ to cast stones" (2 Chronicles 26:14)
6. Mushi's brother (Exodus 6:19)
7. Village in Judah (1 Chronicles 4:32)
8. Witch
9. Metallic element's symbol
10. Rescue
11. "How long ____ I cry" (Habakkuk 1:2)
13. Ancient
16. "Of Keros, the children of ____" (Nehemiah 7:47)
22. Eating surface
24. Thatch
26. Son of Amoz (abbr.)
27. Dine
29. Wall-building governor (abbr.)
30. From
33. Chariot-of-fire prophet (Greek)
34. Evildoer
35. Gourmets
36. "____ we are at home in the body" (2 Corinthians 5:6)
37. Philistine city
38. Paralyze
41. Old French coin
44. Look over quickly
45. Abel's brother
49. To one side (abbr.)
52. Physical education (abbr.)

53. Pearl Harbor state (abbr.)
55. All right

by
N. Teri Grottke

ACROSS

1. Perspire
6. Nagge's father (Luke 3:25-26)
11. Shobal's son (Genesis 36:23)
12. Shem's son (Genesis 10:22)
14. Alloy element's symbol
15. Head of exilic family (Nehemiah 7:63)
17. "____ man hath ascended up to heaven" (John 3:13)
18. Morning (abbr.)
19. "The ____ of the air have nests" (Luke 9:58)
20. "Reel ____ and fro" (Isaiah 24:20)
21. "And ____ also the Jairite" (2 Samuel 20:26)
23. Gnawed
24. Son of Noe (Luke 3:36)
25. City in Gad (Numbers 32:3)
28. "The daughter of Bethuel, ____ son" (Genesis 24:47)
31. Disfigure
32. Mil. rank
33. Gratitude
36. "As darkness ____" (Job 10:22)
39. Cheer
40. Hotel
42. Body of water
43. Chemical compound with ether (suffix)
44. Wilderness encampment (Numbers 33:13)
46. Southern state (abbr.)
47. Twelve Step org.
48. Adversaries
50. Exercise course (abbr.)
51. "If it be a shame for a woman to be shorn or ____" (1 Corinthians 11:6)
53. Smeared
55. "If thou ____ pure and upright" (Job 8:6)
56. Made a mistake

DOWN

1. Jedaiah's father (1 Chronicles 4:37)
2. Midweek (abbr.)
3. Pauline letter (abbr.)
4. Jezebel's husband
5. Nehemiah's adversary
6. Young girl
7. "Nevertheless ____ heart was perfect" (1 Kings 15:14)
8. Fire product
9. Rare earth element's symbol
10. Stalker
11. Blemish
13. Habitations
16. "____ thou he that should come?" (Luke 7:19)
22. Hill near Gibeon (2 Samuel 2:24)
24. Shoe bottoms
26. "And ____ greedily after the error" (Jude 11)
27. Noah's vessel
29. Behave
30. Jolly sounds
33. "Tarried for us at ____" (Acts 20:5)
34. Assyrian district (2 Kings 17:6)
35. Quiet
36. Within
37. Jumped
38. "____ sumptuously every day" (Luke 16:19)

41. Pentateuch part (abbr.)
44. Abraham's ally (Genesis 14:13)
45. Listen
48. Adam's wife
49. Temple gate
52. True measurement (abbr.)
54. "He might ___ revealed in his
    time" (2 Thessalonians 2:6)

by
N. Teri Grottke

PUZZLE 184

ACROSS

1. Explode
6. Darics
11. Warrior in David's army (1 Chronicles 12:6)
12. "Adino the ____" (2 Samuel 23:8)
14. Twelvemonth (abbr.)
15. Begged
17. Poisonous element symbol
18. "For, ____, the winter is past" (Song of Solomon 2:11)
19. Father of the Jews
20. Metallic element symbol
21. Sole
23. Auricle
24. From
25. Idol of the Avites (2 Kings 17:31)
28. Division
31. Paddle
32. Levitical city (Joshua 15:32)
33. Stoves
36. Purpose
39. "But if ____ have caused grief" (2 Corinthians 2:5)
40. Owns
42. Small deer
43. "____ and tell David my servant" (1 Chronicles 17:4)
44. Egyptian servant of Sheshan (1 Chronicles 2:34)
46. Midwest state (abbr.)
47. City near Bethel (Joshua 7:2)
48. Talk
50. "I have not found ____ great faith" (Matthew 8:10)
51. Disengaged
53. Response
55. City where Shimei's family lived (1 Chronicles 4:29)
56. Despised

DOWN

1. Benjamin's original name (Genesis 35:18)
2. It has fifty states (abbr.)
3. Shred
4. Heber's father (Luke 3:35)
5. City in Ephraim (Judges 9:50)
6. Aromatic trees
7. Brother of David (1 Chronicles 2:15)
8. Native American (abbr.)
9. Metallic element symbol
10. Steps
11. Son of Ezra (1 Chronicles 4:17)
13. "____ begat Aram" (Matthew 1:3)
16. Jether's son (1 Chronicles 7:38)
22. Black
24. Better
26. Witch
27. "These ____ the generations of Noah" (Genesis 6:9)
29. Able
30. Strike
33. Saruch's father (Luke 3:35)
34. Apply oil
35. Humiliated
36. Son of Asher (Genesis 46:17)
37. Sounded
38. High-voiced male singer
41. "The sword shall be upon his ____" (Zechariah 11:17)
44. Peter's father (John 1:42)
45. Prophetess in the Gospels
48. Officer (abbr.)
49. Guess (abbr.)

52. "____ not ye yet understand"
(Matthew 15:17)
54. Pronoun

by
N. Teri Grottke

ACROSS

1. "And, lo, my ____ arose, and also stood" (Genesis 37:7)
6. "And ye shall ____ every fenced city" (2 Kings 3:19)
11. "____ then hast thou that living water?" (John 4:11)
12. Despising
14. Metric acre (abbr.)
15. Bureau part
17. Judah's firstborn (Genesis 46:12)
18. Part of British Isles (abbr.)
19. Descendant of King Saul (1 Chronicles 8:39)
20. Its cap. is Augusta (abbr.)
21. Kettle
23. Best
24. Vision member
25. Traps
28. "Why ____ thou, She is my sister?" (Genesis 12:19)
31. Dinner item
32. "Shallum, and Telem, and ____" (Ezra 10:24)
33. Rocks
36. Precipices
39. Pronoun
40. Coke
42. Even
43. Cascade Mts. state (abbr.)
44. "Tarried for us at ____" (Acts 20:5)
46. "He could swear by ____ greater" (Hebrews 6:13)
47. "____ not dismayed at their faces" (Jeremiah 1:17)
48. Avenue of communication
50. Magnetic metal symbol
51. Son of Izrahiah
53. Brought to pass
55. Sponsors
56. Elder that remained in the camp (Numbers 11:26)

DOWN

1. "Rose of ____" (Song of Solomon 2:1)
2. Balloon gas symbol
3. "Thou hast shewed more kindness in the latter ____" (Ruth 3:10)
4. Parcel of land
5. Banquets
6. Wolf in ____ clothing
7. Gospel
8. Appenines' country (abbr.)
9. Alloy element's symbol
10. Adversary's
11. Scourges
13. "____ them that love us" (Titus 3:15)
16. Disease-fighting group (abbr.)
22. "Barak went down from mount ____" (Judges 4:14)
24. "____ one another, even as also ye do" (1 Thessalonians 5:11)
26. Sprint
27. Carbon compound (suffix)
29. "Bore his ear through with an ____" (Exodus 21:6)
30. Son of Bela (1 Chronicles 7:7)
33. Son of Nahash (2 Samuel 17:27)
34. Traitorous servant of King Ahasuerus (Esther 2:21)
35. "Hagar the Egyptian, ____ handmaid" (Genesis 25:12)
36. Opportunity
37. Enclosed
38. Upright

41. "Came to Joel the _____ of Pethuel" (Joel 1:1)
44. "And I _____ am the Lord thy God" (Hosea 12:9)
45. Closure
48. "Saul the son of _____" (Acts 13:21)
49. "And _____, that draw the bow" (Isaiah 66:19)
52. "_____, come forth, and flee" (Zechariah 2:6)
54. Rio de Janiero's cont.

by
N. Teri Grottke

ACROSS

1. "Cast out into ____ darkness" (Matthew 8:12)
6. Eve was the first
11. Faithful advisor to David (2 Samuel 15:32)
12. Major prophet
14. Radioactive element symbol
15. Got away
17. College requirement (abbr.)
18. Dublin's country (abbr.)
19. "She hid him ____ months" (Exodus 2:2)
20. Bible history books (abbr.)
21. Sprint
23. Ingest
24. Type of tree
25. Traps
28. "They hanged ____ ten sons" (Esther 9:14)
31. Falls at night
32. "Between Bethel and ____" (Genesis 13:3)
33. "The Emims in ____" (Genesis 14:5)
36. Gasped
39. Minor prophet (abbr.)
40. Prior
42. "Aaron and ____ stayed up his hands" (Exodus 17:12)
43. Canadian prov.
44. Exhibits
46. "There...now ____ condemnation" (Romans 8:1)
47. Altar (Joshua 22:34)
48. Sweet spice
50. Small land body (abbr.)
51. Lead astray
53. "____ servants digged in the valley" (Genesis 26:19)
55. Delighted in
56. Tenth

DOWN

1. "The other disciple did ____ Peter" (John 20:4)
2. NA nation
3. God (comb. form)
4. "We have seen his star in the ____" (Matthew 2:2)
5. Wealth
6. "She eateth, and ____ her mouth" (Proverbs 30:20)
7. "As he saith also in ____" (Romans 9:25)
8. Insane
9. City near Bethel (Joshua 7:2)
10. Diaper (Brit.)
11. God knows their number
13. Inheritors
16. Jether's son
22. Presumptuous son of Aaron (Exodus 6:23)
24. Evidence of things not seen
26. NT prophetic book
27. Female sheep
29. "Against Jerusalem, ____, she is broken" (Ezekiel 26:2)
30. "The blind ____ said unto him" (Mark 10:51)
33. Footwear
34. Gave over
35. Made well
36. Allow
37. Timothy's mother
38. Metal impurities
41. Radioactive antigen (abbr.)
44. Visage

45. Father of Gaddi
    (Numbers 13:11)
48. Slice
49. What Lot did in the gate of
    Sodom
52. Copy (abbr.)
54. "____ Lord God! behold"
    (Jeremiah 1:6)

by
N. Teri Grottke

ACROSS

1. Something Jonah appreciated
6. "I take my journey into ____" (Romans 15:24)
11. Son of Michah (1 Chronicles 24:24)
12. Tikvath's father
14. Exercise course (abbr.)
15. "And one of the king of ____ servants" (2 Kings 3:11)
17. "Reel ____ and fro" (Isaiah 24:20)
18. "I will make ____ everlasting covenant with you" (Isaiah 55:3)
19. Son of Lotan (1 Chronicles 1:39)
20. Tiny land mass (abbr.)
21. City in Moab (Isaiah 15:1)
23. Large rodent
24. Wife of Adam
25. Descendants of Eri (Numbers 26:26)
28. "They have ____ the children of Lot" (Psalm 83:8)
31. Promise
32. Governor of Jerusalem (abbr.)
33. Masticated
36. Aromatic trees
39. Paddle
40. Hearing
42. Encampment before Dibongad (Numbers 33:45)
43. City of Moab (Deuteronomy 2:9)
44. Minor prophet
46. Johannesburg is its cap. (abbr.)
47. Rare-earth element's symbol
48. City on Cyprus (Acts 13:5)

50. Judah's firstborn (1 Chronicles 2:3)
51. "Mother of James the less and of Joses, and ____" (Mark 15:40)
53. "Sanctify the ____ of the wave offering" (Exodus 29:27)
55. Planter
56. "What thou ____, write in a book" (Revelation 1:11)

DOWN

1. "From the top of ____ and Hermon" (Song of Solomon 4:8)
2. Metric acre (abbr.)
3. Head of exilic family (Ezra 2:57)
4. Plate
5. Mistakes
6. Covering for a sword
7. Tropical tree
8. Donkey
9. Metallic element's symbol
10. Indigenous
11. "And God ____ unto Noah" (Genesis 8:15)
13. "Were bound in their coats, their ____" (Daniel 3:21)
16. Doc's org.
22. "Baptized of him in the ____ of Jordan" (Mark 1:5)
24. Family left behind in captivity (Jeremiah 40:8)
26. "As a thread of ____ is broken" (Judges 16:9)
27. Ram's mate
29. Single
30. Commanded militarily
33. Outer coverings
34. Shallum's grandfather (2 Kings 22:14)

35. Merchant
36. Bread leftover
37. "When thou liest down, and when thou ____ up" (Deuteronomy 6:7)
38. Intelligent
41. "Tyrus hath said against Jerusalem, ____" (Ezekiel 26:2)
44. "That at the ____ of Jesus" (Philippians 2:10)
45. Mud
48. Producing pig
49. "____ that ye refuse not him that speaketh" (Hebrews 12:25)

52. "____, I will bring a nation upon you from far" (Jeremiah 5:15)
54. Poisonous element's symbol

by
N. Teri Grottke

PUZZLE **188**

ACROSS

1. City in Judah
   (2 Chronicles 28:18)
6. Duke of Edom
   (1 Chronicles 1:51)
11. Christian teacher at Antioch
    (Acts 13:1)
12. Bring together
14. Exists
15. Prize
17. Required course (abbr.)
18. Place of worship (abbr.)
19. Infants
20. Balloon gas symbol
21. Head of exilic family (Ezra 2:57)
23. Grain (Isaiah 28:25)
24. Commanded militarily
25. Stalked
28. "Sow thy vineyard with ____
    seed" (Deuteronomy 22:9)
31. Moisture
32. "After the ____ Satan entered
    into him" (John 13:27)
33. "As a jewel of gold in a ____
    snout" (Proverbs 11:22)
36. "Thou ____ iron mixed with
    miry clay" (Daniel 2:43)
39. "Tyrus hath said against
    Jerusalem, ____" (Ezekiel 26:2)
40. Pauline letter (abbr.)
42. Uncooked
43. Business (abbr.)
44. Gained more knowledge
46. Titanium (abbr.)
47. Southern state (abbr.)
48. "____, come forth" (John 11:43)
50. Jan. through Dec.
51. Rake away

53. Foreigners
55. Stitched
56. Leaders

DOWN

1. "It is reported among the heathen, and ____ saith it"
   (Nehemiah 6:6)
2. Indianapolis is its cap. (abbr.)
3. Disfigure
4. Prince of Midian (Judges 7:25)
5. "Israel went ____ in all their
   journeys" (Exodus 40:36)
6. Concurred
7. Boys
8. Naples' country (abbr.)
9. "saying, ____ my brother!"
   (Jeremiah 22:18)
10. Son of Gilead (Numbers 27:1)
11. Minor prophet
13. Measure of length
    (Ezekiel 42:16)
16. Hezekiah's mother
    (2 Kings 18:2)
22. "From ____ even" (Esther 1:1)
24. "The house of Simon the ____"
    (Mark 14:3)
26. "Hundred and ____ years old"
    (Joshua 24:29)
27. Lamb's mother
29. Major prophet (abbr.)
30. Promise
33. Ahiam's father
    (1 Chronicles 11:35)
34. "Separated with ____"
    (Hosea 4:14)
35. Grabbed
36. Beriah's daughter
    (1 Chronicles 7:24)
37. "Even where ____ seat is"
    (Revelation 2:13)

38. Esau and Jacob
41. OT hymns (abbr.)
44. "___ the sheaf before the Lord"
    (Leviticus 23:11)
45. Law
48. Poor
49. "Of Keros, the children of ____"
    (Nehemiah 7:47)
52. Portland's state (abbr.)
54. Altar (Joshua 22:34)

by
N. Teri Grottke

ACROSS

1. Head of returning exile family (Ezra 2:44)
6. Assyrian city (Genesis 10:11)
11. "Behold, a ____ shall conceive" (Isaiah 7:14)
12. Began
14. Key (abbr.)
15. Got away
17. "___, the star, which they saw in the east" (Matthew 2:9)
18. Typesetter's mistake (abbr.)
19. Large boats
20. "He shall ____ like a tree planted by the rivers" (Psalm 1:3)
21. Slip
23. Lone
24. Ancient Hebrew measurement
25. Reviler
28. Conquerors of Israel
31. Oslo is its cap.
32. "Before Abraham ____, I am" (John 8:58)
33. Worn out
36. City in Reuben (Numbers 21:30)
39. Donkey
40. Major prophet (abbr.)
42. Son of Noe (Luke 3:36)
43. 2.47 acres (abbr.)
44. Capital of Edom (Genesis 36:35)
46. Mt. Katahdin state
47. "____, Lord God! behold" (Jeremiah 1:6)
48. Sheep barber
50. Windsor prov.
51. "Mountains of ____" (Song of Solomon 2:17)

53. Chislon's son (Numbers 34:21)
55. "Were ____ in ambush against him" (Joshua 8:14)
56. Amorite town (Numbers 21:30)

DOWN

1. Jael's victim (Judges 4:22)
2. Metallic element's symbol
3. Time period
4. Snake noise
5. Boat's stabilizing weight
6. Burnished metal
7. Primates
8. Headed
9. Jan. to Dec.
10. "The wine of ____" (Ezekiel 27:18)
11. Snake
13. "____ of the law shall be justified" (Romans 2:13)
16. Levitical city (Joshua 21:16)
22. Circles
24. Boxes
26. Timber
27. Before
29. Indebted
30. Insane
33. Hebrew spy hider
34. Joab's brother
35. "____ weights are an abomination" (Proverbs 20:23)
36. Mehetabel's mother (Genesis 36:39)
37. Complain
38. Improve
41. "Of Keros, the children of ____" (Nehemiah 7:47)
44. Ir's father (1 Chronicles 7:12)
45. Jesus' grandfather (Luke 3:23)
48. Female

49. "And the _____, which the Lord
    God had taken from man"
    (Genesis 2:22)
52. Alloy element's symbol
54. Repeat (abbr.)

by
N. Teri Grottke

ACROSS

1. Ammonite mighty man
   (2 Samuel 23:37)
6. Duke of Edom
   (1 Chronicles 1:51)
11. Mock
12. Well near Gerar (Genesis 26:21)
14. Lira's country (abbr.)
15. Kings' dwellings
17. Artificial radioactive element's
    symbol
18. "Let them not say in their hearts,
    ____" (Psalm 35:25)
19. Traditions
20. Poisonous element's symbol
21. Nix, slang
23. "Hundred and ____ years old"
    (Joshua 24:29)
24. Solo
25. "Mount Sinai in ____"
    (Galatians 4:25)
28. Point
31. "And ____ greedily after the
    error" (Jude 11)
32. 100 square meters
33. Mistreated
36. "A man of ____, Simon by
    name" (Matthew 27:32)
39. "Built a city, and called the name
    thereof ____" (Judges 1:26)
40. Pauline epistle (abbr.)
42. "rejoice ____ his birth"
    (Luke 1:14)
43. Mouth
44. Bottoms
46. "Lament thee, saying, ____
    lord!" (Jeremiah 34:5)
47. Univalent hydrocarbon group
    (abbr.)
48. "For the Lord shall rise up as in
    mount ____" (Isaiah 28:21)
50. Augusta is its cap.
51. Consecutive
53. Son of Kohath (Numbers 3:19)
55. Song
56. City of Hadadezer
    (2 Samuel 8:8)

DOWN

1. Chamberlain of King Ahaseurus
   (Esther 1:10)
2. Judah's firstborn
   (1 Chronicles 2:3)
3. Mouth part
4. Watchtower (Genesis 35:21)
5. Assistant to Ezra
6. Rise
7. Untruths
8. Possessive pronoun
9. "Make thee ____ ark of gopher
   wood" (Genesis 6:14)
10. Heman's son (1 Chronicles 25:4)
11. "Great is ____ of the Ephesians"
    (Acts 19:28)
13. Firefighters' needs
16. "Took the little book out of the
    angel's hand, and ____ it"
    (Revelation 10:10)
22. Meshullemeth's father
    (2 Kings 21:19)
24. "As he saith also in ____"
    (Romans 9:25)
26. College degrees (abbr.)
27. Chemical substance (suffix)
29. Cattle feed
30. Miss
33. Healing plants
34. Broken

35. Affectionately
36. "He was at ____, when she bare him" (Genesis 38:5)
37. Sister of Tubal-Cain (Genesis 4:22)
38. Judean town (Joshua 15:42)
41. Free radio ad (abbr.)
44. Pound
45. Dimensions
48. Deep hole
49. Became acquainted
52. Northeast state (abbr.)
54. Laugh sound

by
N. Teri Grottke

ACROSS

1. Abraham's brother
   (Genesis 11:26)
6. Stable enclosure
11. Take away
12. Gullet
14. City of Moab (Deuteronomy 2:9)
15. "Pitched in the valley of ____"
    (2 Samuel 23:13)
17. Teen's greeting
18. Required class (abbr.)
19. Metal pegs
20. Judah's firstborn
    (1 Chronicles 2:3)
21. Aram's son (Genesis 10:23)
23. Color
24. Free radio ad (abbr.)
25. Shark
28. "Which ____ the upright in
    heart" (Psalm 7:10)
31. "And went away with them,
    ____ and all" (Judges 16:3)
32. Armoury (abbr.)
33. Jedaiah's father
    (1 Chronicles 4:37)
36. "And ____ old is ready to van-
    ish" (Hebrews 8:13)
39. Man's nickname
40. Wall rebuilder (abbr.)
42. "Man will ____ thee at the law"
    (Matthew 5:40)
43. Egg (comb. form)
44. Son of Korah
    (1 Chronicles 6:22)
46. Alloy element's symbol
47. Magnetic-field strength unit
    (abbr.)
48. Jonah's father (Jonah 1:1)

50. Columbia River state (abbr.)
51. "A goodly price that I was ____
    at of them" (Zechariah 11:13)
53. Mistakes
55. Site
56. Checks

DOWN

1. "Philologus, and Julia, ____, and
   his sister" (Romans 16:15)
2. Graduate deg.
3. Aaron's grave (Numbers 20:23)
4. Baking place
5. Fix
6. Stems
7. "____ people refuseth the
   waters" (Isaiah 8:6)
8. Ready for battle
9. "___ I have sinned"
   (2 Samuel 24:17)
10. "Then ____ thou a snare for my
    life" (1 Samuel 28:9)
11. Benjamite Promised Land spy's
    father
13. Pentateuch
16. Ancient Hebrew liquid measure
22. "Put and ____ were thy helpers"
    (Nahum 3:9)
24. "____; thy kingdom is divided"
    (Daniel 5:28)
26. Ewe's mate
27. Fail
29. "Against Jerusalem, ____, she is
    broken" (Ezekiel 26:2)
30. "Awake that shall ____ thee"
    (Habakkuk 2:7)
33. Bend over
34. Hangs over
35. Within
36. "I shall be ____ than snow"
    (Psalm 51:7)

37. Teachers
38. Inheritors
41. Guess (abbr.)
44. "Lord Jesus Christ be with your spirit. ____" (Philemon 25)
45. Unusual
48. Enzyme (suffix)
49. Son of Bela (1 Chronicles 7:7)
52. Consisting of (suffix)
54. Noble gas (suffix)

by
N. Teri Grottke

ACROSS

1. Brisk
6. Son of Ephraim (Numbers 26:35)
11. Elijah's apprentice
12. Mahath's father
14. "I had ____ rest in my spirit" (2 Corinthians 2:13)
15. "With lanterns and ____ and weapons" (John 18:3)
17. "for the kingdom of God is ____ hand." (Matthew 3:2)
18. Meridian (abbr.)
19. Decorate
20. Pinetree state (abbr.)
21. "Shallum, and Telem, and ____" (Ezra 10:24)
23. Female sheep
24. Toast spread
25. Jewish queen of Persia
28. "Go now to thy brother ____ house" (2 Samuel 13:7)
31. "Zur, and ___, and Reba, five kings" (Numbers 31:8)
32. Auris
33. Climbs
36. City in Judah (1 Samuel 30:30)
39. Father of Hophni
40. Nineteenth NT book
42. "Between Bethel and ____" (Genesis 13:3)
43. "____ and search diligently" (Matthew 2:8)
44. Cow groups
46. Judah's firstborn (1 Chronicles 2:3)
47. NA nation
48. Fighter

50. Direction (abbr.)
51. Look
53. Chislon's son (Numbers 34:21)
55. Booths
56. "Uzziah the king was a ____" (2 Chronicles 26:21)

DOWN

1. Walking surfaces
2. Newport's state (abbr.)
3. Rate (abbr.)
4. "Pekod, and ____, and Koa" (Ezekiel 23:23)
5. More difficult
6. Micah's son (1 Chronicles 9:41)
7. "____. Praise ye the Lord" (Psalm 106:48)
8. Possesses
9. "Thou shalt love thy neighbor ____ thyself." (Matthew 19:19)
10. Leper healed by Elisha (2 Kings 5)
11. Result
13. Things
16. Female bovine
22. Valiant man (1 Chronicles 11:31)
24. Head of exilic family (Ezra 2:18)
26. Aram's son (Genesis 10:23)
27. Before
29. Saw
30. Nix (slang)
33. Hiel's son (1 Kings 16:34)
34. "And the bride out of her ____" (Joel 2:16)
35. "Break the ____" (Ezekiel 23:34)
36. Guni's son (1 Chronicles 5:15)
37. Roman emperor's title
38. Rented
41. Slip
44. Stop

45. Shoe bottom
48. "Without the word be ____"
    (1 Peter 3:1)
49. Tear
52. Balloon gas symbol
54. Diamond state (abbr.)

by
N. Teri Grottke

ACROSS

1. "Melech, and ____"
(1 Chronicles 8:35)
6. "Create in me a ____ heart, O God" (Psalm 51:10)
11. Crowd
12. Resheph's brother
(1 Chronicles 7:25)
14. Judah's firstborn
(1 Chronicles 2:3)
15. Labored
17. Jolly sound
18. "For, ____, the winter is past"
(Song of Solomon 2:11)
19. Bench
20. Poisonous element's symbol
21. Old (abbr.)
23. Orb
24. Audit (abbr.)
25. "An ____ cried aloud"
(Daniel 3:4)
28. Metalworkers
31. "Hast thou not heard long ____"
(2 Kings 19:25)
32. Ember
33. But the fool ____, and is confi-dent (Proverbs 14:16)
36. "Fat on his ____" (Job 15:27)
39. Donkey
40. "Against Jerusalem, ____"
(Ezekiel 26:2)
42. Characterized by (suffix)
43. Metric acre (abbr.)
44. "The ____ of thine heart hath deceived thee" (Obadiah 3)
46. CA city
47. City near Bethel (Ezra 2:28)
48. Center
49. Character (suffix)
51. Wolverine state (abbr.)
52. "I rent my garment and my ____" (Ezra 9:3)
54. Cravat apparatus
56. "Were bound in their coats, their ____" (Daniel 3:21)
57. Seven (comb. form)

DOWN

1. "A rainbow round about the ____" (Revelation 4:3)
2. City of Moab (Isaiah 15:1)
3. "The first ____ shall be a sardius" (Exodus 28:17)
4. Seth's son (Luke 3:38)
5. Concurred
6. "____ and Arabians" (Acts 2:11)
7. Guided
8. Longer game (abbr.)
9. "____, Lord God! behold"
(Jeremiah 1:6)
10. Shobi's father (2 Samuel 17:27)
11. Tahan's father
(1 Chronicles 7:25)
13. Sponsors
16. Round Table knight
22. Tors
24. Zerah's son (1 Chronicles 6:41)
26. Era
27. Abraham's nephew
29. Bad (prefix)
30. Major prophet (abbr.)
33. Shema's son (1 Chronicles 2:44)
34. Servant of the king
(2 Chronicles 34:20)
35. "I will ____ Pharaoh's heart"
(Exodus 7:3)
36. "____ not away" (1 Peter 5:4)
37. Mountain laurel
38. Killed

41. Aloha state (abbr.)
44. "Make the ____ for fire great"
    (Ezekiel 24:9)
45. Great Lake
48. Bergs (abbr.)
50. Yes (slang)
53. "I will ____ more have mercy"
    (Hosea 1:6)
55. Jewelry metal's symbol

by
N. Teri Grottke

ACROSS

1. Udders
6. Used a broom
11. Deep sadness
12. Messenger bird
14. Rare-earth element's symbol
15. Working
17. Midi (abbr.)
18. Radioactive element's symbol
19. Rap
20. Chile's cont.
21. Doc's deg.
23. Lamb's mother
24. Governor of Jerusalem (abbr.)
25. "Heard him read the prophet ____" (Acts 8:30)
28. "Dwelt in their ____ until the captivity" (1 Chronicles 5:22)
31. "Saul the son of ____" (Acts 13:21)
32. Acorn's tree
33. City in Judah (Joshua 15:40)
36. Positively
39. "____, our eye hath seen it" (Psalm 35:21)
40. Uraeus
42. Appointed portion
43. Historical OT books
44. "____ them that love us" (Titus 3:15)
46. 2.47 acres (abbr.)
47. Abraham's birthplace
48. Affairs
50. Metallic element symbol
51. Amasai's son (1 Chronicles 6:35)
53. Ark's measuring units (Genesis 6:15)

55. Menan's son (Luke 3:31)
56. "Be like the ____ in the desert" (Jeremiah 17:6)

DOWN

1. "Shall let him go free for his ____ sake" (Exodus 21:27)
2. Judah's firstborn (1 Chronicles 2:3)
3. "For dust thou ____ " (Genesis 3:19)
4. Captured
5. "As a jewel of gold in a ____ snout" (Proverbs 11:22)
6. Food flavoring
7. Eye signal
8. "Taste in the white of an ____?" (Job 6:6)
9. Typesetter's mistake (abbr.)
10. Thrown
11. "Bodily ____ like a dove" (Luke 3:22)
13. "____ wife, and the three wives of his sons" (Genesis 7:13)
16. Small
22. Russian cottage
24. Without clothes
26. Encampment before Dibongad (Numbers 33:45)
27. Solomon's great-grandson (1 Kings 15:8)
29. King of Hamath (1 Chronicles 18:9)
30. Aurical
33. Town in Naphtali (Joshua 19:33)
34. "Ashbelites: of ____ " (Numbers 26:38)
35. Mary's work-worn sister
36. Talk
37. City in Moab (Isaiah 15:5)

38. "Six ____ thou shalt sow thy field" (Leviticus 25:3)
41. Place
44. Entrance
45. "How long, O Lord, holy and ____" (Revelation 6:10)
48. Bad (prefix)
49. Aid for new companies (abbr.)
52. Balloon gas symbol
54. Lira's country

by
N. Teri Grottke

ACROSS

1. Set free
6. City of refuge (Deuteronomy 4:43)
11. Ocran's son (Numbers 1:13)
12. Useless
14. Metric acre (abbr.)
15. Free time
17. "Reel ____ and fro" (Isaiah 24:20)
18. Altar (Joshua 22:34)
19. Female servants
20. Masculine pronoun
21. "Discern between good and ____" (1 Kings 3:9)
23. Sack
24. Saul's grandfather (1 Chronicles 8:33)
25. Adversary's
28. Older ones
31. Shelter
32. Acorn's tree
33. Acquired knowledge (Brit.)
36. Proprietors
39. Quality (suffix)
40. Rose fruit
42. Small amount
43. Platinum ore element's symbol
44. Assists
46. Business (abbr.)
47. Twelve Step org.
48. "He that keepeth company with ____" (Proverbs 29:3)
50. Rare-earth element's symbol
51. Spunk
53. Traveled by sea
55. Other
56. Fumble

DOWN

1. Ammihud's father (1 Chronicles 7:26)
2. "And ____ the king of Bashan" (Numbers 21:33)
3. Petroleum product
4. Appear
5. "____ anger was kindled against David" (1 Samuel 17:28)
6. Resentment
7. Belonging to us
8. Untruth
9. Yr.
10. "Stood at the ____ part of the mount" (Exodus 19:17)
11. "___ our sister" (Romans 16:1)
13. Accomplishers
16. "Of Keros, the children of ____" (Nehemiah 7:47)
22. Postponement
24. City in Naphtali (Joshua 19:33)
26. Member of a class (comb. form)
27. Craving
29. Base
30. Son of Jacob
33. Italian money
34. Colorless gas
35. "____ will I sit" (Joel 3:12)
36. Stand against
37. Wealthier
38. Upright
41. Sick
44. Own
45. "What time the ____ appeared" (Matthew 2:7)
48. Day parts (abbr.)
49. Knight's title
52. Aboveground transportation
54. "____ he is strong" (Job 9:19)

by
N. Teri Grottke

ACROSS

1. A.D. equivalent
3. "____, and do thou likewise" (Luke 10:37)
5. Holy ones (abbr.)
7. "Because I ____ a man of unclean lips" (Isaiah 6:5)
9. "In letters of Greek, and ____ " (Luke 23:38)
11. "Drive out the inhabitants of ____ " (Judges 1:31)
13. Perform
14. Metric measure (abbr.)
15. Symbol for pool chemical
16. Spar
18. Mouth
19. Son of King Rehoboam
22. Beneficiary (suffix)
23. Corn Husker state (abbr.)
24. "Taanach and her towns, nor the inhabitants of ____ " (Judges 1:27)
25. Desire
28. Move
30. Wing
33. Because
34. Symbol for metal in nickel
35. Matrix
36. Laughter sound
37. "Thou hadst cast me into the ____ " (Jonah 2:3)
39. Midi (abbr.)
40. Father, in Aramaic
43. America (abbr.)
44. "The children of ____, the children of Padon" (Nehemiah 7:47)
47. Cave
49. Muncie's state (abbr.)
50. Chile's cont.
51. Fetch
53. Investment option (abbr.)
54. Agave
55. Cerulean (abbr.)
56. "The land from ____ to the wilderness" (Isaiah 16:1)
58. Sixty mins.
59. "And ____, the son of Ahitub" (1 Samuel 14:3)
62. "The children of Giddel, the children of ____" (Ezra 2:47)
64. Likewise
65. Metallic element (abbr.)
66. Expression of surprise
67. Two (comb. form)

DOWN

1. "When thou prayest, enter into thy ____" (Matthew 6:6)
2. Apiece (abbr.)
3. "Timnah with the villages thereof, ____ also" (2 Chronicles 28:18)
4. Ottawa's prov.
5. "Which was the son of Heber, which was the son of ____" (Luke 3:35)
6. Branch of ed.
7. "And saith, ____, I am warm, I have seen the fire" (Isaiah 44:16)
8. Where Aaron died
10. Weekday (abbr.)
12. Gal (abbr.)
13. Wears
15. Padre (abbr.)
17. "Enlarge the place of thy ____ " (Isaiah 54:2)
20. "And the sons of Ulla: ____, and Haniel, and Rezia" (1 Chronicles 7:39)

21. Tenth of an aeon (abbr.)
24. Falls
26. Levite singer
    (1 Chronicles 15:19)
27. Jezebel's husband
29. Frost
31. Moo
32. Friend of Shadrach
37. Clean
38. "Well hath ____ prophesied of
    you" (Mark 7:6)
41. Ancestor of Sheba
    (2 Samuel 20:1)
42. Male (comb. form)
45. Judge of Israel

46. Middle Eastern lang.
48. Wife of David
52. "The grace that ____ to be
    brought unto you" (1 Peter 1:13)
55. "There was not a man left in
    ____" (Joshua 8:17)
57. "____ sinful nation, a people
    laden" (Isaiah 1:4)
60. Jolly sound
61. Greeting
63. Sign

by
Pauline Grottke

ACROSS

1. "Thy word is a ____ unto my feet" (Psalm 119:105)
5. Bundle
9. "I will abide, yea, and ____ with you" (1 Corinthians 16:6)
11. Remote
14. "My soul ____ exceeding sorrowful" (Mark 14:34)
15. "Let us ____ up to the mountain" (Isaiah 2:3)
16. Decay
17. Sigh sound
18. Son of Caleb
21. Son of Cush
24. Father of King Menaham
25. Printer's measures
26. "Built Ono, and ___" (1 Chronicles 8:12)
27. Makes goals
29. "She is ____ precious than rubies" (Proverbs 3:15)
30. Off the rack (abbr.)
31. "Milk, and not of strong ____" (Hebrews 5:12)
33. Tower in Jerusalem
35. Places of worship
39. Prince of Midian
40. Ambassador's title (abbr.)
41. "The children of ___ answered Abraham" (Genesis 23:5)
42. Father of Pekah
46. "Sons of Appaim; ____" (1 Chronicles 2:31)
47. Welding gas symbol
48. Melted
50. US
51. "And a ___, among all nations" (Deuteronomy 28:37)
53. "Call his name ___: for ye are not my people" (Hosea 1:9)
56. Remnants
57. "___; God hath numbered thy kingdom" (Daniel 5:26)

DOWN

1. Byway (abbr.)
2. Atmospheric condition
3. Nickname for Margaret
4. Gossips
5. Arrow points
6. Many (2 words)
7. Mineral (comb. form)
8. Person who performs action (suffix)
9. Pinna
10. Abraham's son
12. Grandfather of Abraham
13. Shelter from light
19. City of Judah
20. Merriment
22. Morning (abbr.)
23. Garments
28. Military female
29. "Geuel the son of ___" (Numbers 13:15)
31. Greek letter
32. "And ____ and Onan died in the land" (Numbers 26:19)
33. Saul's daughter
34. "Bring forth with thee ____ living thing" (Genesis 8:17)
35. Toddler's
36. High temperature
37. "Pitched in ___, which is in the edge of the wilderness" (Numbers 33:6)
38. "Libni, and ___" (Exodus 6:17)

43. Josiah's father
44. Ruler
45. Stern
49. "As it was in the days of ____"
   (Luke 17:26)
52. Midweek (abbr.)
54. Yr.
55. Pinetree state (abbr.)

by
Pauline Grottke

ACROSS

1. Short form of Jehucal
6. Son of Zophah
   (1 Chronicles 7:37)
11. "And ____, and Gaba; twelve cities" (Joshua 18:24)
12. Hair-cutting device
13. Poisonous snake
14. Publisher's staff member (abbr.)
15. Son of Phares (Matthew 1:3)
16. Cut
18. Hit
19. Small point
21. "Be ____ your sin will find you out" (Numbers 32:23)
22. Name (abbr.)
23. Son of Jacob (var.)
24. Johannesburg's country (abbr.)
25. "Fear ye not, ____ be afraid" (Isaiah 44:8)
28. Meridian (abbr.)
29. "And ____, the firstborn of Judah" (1 Chronicles 2:3)
30. "He ____ up his father's hand" (Genesis 48:17)
31. "I ____ filled with comfort" (2 Corinthians 7:4)
33. Fighting forces
35. Perform
36. Laughter sound
38. Large tanks
40. Yr.
41. "Inhabitants of ____" (Joshua 17:11)
43. "Because thou saidest, ____, against my sanctuary" (Ezekiel 25:3)
44. "The best of them is as a ____" (Micah 7:4)
46. Handicraft
47. "And ____ went before the ark" (2 Samuel 6:4)
49. Environment (abbr.)
50. Defensive weapons
51. Language of Rome in Paul's day
53. Fourth son of Midian (1 Chronicles 1:33)
55. Notre Dame's state (abbr.)
56. Behold!
57. Its capital is Augusta (abbr.)
58. Sigh sound

DOWN

1. Man who succeeded Moses
2. "They laid her in an ____ chamber" (Acts 9:37)
3. Padre (abbr.)
4. "The men which went with me, ____, Eshcol, and Mamre" (Genesis 14:24)
5. Cover
6. Live
7. "The land of Nod, on the ____ of Eden" (Genesis 4:16)
8. Ezra (abbr.)
9. Origins
10. "Turned to flight the ____ of the aliens" (Hebrews 11:34)
13. "Sitting on an ____ colt" (John 12:15)
17. Man with palsy healed by Peter
18. "They assayed to go into ____" (Acts 16:7)
20. Expert
22. Toi
23. Son of Caleb
26. Go astray
27. Church official

31. "Men from Babylon, and from Cuthah, and from ____" (2 Kings 17:24)
32. Son of Merairi (Ex. 6:19)
34. Dent
36. "And smote them, and discomfited them, even unto ____" (Numbers 14:45)
37. Industrial ____
39. "Of ____, the family of the Tahanites" (Numbers 26:35)
42. "And ____, the sons of Mahol" (1 Kings 4:31)
44. Bubble

45. "He built even Bethlehem, and ___" (2 Chronicles 11:6)
48. Naples' country (abbr.)
50. "The men went up and viewed ____" (Joshua 7:2)
52. "There shall be ____ night there" (Revelation 22:5)
54. "The Lord Jesus shall ___ revealed from heaven" (2 Thessalonians 1:7)

by
Pauline Grottke

ACROSS
1. Tax preparer (abbr.)
4. Music recorders (abbr.)
7. Jezebel's spouse
11. Curve
12. Foil (abbr.)
13. "____ cometh one mightier than I" (Mark 1:7)
14. Question
16. Father of Jezebel
18. Mouth
19. Compensate
21. "The city of ____ the father of Anak" (Joshua 15:13)
22. Kansas City state (abbr.)
23. "I have a secret ____ unto thee" (Judges 3:19)
25. "That which groweth of ____ own accord" (Leviticus 25:5)
27. Gate (2 Kings 11:6)
28. Baton Rouge is its cap.
30. "Let him ____ evil, and do good" (1 Peter 3:11)
33. Son of Cush
36. "All that thou sayest...I will ____" (Ruth 3:5)
37. "Saul the son of ____" (Acts 13:21)
39. "The ____ and stars to rule by night" (Psalm 136:9)
40. Chewed
43. Dwelling (abbr.)
44. Distant
46. Car parts
48. Middle Eastern nation (abbr.)
50. Investment result (abbr.)
51. Metallic element symbol
52. "Amasa was a man's son, whose name was ____ an Israelite" (2 Samuel 17:25)
54. Son of Issachar (1 Chronicles 7:1)
56. Prevalent
58. Infantry officer (abbr.)
59. Pace
60. Saw
61. Cook's measure (abbr.)

DOWN
1. Churl
2. Experts
3. Biking group (abbr.)
4. Cot
5. Condensation temperature (abbr.)
6. "Their ____ into pruninghooks" (Micah 4:3)
7. Son of Abishur (1 Chronicles 2:29)
8. "And God ____ the voice of the lad" (Genesis 21:17)
9. "____, and Dumah, and Eshean" (Joshua 15:52)
10. Son of Benjamin
13. Weekday (abbr.)
15. Soup
17. Tyre (var.)
20. Typesetter's mistake (abbr.)
22. OT prophet
24. "Kemuel the father of ____" (Genesis 22:21)
26. Denomination
28. "Cometh thither with ____ and torches" (John 18:3)
29. Electricity measure (abbr.)
30. Publisher's staff member (abbr.)
31. "____ have we been in thy sight" (Isaiah 26:17)
32. Dry up
34. Praise oneself

35. Upper surface
38. "The third to Harim, the fourth to ____" (1 Chronicles 24:8)
40. "From ____ of Judah, to bring up from thence the ark of God" (2 Samuel 6:2)
41. Erin (abbr.)
42. "And there shall be ____ more curse" (Revelation 22:3)
44. Trivium
45. "Crushed Balaam's ____ against the wall" (Numbers 22:25)
47. Food planning
49. Croak

53. With up, upset
55. Sent ones (abbr.)
57. Iron's symbol

by
Pauline Grottke

ACROSS

1. Pastor (abbr.)
3. "When they ____ ordained them elders" (Acts 14:23)
6. Metric acre measurement (abbr.)
8. Lengthen
11. Look!
12. "____ the brother of Joab was on to the thirty" (2 Samuel 23:24)
14. "The children of Keros, the children of ____" (Nehemiah 7:47)
15. "The children of Dishan are these; Uz, and ___" (Genesis 36:28)
17. "His hands are as gold ____" (Song of Solomon 5:14)
19. Champion athlete's goal (abbr.)
20. Marriage ceremony
22. "____ the Son of man be risen again" (Matthew 17:9)
24. "They had a few ____ fishes" (Mark 8:7)
25. Father of Shechem
27. Grain
29. Lack
32. Nor
34. "And ____, and Ader" (1 Chronicles 8:15)
36. "The Telltale Heart" author
37. Joints
39. Deer
41. Sodium, to scientist
42. Skill
43. Animal enclosure
45. Chaldean city
46. Weekday

47. "The Amorites would dwell in mount Heres in Aijalon, and in ____" (Judges 1:35)
50. Gate (2 Kings 11:6)
51. "And with all thy ____ get understanding" (Proverbs 4:7)
54. Sold-out theater (abbr.)
55. Peach state (abbr.)
56. "Chedorlaomer king of ____" (Genesis 14:1)
57. "The ____ of Sodom were wicked" (Genesis 13:13)
58. Printer's measure
59. Eastern European person

DOWN

1. Hooked nails
2. "And Iron, and Migdalel, ____" (Joshua 19:38)
3. Conducting
4. Rate of flight (abbr.)
5. Mend
6. Son of Zephaniah
7. "And ____ trees" (2 Chronicles 2:8)
8. Artificial radioactive element symbol
9. Fuzzy fruit
10. British nobleman
13. More elevated
16. "As an ____ harder than flint" (Ezekiel 3:9)
18. "Garment was white as ____" (Daniel 7:9)
21. Unwell
23. Imprison
26. "Threshingfloor of ____" (Genesis 50:10)
28. City on Crete (Acts 27:8)

30. Nun (var.)
31. Popular beverage
32. Melt
33. Rent
35. Question
38. "Field of _____ the son of Zohar" (Genesis 25:9)
40. Descendants of Eri (Numbers 26:16)
44. Father of Esli (Luke 3:25)
47. Certain
48. Thin

49. Place to grind corn
50. Noncom military rank (abbr.)
52. Bowman's org.
53. Physicist's measure (abbr.)

by
Pauline Grottke

ANSWERS

Puzzle 1

A	T	O	P		F	I	R		B	O	N	E
H	O	L	A		O	R	E		E	D	E	R
A	R	I	D		R	I	A		N	E	R	I
B	E	C	O	M	E		P	L	E	A	S	E
			N	E	V	A		O	F			
E	A	R		N	E	B		S	I	M	O	N
B	L	O	C		R	A	L		T	A	L	E
B	L	O	O	M		N	E	R		R	E	D
			N	O		A	B	E	L			
O	L	I	V	E	S		A	B	A	T	E	D
N	U	D	E		E	E	N		T	I	L	E
A	T	O	R		E	T	O		I	M	L	A
M	E	L	T		R	A	N		N	E	E	D

Puzzle 2

E	R	E		M	A	U	L		P	A	S	S
N	A	P		A	B	D	A		A	R	A	L
O	N	E		R	O	O	M		R	A	K	E
S	I	E	S	T	A		E	S	C	H	E	W
			T	Y	R		N	E	E			
U	P	W	A	R	D		T	A	L	E	N	T
A	U	I							A	I	R	
R	A	N	S	O	M		C	A	S	T	L	E
			I	R	A		O	R	A			
V	E	S	S	E	L		M	E	D	D	L	E
O	S	E	E		L	I	E	N		O	I	L
I	T	E	R		O	L	L	A		N	O	B
D	E	K	A		W	A	Y	S		E	N	E

Puzzle 3

A	A	R		C	L	A	P		S	C	O	T
B	R	A		L	I	M	A		O	A	T	H
B	A	G		E	V	A	N		P	L	I	O
A	B	I	G	A	I	L		B	O	A	S	T
			E	N	D		H	A	R	M		
A	M	E	N	S		M	A	R		I	E	R
W	A	N	E		R	A	M		E	T	T	U
E	N	T	R	E	A	T		R	A	Y	O	N
			R	A	T	E		E	E	R		
D	E	A	T	H		A	N	A	N	I	A	S
R	A	N	I		O	L	D	S		A	B	E
A	R	C	O		O	M	O	O		M	E	N
G	L	E	N		T	A	R	N		B	L	T

Puzzle 4

O	M	R	I		P	E	P		R	A	G	S
A	D	A	M		O	R	R		E	S	A	U
R	A	M	P		W	E	E		S	H	E	D
			U	S	E		S	H	I	E	L	D
O	R	A	T	O	R		E	M	S			
R	A	V	E	N		A	N	O	T	H	E	R
A	N	I		E	N	T			O	V	A	
D	I	S	T	A	N	T		L	E	P	E	R
			R	M	C		R	E	F	I	N	E
J	O	S	E	P	H		A	E	F			
U	S	I	A		A	T	I		E	N	O	S
D	A	R	D		N	O	S		C	A	N	A
E	Y	E	S		T	R	E		T	E	E	D

Puzzle 5

```
S A R D I S   U P S I D E
T H I R S T   N A T I O N
R A   A H A   C I A   C G
I S   G I B B O N     T A
F A T   S A V   F R O G
E I D E R   R E Q U I R E
    Q U A R R E L
A U G U S T E   L A I C
F R I A   A L S   Y E T A
F A L L   B   Y E   F E N
E L     L A   R A E     T
C   R E E L   I N D I T E
T H E M I S   A S H D O D
```

Puzzle 6

```
H E E   A D I N   D O V E
E N D   P E R O   E T O N
E T O   I C E D   V O W S
P O M M E L   A T I
    U C A   B E S I D E
P R A Y E R S   L E P E R
A I L   E E E     S A G
C O U C H   E M E R O D S
S T R A I T   I N E
    N E A   N O V I C E
L A C K   B L E U   R A Y
A C H E   L O N G   O N E
P E A R   E S T H   N E D
```

Puzzle 7

```
H O L E   A W L   M A R A
A D A R   L I E   O V E N
L I K E W I S E   V A L E
E N E   E V E   I E
    O N E   E N D U R E
B E G A T   M L S   R A N
L O O K   H A M   T I T O
U N A   P E R   N A M E S
E S T H E R   B E G
    O D   N E B   L A P
R O A R   D E S O L A T E
E A R S   O R O   A V O N
T R E E   R I M   D A R N
```

Puzzle 8

```
H E W   T I N E   M A D E
I R A   I R O N   O B E Y
S I S E R A   E S S E N E
    B E N D   W E L T S
S I L A S   E N O S
A Z U L   E W E R   A L A
V E S S E L   A N A M I M
E S T   L I S T   B O L O
    P O M P   B A R A K
A M I S T   Y U A N
S E L A H S   P R A I S E
S A I L   A N O N   C A R
E L A M   P E N S   E W E
```

Puzzle 9

```
L O F T   E R R S   B S A
A M O R   R E E M   E K E
C A R E S   D E A D L Y
    S E A R E D   O I E
L E A   D O E   A T E
I N K S   U M M A H   A B
F I E L D S   O R A C L E
T D   I D E A L   N A I N
    A G E   R E D   R T E
    A S H   B E S I D E
R E T U R N   D E F E R
D O R   R I A S   A U R A
O D S   B E S T   F L E E
```

Puzzle 10

```
N A R D   R A H   S A F E
A G U E   A B E   I T E R
D E T S   N B A   M O T E
A S H E R   A R T E M A S
    R E U   T I O
R E S T O R E   E N O C H
O L E   I A M   T A I
B L E S S   N A T I O N S
    A H A   P E N
E L E M E N T   A V O I D
L I D S   G O D   A B D A
I N D O   E H I   D E L I
M E A N   R U N   E Y E S
```

Puzzle 11

H E I R		P E P		E M S
I	D E	T R E E		V E E
P R O M		O I N T M E N T
S O L O M O N	E I	
	V A N C E	S H A D
B A R A K	E L S	A N O
C H O L E R	F I N I N G
D A B	R A W	N U R S E
E B E R	T A M A R	
	A S	N E I T H E R
E V E N T I D E	U E L E
T A P	A B E T	R A D
A N I	B A R	E P E E

Puzzle 12

| M O W | H A N D | A G A G |
| E P A | O D I O | R A T E |
| S E C O N D T R U M P E T |
S C O R E	A N O	
	P Y R E	C R A V E
I D E A	O L L A	B I S
R I G H T E O U S N E S S
I N A	A S N A	O D E A
S A L E M	S U P S	
	V A N	A E N O N
U N D E R S T A N D I N G
S A A R	E R I E	L E A
E M M Y	W A R S	E R I

Puzzle 13

L A M P	L A D D	A D D
O V A L	F I R E	R A E
P A N E S	D E C L A R E
I D O L	D E E M E D
A F G	I B	A V
A L O E	B E S S E M E R
R E L	S Y E N E	I T E
M E D I T A T E	P R A Y
O R	S A	E A T
A B A N A S	K R O C
R E P E N T S	S P L A T
I L E	G A I N	L E T O
L A X	E R A T	E S E R

Puzzle 14

C A P	B O R E D	T A M
U L U	O R A T E	R I A
P E R S I A	A S S U R E
P A L L S	I E S
H A L L S	P I R A T E D
A N E T	E Y R E	S T R
T A	S U N	A S E	H E
E N A	P O E M	M B A S
D I V E R S E	W O R M S
O E I	L I E T O
B R I N G S	S E E K E R
A I D	H I R E D	E R A
Y E S	T A R E S	N E W

Puzzle 15

C A U L	P A N T	J E W
O M R I	E K O I	U M E
M A I M	T A L E	D I N
E N A B L E	O R N A N
E R R	E A S E S	
A D E	A L D A	N O
I S R	R I O	M O T
A M	E A R S	B	N
T A M A R	E S E	
G O M E R	I D U M E A
T I N	L O O M	R O L L
E N E	I S N O	I R A M
N E T	S E E N	M E N S

Puzzle 16

M A N	A B B A	B I T
A D O	T H R O W	E N A
Y E T	A A A	H A G A R
A B I B	W I R E	
M B A	T A L I T H A
G O L D	F I X E D	E N
A N E	E R E	B I D
I T	S O W E D	V E R Y
T H R O N E S	I N S
H A I R	O S E E
F I E R O	O V I	F A R
A N S	N E V E R	I R U
T E A	S E A R	T E N

Puzzle 17

A T L		N O M		S E A T
D R A G		O R O		E L L E
A U R A		I E R		L I M E
R E A R		S O N O F M A N	
	D U E		I N	
L A D E N		E N T E R E D	
A L A N		N A G		L E V E
D A Y S T A R		D E V I L	
	I T		R A M	
I N F I N I T E		E N O S	
D O O M		O R A		N E M O
D E A N		N O D		T A R O
O L L A		S P Y		R I N

Puzzle 18

A R E		C A B		E N O S
H O L D		O D E		N E N E
A B I A		A I S		D E C A
	M U L T I T U D E S	
M O S E S		E V E	
B A B E L		A G A		A B A
A R A L		R T E		A S I A
D A D		S E T		O S H E A
	A I M		E N T E R	
W H O M S O E V E R	
H O L A		V I I		A L M A
A M O S		A R C		Y E A R
T E R A		L E T		A N T

Puzzle 19

H I S		V I T A L		R N A
I R E		E P H A I		H A I
D I V E R S E		K N E E L	
	E L S E		T E E S	
L A R U E		S U N D A Y S	
O D E D		R O M E		S O P
C I		E M E R O D S		K A
A N A		E S E R		T I E R
L O C U S T S		B A R D S	
	C A S S		H A R P	
O P E R A		C A U S E R S	
L O P		G R A V E		E A T
D E T		E N T E R		L T D

Puzzle 20

A S A		U T E		T E L
R A D		A S E R		G A V E
C H A M B E R		N A K E D	
	M O B S		W A V E	
S H A M A		D I V I N E R	
H A N S		H A V E N		L A
E V T		L O V E S		R E V
R O		B A L I S		R E N E
I C H A B O D		G O L A N	
	E B A N		W H O A	
W O M A N		S H A M B L E	
R E A R		T H A T		E E R
Y O N		O A T		L I E

Puzzle 21

E S L I		D A M		C A S T
C O A T		E R A		A G U R
C O M B		R E S		N E R I
	E L I		T A N	
C L O S E D		E X O D U S	
R E M O V E		R E T I N A	
I V E			T I C	
B E G O N E		P A S T O R	
S E A S O N		A R M O N E	
	P R O		C M I	
A F A R		U R I		T H A T
S E B A		G A F		H A V E
A W A Y		H E Y		S P E D

Puzzle 22

P A T		S A D		T R O W
A H A B		A B E		A E T A
C A R E		L E V		M A R S
	A H O L I B A M A H	
B R U I N		C O R	
R O O T S		L E W		W P A
O L A Y		D O S		B O A T
B E D		D O T		S I R W E
	A I L		P A L M S	
E B E D M E L E C H	
D O R M		F I N		A D A H
A R I A		U R N		H A R E
R E S H		L A Y		D A M

Puzzle 23

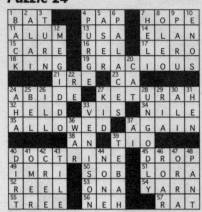

Puzzle 24

Puzzle 25

Puzzle 26

Puzzle 27

Puzzle 28

Puzzle 29

Puzzle 30

Puzzle 31

Puzzle 32

Puzzle 33

Puzzle 34

Puzzle 35

F	E	A	R		R	I	B		T	H	A	T
E	S	T	E		E	R	E		H	A	L	E
N	E	E	D		T	E	A		R	I	P	E
		O	N	I		S	P	A				
A	N	S	W	E	R		T	I	L	L	E	D
P	I	L	A	T	E		S	A	L	U	T	E
A	G	A						C	H	E		
R	E	V	E	A	L		R	E	A	R	E	D
T	R	E	B	L	E		E	A	T	E	R	S
			R	I	G		S	T	A			
N	E	B	O		I	I	I		R	A	R	E
O	D	I	N		O	N	S		A	W	A	Y
R	E	B	S		N	O	T		H	E	M	E

Puzzle 36

L	A	I	C		H	O	S		L	O	L	A
A	L	T	O		E	R	A		O	M	E	R
S	T	E	N		R	E	V		W	A	I	T
A	S	T	R	O	L	O	G	E	R	S		
			E	N	D		U	A	R			
P	A	I	N	S		C	R	Y		S	E	N
A	B	E	T		C	O	Y		D	O	T	E
T	A	R		P	O	T		W	E	N	C	H
			E	O	N		P	A	L			
M	I	N	I	S	T	E	R	I	N	G		
H	A	N	D		U	S	A		V	E	R	Y
I	N	T	O		M	A	C		E	B	E	R
P	E	O	R		E	R	E		R	O	Y	S

Puzzle 37

C	H	I	C		D	A	R		A	R	O	E
L	O	G	O		E	V	E		L	E	V	I
A	N	O	N		B	I	C		L	A	I	N
P	E	R	C	E	I	V	E	W	O	R	D	S
			E	R	R		I	O	N			
P	A	R	I	S		A	P	T		R	E	L
A	L	I	T		S	I	T		P	U	S	H
R	E	D		S	E	L		P	R	E	S	S
			D	I	A		T	A	U			
U	N	D	E	R	S	T	A	N	D	I	N	G
S	E	E	M		O	R	R		E	V	E	R
E	S	C	A		N	E	R		N	A	V	E
S	T	A	S		S	K	Y		T	H	A	W

Puzzle 38

H	I	P		D	O	E	R		S	A	I	D
O	R	A		E	S	T	E		H	I	D	E
M	I	R		A	T	A	P		A	S	E	R
E	S	T	A	T	E		R	I	P			
		A	S	H		C	O	V	E	R	E	D
T	A	K	E		L	O	V	E		U	S	E
I	C	E		W	I	L	E	S		D	A	N
E	R	R		E	K	E	D		P	I	U	S
D	E	S	I	R	E	S		R	A	M		
			N	E	W		R	E	D	E	E	M
T	O	W	N		I	L	A	I		N	I	E
A	L	O	E		S	I	G	N		T	R	E
O	D	E	R		E	V	E	S		S	E	T

Puzzle 39

S	E	E		D	S	C		B	O	N	E
H	A	V	E		O	O	H		E	P	O	S
E	T	E	S		U	M	A		G	E	I	N
		T	A	B	E	R	N	A	C	L	E	
	S	H	A	L	T		G	O	T			
R	H	E	T	T		B	E	N		A	S	H
Y	U	L	E		G	U	R		B	L	O	T
E	N	D		O	A	T		R	E	I	N	S
			E	L	I		M	O	S	E	S	
C	O	N	V	E	N	I	E	N	T			
A	L	O	E		S	S	A		O	M	R	I
P	E	O	R		A	L	L		W	A	I	L
T	O	N	Y		Y	E	S		N	A	E	

Puzzle 40

L	A	P		F	I	N	E		K	I	N
E	R	R		W	O	M	A	N		O	R	A
D	E	E		E	L	F		S	O	R	R	Y
		S	E	N	D		A	I	R	E		
	P	E	N		E	N	G	R	A	F	T	
S	E	N	T		M	A	G	N	A		R	I
E	A	T		O	R	E			C	O	N	
E	L		R	E	P	E	L		W	O	N	T
R	E	F	U	S	E	D			A	N	T	
		L	E	S	S		L	A	S	S		
A	B	A	S	E		W	A	R		U	R	I
R	A	M		N	A	O	M	I		M	A	D
A	N	E		E	R	N	E		E	G	O	

411

Puzzle 41

K I N D	W I S	F O R D
I R A E	A A A	I S U I
D A M S	D M V	G E N S
M E P H I B O S H E T H
I T S	U L T
H A R T S	W R Y	M L A
E R I E	S A Y	L I A R
R E D	T O Y	B E S O M
B E L	H A S
M Y B E L O V E D S O N
E A R L	M I R	I V A H
D R E I	O T O	N E S S
O N D E	N O D	G N A T

Puzzle 42

T O R	H A S	B R O W
A L E C	A L O	R O M A
I D D O	N A T	U T O R
M E D I T A T I O N
N A M E S	I L E
B E S O R	B S A	E W E
A N O N	B A H	B A I L
R E P	L E T	T A S T E
P A S	W O R T H
T A L E B E A R E R
A N E T	E R E	E N V Y
K I T E	C E S	N E A R
E M I R	H S T	W T S

Puzzle 43

S I A L	E N C	A F A R
E S L I	N E O	F I L E
A N A K	D I M	O R E N
T O B E C O N F O R M E D
N O R	O N E
F A R E D	F R O	L E E
A L A D	D E T	S E E R
T A M	P E N	R A V E N
P A C	S I C
M A D E P A R T A K E R S
A S E R	Y E A	B R A E
S E M I	E A R	U R G E
T A I L	D D E	T S A R

Puzzle 44

| M A C | W I T | T W O |
| A B A | A B I | S H O W |
| S U P P L I C A T I O N |
S T E R E S	D A N
R E S	P O V E R T Y
S I N S	D A R E	E R E
O P A S	I R A	A S E A
L S U	A V I M	H U E S
D A M A R I S	M I R
D O N	H E A R T S
F A L S E W I T N E S S
B R A E	O D E	C A T
I R I	T E D	T R S

Puzzle 45

D O O R	A L S	T O M E
E R N E	S E A	A B E T
N E E D	S A H	R A R E
E N E	A R M
G A R E B S	R E A G A N
E D E M A S	A C C E D E
D E L	R O B
O L I V E S	G A D A R A
R A C I N E	A R A R A T
R T E	R A N
S I N G	T E L	I V A H
E Z R I	H A I	E I R E
W E A N	E T C	L A T E

Puzzle 46

O B I S	A N S	S L I P
R A S H	V A T	H A K U
B L E U	O I E	A L A S
M E S H I L L E M O T H
H U D	L I E
B E G A T	R A N	D E B
E R A N	S I R	B A K E
N E T	B A D	R E B E L
S A V	C A N
B A R T H O L O M E W S
A B I A	U I T	F E E T
S E M I	R A E	I R A E
E D E N	Y R S	T E L L

Puzzle 47

C	A	N		W	O	R	M		C	A	R	E
A	R	E		O	N	C	E		A	G	U	R
S	A	I		R	U	D	D		L	A	M	E
A	N	G	E	L	S		I	A	N			
	H	O	D		A	C	C	O	U	N	T	
J	O	B	S		M	A	I	N		N	O	E
A	S	O		B	E	R	N	E		D	O	N
M	S	U		A	D	O	E		B	E	N	D
B	A	R	G	A	I	N		F	U	R		
	U	L	A		B	E	S	T	O	W		
S	A	V	E		T	A	R	E		A	V	A
O	R	E	S		O	B	E	D		K	E	Y
N	E	X	T		R	E	D	S		E	R	S

Puzzle 48

A	I	R		V	A	I	N		V	C	O	N
R	T	E		O	N	A	M		E	A	R	N
R	O	M		W	O	N		S	L	O	E	
	O	R	E	N		N	O	T	E			
S	A	V	E	D		P	A	R	A	B	L	E
N	E	E	D		B	A	B	E	L		I	V
A	N	D		L	E	G	A	L		I	N	E
R	O		B	A	G	E	L		O	M	E	R
E	N	T	R	E	A	T		P	L	A	N	T
	H	O	L	T		F	L	A	G			
B	O	O	K		M	E	A		I	T	E	
B	A	S	E		F	L	A	T		N	E	W
B	R	E	N		T	I	R	E		E	N	E

Puzzle 49

C	O	N	E		B	I	D		S	L	I	P
O	M	A	N		R	B	I		A	E	R	O
B	R	I	C		I	R	S		I	S	I	T
	I	N	H	A	B	I	T	A	N	T	S	
	A	R	E			A	N	T				
F	R	O	N	T		D	N	A		C	A	T
A	U	N	T		R	O	T		G	A	V	E
D	E	E		S	E	E		N	A	B	A	L
		R	I	B		G	E	L				
	T	R	I	B	U	L	A	T	I	O	N	
T	H	U	S		K	I	T		L	A	E	L
V	A	L	E		E	V	E		E	R	S	E
A	T	E	N		D	E	S		E	S	T	E

Puzzle 50

A	K	O	V		C	O	R		A	L	A	C
D	E	M	I		U	N	E		L	A	B	A
S	E	E	N		R	E	S		O	R	E	N
	P	R	E	D	E	S	T	I	N	A	T	E
	G	A	D			I	S	E				
B	E	G	A	N		T	N	T		S	R	S
O	M	A	R		C	O	G		S	O	U	L
Y	E	T		E	O	N		M	O	N	E	Y
		A	W	N		S	A	L				
P	E	R	S	E	C	U	T	I	O	N	S	
I	T	I	S		E	V	E		M	E	T	E
T	A	L	C		I	E	R		O	B	E	D
A	S	E	S		T	A	N		N	O	M	O

Puzzle 51

T	R	E	E		A	S	K		L	O	R	D
A		A	A	S		O	P	E	N			O
L	U	S	T	S		A		N	E	T	S	
M	E	T	E		A	D	D		D		O	
A	L	W	A	Y	T	A	B	L	E		B	E
I		A	T	E		M		U	R	I		R
	U	R		A	I		O	N		N	O	
L		D	A	R		E		G	O	D		S
O	F		I	S	H	B	O	S	H	E	T	H
	A	L	L		P	E	T		A	B	I	A
T	R	E	E			R		S	T	E	M	
U		S	T	U	B		H	A	T	E		E
B	O	T	H		Y	E	A		E	D	A	R

Puzzle 52

J	U	S	T	I	F	I	E	D		S	O	P
U	S	O		R	A	C	E		P	I	N	E
D	E		F	A	R	E		O	A	R		R
G		B	A	D		A	N	Y		A	S	
E	N	A	N		E	D	G	E		A	G	O
I	N	T	E	R	C	E	S	S	I	O	N	
A	M	N	O	N			I			N		
P	R	E	D	E	S	T	I	N	A	T	E	
P	A	R		M	E	A	T		J	O		N
A	H		E	Y	E		G	A	P		A	
R		W	A	S		A	D	A	H		A	M
E	D	A	R			G	O	D		P	R	E
L	O	Y		G	L	O	R	I	F	I	E	D

Puzzle 53

	R	A	G	E		A	C	T	S	
S	A	N	E	R		M	A	R	A	H
B	L	I	N	D			L	O	V	E	S
R	O	S		N	B	A		P	E	A	L
I	T	E	M		A	I	N		E	S	L	I
M	S		S	E	A	S	O	N	S		S	T
		A	R			N	E					
S	O		S	T	A	R		B	M		M
E	R	S	E		T	E	E		E	D	G	E
A	D	A	M	A	H		R	E	A	R	E	D
S	E	T				D	O	N	E	
R	A	H	A	B			R	O	P	E	
	N	E	T	S			L	A	W	S	

Puzzle 54

H	E	I	R	S			F	O	L	D	S
E	N	T	I	C	E		A	R	A	R	A	T
A	D		D	A	N	D	L	E	D		M	E
R	U	B		B	R	A	S	S		N	U	N
S	E	A	S		A	T	E		F	E	E	T
	D	R	E	D	G	E		M	E	A	L	S
		T	R	U	E		F	E	A	R	
S	P	E	E	D		S	E	N	S	E	S
C	A	R	D		W	E	N		T	S	A	R
A	S	S		S	I	N	C	E		T	I	A
R	T		A	U	S	T	E	R	E		L	I
F	E		A	R	E		D	A	R		E	N
		H	E	R			N	E	E	D	Y

Puzzle 55

S	I	S		S	T	O	A		E	V	E	N
A	S	H		T	A	R	G	E	T		D	O
	O	M	E	N		A	N	A	K		N
S	H	E	E	P		A	I	D		I	C	E
L	A	S	T		A	W	N		A	N	A
E	T		A	R	E		S	I	G	N	S
P		F	O	R	M		B	A	R	S		P
T	H	I	N	K		B	A	T		I	O
	A	N	T		H	O	D		F	A	D	O
O	D	E		D	A	Y		H	A	M	A	N
V		R	I	N	G		D	A	R	E	
E	M		N	A	A	M	A	N		N	A	B
R	A	I	N		R	E	N	D		D	U	E

Puzzle 56

A	L	E	E		F	A	R		E	A	S	T
H	E	A	R	S	A	Y		W	I	T	H
A	V		O	R		S	H	E		R	E
Z	I	A		L	A	S	E	A		B	E	E
		R	A	I	D		T	H	R	E	E
N		A	B	D		S	A	I	N	T	S
O	H		I			T		S	O
N	O		I	D	O	L		T	O	E	S	N
	S	C	E	N	E		H	U	S	K
O	T		H	O	O	T		Y	E	N
D	A		R	E	I		L	E	E		A	O
O	G	L	E			M	E	R	G	E	R	S
R	E	A	D		S	O	S		O	R	L	E

Puzzle 57

T	O	B		B	L	O	O	D		R	O	T
O	N	E		L	A	R	G	E		I	N	N
W	E		L	E	S	T		F	A	C	E
	W	A	I	S	T		N	E	C	H	O
S	A	C	K	S		R	E	N	T		N	E
T	Y	R	E		M	A	I	D	S		T	X
R	O	E		A	K	E		A	H	I
I	R		A	N	G	E	L		E	V	I	L
P	O		R	O	O	M		T	H	E	S	E
	T	W	A	N	G		S	H	U	N	S
T	H	I	N	E		S	H	E	D		I	N
H	E	N		O	U	T	E	R		A	D	O
E	R	E		F	R	A	M	E		R	E	D

Puzzle 58

S	E	A		S	L	A	I	N		C	R	Y
E	G	G		T	O	N	E	D		R	O	E
T	O	O	K	E	S	T		L	E	S	S
	E	R	E			B	R	E	E
T	O	K	E	N		S	L	E	E	P	E	R
A	R	A	N		S	P	E	A	K		N	O
R	I	B		S	P	E	N	D		E	T	A
T	O		A	I	R	E	D		A	W	E	S
S	N	U	F	F	E	D		A	L	E	R	T
	R	A	T	E			F	T
S	T	I	R		R	E	T	O	U	C	H
T	O	E		H	O	U	S	E		R	O	O
A	W	L		A	N	G	E	R		N	O	W

414

Puzzle 59

```
F I R E   G O D   A C T S
A N O N   E W E   M A I L
S T A R   D E N   P U R E
T O M A T O   Y E L L E D
    G A R L I C Y
C A L E B   I N C   L B S
A D E   R I N G   A O R
N O T A E N D   N E B A I
    A T T A L I A
C O U R S E   O M R I
O S L O   N O W   L O B
L E A N   T I L   N A I L
D E M S   S L Y   B I L E
```

Puzzle 60

```
R E N D   I N T O   E K E
O V E R   F O U R   R E D
D E T E R   T B A   R E I
    A E R   A C C E P T
T R I M M E D   L A D
I O N S   P E T E R   A D
M A N   M A L E S   U G H
E D   R O Y A L   U R E
    S U R   Y E A R N
L A M E N T   M U G
A H A   I R E   K E N A N
O I L   N U T S   N A I N
S O L   G E A R   T Y R E
```

Puzzle 61

```
R O S E   M I N E   H O W
A N O N   A V O N   A W E
M E   D E G   E A G L E
    H U N   S M U G
T H I R D   S H I N I N G
R O D E   S W E E T   O R
A R E   E L I A S   L I E
I S   C L I F F   R A S E
N E G L E C T   H O S E N
    R A C E   N E T S
S L A N T   W E N T   T O
P E N   E W E S   E D E N
A D D   D E B T   N O N E
```

Puzzle 62

```
T A N   T R E E   C H A T
A N Y   R E A P   H A T E
L T   T I E   I C E   E N
E S T A B L I S H E D
    O R E   S T O R I E S
D A R E   G U L P   S H E
O U T S   O N E   S C U M
G N U   O R D   P E D I
S T R A N G E   B A R
    E N T E R T A I N E D
H E   T O O   R A N   S O
U L A I   U R A L   D A N
Z I N C   S I P   D U E
```

Puzzle 63

```
D E A T H   U N T O   A M
O R D E R   N E A R   H O
    O N   A D E R   H A S
A M   T A X E D   C A V E
L O T   N E R   M O   A S
S O O N     O A R
O N I O N   P S A L M
    L I E   T I E S
T O   S T   N U N   D E E
R U L E   B A S O N   S C
I T O   T A M E   O G
B E   M O R E   A N A N I
E R   L E S S   L E D G E
```

Puzzle 64

```
E D   S L I D E   A I A H
R O T T E N   L A I D   E
    H O T   F I B   U R
S H I P   L A U D   O N E
H U S   V O I D   C A N
I T   M O A N   S A R I D
P   M O U N T A I N S   E
S E A T S   N O T E   W E
    O R E   D E N S   H A D
A N Y   N O S E   P A S S
I S   A N T S   A R T
J   T R E E   E R A S E R
A M O K   D E L A Y   N A
```

Puzzle 65

```
L O N E   A S I D E   A T
I   O R E N   N E W   S O
V A   E D O M   N E S T
E N D   G N A T   S E E D
  N A M E   L E T   T R I
M A R A   E N O S   S E
A   E K E   B A T   T
I T   E A R S   L A D Y
D O R   T I E   S T I R
S W A N   D E C K   L O G
  E N A N   R O I L   P O
M R   I I M   O N E S   R
A S   L E E K S   D O V E
```

Puzzle 66

```
H I P   E R E   I W W
A R E   S O O N   M A I N
S E R V A N T S   P I T S
    J A W S   N A U T
A R U I N   H A S T
D A R N   D A R K E N E D
A T E   N O T E S   A R A
R E D E E M E D   A Z A L
    A R I D   I N A N E
S E I S I N   A D E R
A S S T   I G N O M I N Y
I L L   O R A L   T O E
L I E   N E   E T A
```

Puzzle 67

```
B E   P O R E D   B E A R
E N   E A T   A M O N   O
A D D E R   A R M Y   A A
  U E L   L I K E   S N R
U R N   S O R E   T I N
L E   F A T   N E R G A L
L   S E W   G U N   O
A S C E N D   A G E   O F
  P A L   E A R S   A L T
W I N   P A C E   E H I
O N   H E R E   S L A V E
R   W E N T   I O U   E L
D E E R   H A M U L   T I
```

Puzzle 68

```
S E M E I   S H A F T
S P R I N G   T A S T E D
O R   L O A D E T H   R A
R E D   S L I M E   A M I
R A R E   R   L A E L
Y D   D E S T R O Y   D Y
  F I R E   A N I M
A T   F R E E M E N   U S
D E F Y   V   G A S H
A R A   D O E S T   N E O
M E   F E W N E S S   D E
I S R A E L   B A A L   S
  H E R D S   A R D O N
```

Puzzle 69

```
P R O D   W E A R Y   S O
R E F I N E   T I E   I R
A D   P O L E   B A R S
M E N   E L A N   R I T E
  E A R   S O B   D E W
O M R I   J E T U R   R E
  E S A U   E Y E S
A S   E N D E D   N E
L E G   T A N   T A T
P A I L   H A N D   S O W
  S E A T   M A I D   W A
N O   M E N   M E A G E R
I N   P E A C E   N O R M
```

Puzzle 70

```
E M S   I C O N   S E L A
L A P   C A P E R N A U M
B U R R O   T R U E   Z O
A L I E N S   O B A L
  G A I T S   S K I E S
T B   P U R I M   S N A P
A I D   M A T E S   G S A
S T A Y   Y E A H S   E N
K E R O S   S L E P T
  R U T H   S C A R E S
A T   T E A M   H E A R T
B E T H P H A G E   P I E
E N D S   A N E M   S E M
```

416

Puzzle 71

```
A R T | J O A S H | S O P
W A R | O S H E A | T W O
E M I M S | I N N | R E D
    B E E S | I D D O
F E E T | T O R M E N T S
I R S | P A R | A N G E L
E R | U R G E D | N A
L O W E R | A G E | I S T
D R O P P I N G | K N E E
    L I O N | S O I L
L I V | S A P | A N A T H
A R E | E N T E R | N O E
Y E S | S E A L S | D O R
```

Puzzle 72

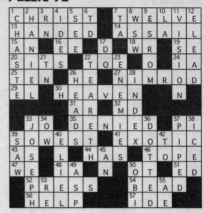

```
C H R I S T | T W E L V E
H A N D E D | A S S A I L
A N | E E | D | W R | S E
S I T S | T O E | O | I A
T E N | H E | N I M R O D
E L | H E A V E N | N
      A R | M D
J O | D E N I E D | P I
S O W E S T | E X O T I C
A S | H A S | T O P E
W E | I A N | O T | E D
P R E S S | B E A D
H E L P | I D E
```

Puzzle 73

```
I N T I M E | T R A N C E
S T A T E S | R A M O T H
  B E T H L E H E M
P E | M | T O N | N | H O
E S S | M O O C H | P A D
A C T I O N | H E R A L D
  A E R O | R E S T
S P E E D S | R O T T E N
P E P | S E L E D | A T E
Y D | W | R E L | K | H E
    P E T I T I O N S
A R A B I A | E N O U G H
D A M S E L | D E T E S T
```

Puzzle 74

```
  S H A R E | R E B A T E
R | E L O T H | D I B O N
I V | I S A A C | R I N D
D E L A Y | D A R D A
E N A N | S I L O S | H A
R U N | T O D A Y | B O X
  S E C H U | H A M O R
B | S H I N E | L O R D S
A T | A N D R O | R E E D
T H A N K | U R G E D
T E S T | E P O S | T O
L I P | S A T | F U E L
E R S | O N | F R E D
```

Puzzle 75

```
W E E | T A M A R | S O P
A L L | W H E R E | M A T
S I N A I | T A T | E R A
    A U N T | B A A L
A N A K | R E S I S T E D
R A M | S O N | N A S T Y
I O | A D O R E | H E
E M P T Y | W A D | H E R
H I R E | G | F U R S
    A N E R | E A R N
L A Y | T A U | I O T A S
O R E | A T T A R | E N E
P E R | S E E M S | R Y E
```

Puzzle 76

```
H A S | H E L O T | M A N
A S A | I V O R Y | E G O
D E R I D E | G E N D E R
    A R E | F A R E D
T R I O | P A N | S L A Y
E A | N A I L | S T E R E
R I D | R E S T S | S R A
A L A R M | E R I E | O R
    M U S | S L Y | D O W N
    S N O W Y | B A A
S L E E P | P A R T E D
E E L | E L I A B | H A I
W A S | S T A T E | S U E
```

Puzzle 77

```
C O S   G A R E B   C U T
O V A   A N I S E   O N E
W E   L I N E   H O R D E
  R E I N A   B O R N E
A S S E S   C E L T   R A
S P E D   S H A D S   S W
A R K   T I N   T A
P E   T R O T S   A N A K
H A   A I R S   S T O N E
  D R I N K   S T A N D
D I A L S   S L E D   I T
I N N   E L I A M   O N O
E G G   D E N T S   A G O
```

Puzzle 78

```
    N I C O D E M U S
    E N A N   T E N T
H E A D   E A N   L U R E
E R R E T H   A P E R C U
R   E R A S   S D   P
E L I D A D   E A S Y   H
A I R   I   S   E
F E A S T   S T E A M
T   H O L D   E A   I
E M P I R E   A S K E R S
R E A P   A H I   E D O M
  N   H E R A L D R I C
    I N N   I S T
```

Puzzle 79

```
A B S   G A R E B   P U T
P A L   E X I L E   L E E
T R O U B L E S   S A L E
  T R E E   E H I
A L T A R   D R I N K S
F E E L   L E A R N   N O
T A D   T E A R S   L O U
E S   B A A R A   F O W L
R E T U R N   N O U N S
  A R E   F A U N
R A I N   S C O U R G E D
A W L   A P A R T   E V A
Y E S   H A N D   R E D
```

Puzzle 80

```
A W L   A H I R A   S P Y
R O E   C A L E B   P I E
T E A C H   B U R N T
  P R E S S   A N E
P R E Y   A E R   I D O L
L E D   P R I E S T   N A
O Z   P A D   N O E   I N
T I   S T I N T S   T O E
S A L A   S E E   P U N S
  I L L   T R U S T
T R E M O R   L I O N S
E A N   B A A R A   R E I
A H S   E P H A I   S E T
```

Puzzle 81

```
J O A N N A   M A N N E R
A D D   A N I A M   O N E
C D   T H A N K E D   D E
O   A H A B   E N A M   D
B A B E L   H   D R A M S
  C R O A T I A   T N
I R A   L O   V I   N O
  E H   B O N D A G E
I S A A C   R   O D O R S
G   M I L E   C L I P   E
E D   R E A D E S T   H E
A I R   A R I D   B I T
L E A R N S   E N D E T H
```

Puzzle 82

```
D A S H   P A R   S A L A
O N T O   A R E   T R O W
E T A   L I E   B R I D E
S I N N E R   G E O D E
  D O T   R E A D
O W E D   H E A R E S T
G A S   P E A R S   H I E
  S T R O L L S   B E E R
  H E L M   C U P
P H O T O   B U S H E L
G O O D S   D A B   E R E
E L S E   B A D   A R N O
L E E S   E Y E   E D E N
```

Puzzle 83

A	M	A	L	E	K		C	A	N	A	A	N
M	A	R	A		E	R		H		E	P	A
O	V	U	M		N		G	I			T	P
S	I	M		H	I	V	I	T	E	S		H
I	N		N	O	T		B	U	L	L	E	T
T		O	R	E		E	B	B		L	A	
E	V	E		O	S	L	O		E	V	I	L
S	I	D	O	N		U	N	I	T		S	I
	C		H	I	N	D		S	H	A	H	
I	T			T		I	D	L	E		A	S
B	O	O		E	L	M		A	L	U	M	
I	R	A			O		A	N		R	A	N
S	Y	R	I	A		A	B	D	I		C	

Puzzle 84

R	O	O	T	S		S	P	R	I	G	
H	E	T	E	R	O		L	A	I	C	A	C
O	S		R	O	A	R	I	N	G		M	O
U	E	L		T	R	A	P	S		M	B	A
S	N	O	W		I			A	R	I	D	
E	D		H	A	R	N	E	S	S		T	S
		L	O	S	E		C	O	S	T		
S	O		S	H	I	L	O	N	I		D	O
T	R	E	E		O			R	E	E	F	
A	D	E		E	L	I	H	U		A	N	T
M	E		R	A	I	S	E	T	H	I	E	
P	R	A	I	S	E		M	A	I	D	E	N
	S	I	D	E	S		S	H	E	R	D	

Puzzle 85

	J	A	C	O	B		S	A	M	O	S	
N	O	T	I	C	E		W	H	A	L	E	S
O	S	E	E		S	E	E		L	E	A	P
M	E	R	L		O	L	E		A	M	A	
E	P			S	M	I	T	E		E	R	
	H	A	L	L		H		D	E	A	D	
	R	E	A	S	O	N	I	N	G			
S	E	M	E	I		R		F	E	E	L	S
I	S		N	E	E	D	Y			U	P	
A	C	T	S		S	P	Y		C	A	S	E
H	A	R	E		T	H	E		A	N	T	E
A	P	I	E	C	E		R	E	N	T	E	D
	E	M	M	O	R		S	T	E	A	D	

Puzzle 86

A	B	I		L	A	B	A	N		B	A	T
R	E	M		E	X	A	L	T		A	D	O
C	H	A	N	G	E	S		A	R	A	N	
	A	G	O		S	E	E	S	T			
E	V	E	R	T		A	W		E	R	A	
D	I		T	H	A	I	S			Y	E	S
G	O	T	H	I	C		E	R	R	E	T	H
E	U	R		G	T		L	O	A		A	E
D	R	Y		H	O	T		S	T	A	I	N
			R	E	D			R	N			
U	N	C	U	S		N	O	I	S	I	E	R
S	E	A		M	A	T	T	E		D	T	H
O	W	N		U	S	H	E	R		H	O	

Puzzle 87

R	I	S	E		L	U	Z		T	R	A	M
A	D	E	R		E	L	I		H	E	N	T
P	L	E	A	S	E	T	H		E	V	E	N
S	E	N	S	E		A	R	R	O	W	S	
		E	A	R	S		U	E	L			
D	E	E	D		E	A	S	T		T	O	B
A	S	S		P	A	R	A	H		E	R	E
M	E	T		A	D	A	M		E	D	E	N
	I	R	U		H	E	I	R				
T	U	M	U	L	T		C	R	O	S	S	
A	Z	A	L		E	T	H	I	O	P	I	A
P	A	T	E		L	I	E		R	A	N	T
S	L	E	D		L	E	N		S	H	O	E

Puzzle 88

Z	A	C	C	H	A	E	U	S		H	E	
E	B	A	L		S		O	V	E	N	S	
B	I	S	O	N		H	A	D	O	R	A	M
E		S	A	T	A	N		I		M	A	
D	O		E	T	H	A	N		D		L	
E	A	R	T	H		H	A	D		R		L
E	T	A		A	D	A		N	O			
	H	M		N	E	S		E	D	G	E	S
A	S	A		A	H		U		E	L	I	
L		T	S	P		T	U	R	T	L	E	
A	S	H	K	E	N	A	Z		N	I	C	E
R	E		I		E	R	A	N		M	T	G
M	E	A	N		T	I	L	E			O	

419

Puzzle 89

```
A B O U T     T I D E S
B U R R O W   A B D U C T
I S   I N H A B I T   R A
E H I   S E L L S   B A M
L E N D   N O E   C A P E
  S C A R C E   D O T E D
    E R I E   H A R T
W A N T   B U N D L E
H I S S   E A R   S E A M
I L E   L A N D S   S S E
L E   G I R D L E S   T A
E T H N A N   E L E V E N
  H O U R S   F E A R S
```

Puzzle 90

```
S U R   S C E N T   T W O
A C T   A L L O W   H A P
N A   I L A I   O W E S T
G L A D L Y   A F A R
  S L Y   S T O N E S T
G H E E   C O L T   E R
H E R   G R A N D   T A U
G I   A L O N E   M A L E
S I T T E S T   S O L
  A L A E   S P O K E N
L I K E N   S H I N   R E
A R E   E A T E N   D A B
P E N   D R A M S   O N O
```

Puzzle 91

```
O   M O U N T S I N A I
F R O G S   A P O S T L E
F   U   T   N   E L L
E   N E M U E L   H   M
R A T   O R N A M E N T
  M O U N T H E R M O N
N   O   R A N   F A
G A R   T H A D D A E U S
S   I   N   B E
  B A B E   C O   A G I O
J A H   B I E R   S B
E T   S O N   E   E C H O
W H I T   A B I D A   E
```

Puzzle 92

```
S A R D I S   T H R O N E
P R A I S E   H E A V E N
I M P   M R I   T E A M
R O T A S   E   H E N R I
I N   T E A S E   E T
T I E   A L P H A   T R Y
  G O Y A   A R A H
F I G   M E G A   M E T
A S   M E N   N O
T A K E S   I   D R O S S
H I E   A C R E   S I S
E A T E S T   C O T   G E
R H O D E S   G R O U N D
```

Puzzle 93

```
B A T   D O A B S   A V A
E R A   E P H A I   T E N
D E L E C T A B L E   G E
  E L I   E A S I E R
R E S I D E S   S A L T
E L   M E T E R   U L A M
S I R   D A T E S   B O
T H A W   S H E A F   L O
  O T E A   F I L L E D
O R E L S E   N E A
R E   L A M E N T A B L E
E P I   P E R I L   A I R
S H T   H U R L Y   N E E
```

Puzzle 94

```
P A T I E N C E   A B I B
U R   N E A   S I D E
R   U N D E R S T A N D
I N T   U D D E R   D O E
T   H O R S E M A N   A
Y E S   E   R A V E N   T
  U T   E   C A   W
S T O R M Y   H I G H E R
T Y R E   I L A I   E
O C E A N   S A   B E A R
O H   T O W   H   B L U E
L U D   P O W   R A   N A
S O   H O W   R I   T D
```

Puzzle 95

T	E	N		R	I	D	E		S	A	L	E
E	A	T		O	R	E	N		P	L	O	W
I	S		O	P	E	N		V	O	I	C	E
L	E	A	V	E	S		D	A	R	K		
		M	E	S		W	A	N	T	E	T	H
E	V	E	R		F	I	R	E	S		R	E
H	I	N		C	O	L	T	S		S	E	A
U	N		H	A	R	T	S		R	E	E	L
D	E	S	E	R	T	S		T	O	E		
	C	A	R	E		L	E	A	D	E	R	
M	E	R	R	Y		H	E	A	R		D	O
O	M	I	T		R	E	A	R		L	E	D
P	U	P	S		A	M	P	S		O	N	E

Puzzle 96

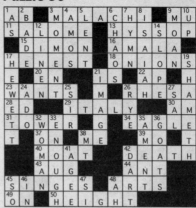

A	B		M	A	L	A	C	H	I		M	U
S	A	L	O	M	E		H	Y	S	S	O	P
D	I	M	O	N		A	M	A	L	A		
H	E	N	E	S	T		O	N	I	O	N	S
E		E	N		I	S		A	P		H	
W	A	N	T	S	M		R	H	E	S	A	
E	D		I	T	A	L	Y		A	M		
T	O	W	E	R		G		E	A	G	L	E
T		O	N		M	E		M	O		T	
	M	O	A	T		D	E	A	T	H		
A	U	G		A	N	T						
S	I	N	G	E	S		A	R	T	S		
O	N		H	E	I	G	H	T				

Puzzle 97

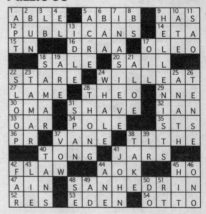

	D	I	E	S		A	S	I	A
	A	C	R	E		N	O	N	E
L	A	V	E	R		N	I	N	T	H
E	H	I		A	A	R	O	N		O	R	E
H	I	D	I	N	G		M	E	A	N	E	R
I	O		D	A	V	I	T	S		E	E	
	E		I	T		P						
H	E		L	E	N	G	T	H		S		
E	S	A	I	A	S		E	A	T	E	S	T
E	A	R		S	T	U	D	S		S	A	E
D	U	R	S	T		T	O	A	S	T		
	O	D	E	D		M	E	N	U	S		
	W	I	R	E		O	N	E	S			

Puzzle 98

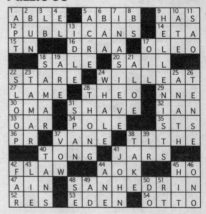

A	B	L	E		A	B	I	B		H	A	S
P	U	B	L	I	C	A	N	S		E	T	A
T	N		D	R	A	A		O	L	E	O	
	S	A	L	E		S	A	I	L			
S	T	A	R	E		W	I	L	L	E	A	T
L	A	M	E		T	H	E	O		N	N	E
O	M	A		S	H	A	V	E		I	A	N
O	A	R		P	O	L	E		S	T	S	
P	R		V	A	N	E		T	I	T	H	E
	T	O	N	G		J	A	R	S			
F	L	A	W		A	O	K		H	O		
A	I	N		S	A	N	H	E	D	R	I	N
R	E	S		E	D	E	N		O	T	T	O

Puzzle 99

L	A	D	E		E	T	A	S		C	O	W
A	T		D	I	V	I	N	E		A	R	E
D	E	W		M	E	N		R	A	N	N	
	E	A	R	S		L	V	I		I	T	
Z	I	B	I	A		H	E	E	D	E	D	
E	N		R	H		E	N	D		R	U	G
A	F	R		B	A	D		E	M	U		
L	O	U		W	A	R		I	S		E	A
R	E	W	A	R	D		S	P	E	A	R	
A	M		O	R	E		S	L	A	T		
M		H	E	N		A	P	E		E	F	T
E	L	I		E	N	M	E	S	H		I	E
N	O	T		D	E	E	D		E	A	R	N

Puzzle 100

T	H	A	D		S	E	A	S		A	R	C
H	A	R	E		T	A	M	E		M	A	R
E	D		A	D	A	R		E	N	E	M	Y
	P	R	A	Y		S	K	I	N			
F	U	L	L	Y		S	P	E	N	D	E	R
A	N	A	Y		H	O	S	E		M	E	
T	I	N		S	H	O	R	T		D	I	S
A	T		S	H	E	E	T		R	A	T	E
L	E	T	T	E	R	S		F	I	R	S	T
	R	A	L	E		H	A	S	T			
S	H	I	R	T		S	E	R	E		E	A
T	O	P		E	B	E	R		S	I	N	G
A	N	E		R	E	N	D		T	R	E	E

421

Puzzle 101

Puzzle 102

Puzzle 103

Puzzle 104

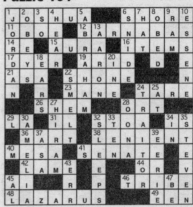

Puzzle 105

Puzzle 106

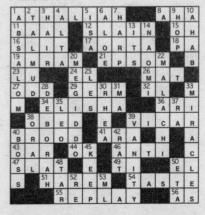

Puzzle 107

Puzzle 108

Puzzle 109

Puzzle 110

Puzzle 111

Puzzle 112

Puzzle 113

	S	O	N	G			S	U	N				D	O	O	R
O	H	I	O			W		U	S	U	R	P				
U		G			M	O	A	N			S			E	N	
L		H	E	A	R	T			A	T	O	N	E			
	S	T	A	N	D			I	N		B		A			
H	E		R			O	F			Y	E	A	R			
	E	R		U	S			J	O	Y						
K	I	N	G		W	E	A	K				A	S			
J	V	A	L	U	E		W	E	I	G	H					
E	N	E	M	Y			I			S	E	A				
W	E	R	E			E	D	G	E				D			
E	T		L	O	N	G		O		M	O	O				
L	S	Y	N	A	G	O	G	U	E				W			

Puzzle 114

Puzzle 115

Puzzle 116

Puzzle 117

Puzzle 118

Puzzle 119

Puzzle 120

Puzzle 121

Puzzle 122

Puzzle 123

Puzzle 124

Puzzle 125

```
A R M O R . . H A N N A H
B O A R . . D E T A I N
L A K E . H A R E . N O T
E D E N . A G O . S E T H
. . C L O D S . . H O
. B A R R E N . L O V E S
J U D E O . . A W A R E
U S . D W E L L I N G
D I M . N . . N . A G E
A N O N . R U N . B A R
S E L A H . R E S T O R E
. S E M E I . R U I N . C
. S . E N Q U I R E D . H
```

Puzzle 126

```
J O S E P H . H I D E S T
E B A L . U N I T . E A R
H E N . T R A V A I L . E
U D D E R . T I L T . I S
. A . U N I T Y . A S P
A L L . E A V E . G A L A
R O S E . B E . L I R A S
P A . L E A . G . D O N S
A V I M . L . A M E N D
D E N . B . T O O . A
. S N A R E . E R N E S T
O . B A A L . E . G O
R E P E N T . T H R O N E
```

Puzzle 127

```
A B E D N E G O . G A D
G A Z A . L U B I M . P A
A C E L D A M A . A . P D
B A K E R S . D E R B E
U . I . S T A I N . E A R
S H E D . I R A D . A S A
. A L . I C E H O C K E Y
J R . A M . . R R
O A K . M E O W . I N T O
S N A R E . F R A M E . A
E . N E R I . A R E T A S
P . A . D A T E . . P I
H A H I R O T H . B E E S
```

Puzzle 128

```
C A L E B . Y E . U Z Z I
A B E L . F E V E R . A T
N I N E . L A E L . A D S
A . T A M A R . N E B O
L . D I M . I A . I K E
J A R . E A S T . D . L
O B O T H . B A H . E L I
R O B E . A B I A H . I S
D R O S S . R A N . R A H
A . A T A D . H . V E R A
N O M I N A L . F A D S
N . F E T E . H I . E
V E R Y . E M M A N U E L
```

Puzzle 129

```
F A I T H . S W O R D . D
A . . A D . O . . . A
L . H . I . O N . N U
S H U R . M O W . D O E G
E A R . A B R A M . B A H
P R . F D A . R O E . S T
R A K E M . . S T A T E
O . . D A G . A E C . R
P A D . H A R P S . L I
H A I L . D A E . G U L F
E . E . D . I G . Z . E
T . . A . N . O . . A
S A T A N . G E R A R
```

Puzzle 130

```
. N O . A L O E S . A C
H O . . E . V . . L P
I F I . H A . A T . C O R
G A R D E N . P I L A T E
H U M . . . . . B . H P
P L A N K S . R E D S E A
R T . M I M . E N D . S R
I . . N O . C E . . A
E M . P S T . O M A . S T
S I . A M E . R I B . P I
T D . P A D . D E E . E O
S A T A N . . S L O A N
. S O W . . . . S U R
```

426

Puzzle 131

Puzzle 132

Puzzle 133

Puzzle 134

Puzzle 135

Puzzle 136

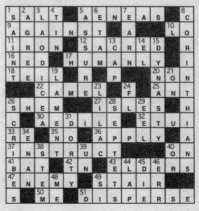

Puzzle 137

```
M U L T I P L Y . S A N D
A N O I N T . . H I . . R
S W I N E . S W E A R . E
T I N . X I . E N D . P A
E N S N A R E . D O G . M
R D . C R A G . W A R S .
. A . T I G E R . D E . .
S I L K . G L E A N . D .
I D L E . A E . N A M E D
N O . D T . S T E E R . .
F L E E C E . O H . M A .
U S . S O . G A M A . E M
L . H O L O N . N O D S .
```

Puzzle 138

```
A A R O N . W E A V E R S
R . N O . A D D . . T A .
K . B Y . U R . A T . C .
. O X E N . S P I C E S .
. A W . V . P I T . O . E
M . . E V E N . R U L E .
O F F E R I N G . R E D .
S . P . E . . . A T E . .
E . C H E R U B I M S . S
S . O N . P E . I . X I .
. O L D . G I L D . S I N
A I . Y A . L O V E . A .
L I N E N . . G . E L I .
```

Puzzle 139

```
S H E P H E R D . H . T A
W I N E . U . A G A B U S
O R D A I N . R U L E R S
R E E K . U N K N O W N .
D . D E A C O N . A S K .
. P . D . H . E D A R . I
D I E . A S P S . M E N .
E G Y P T . A S H . A G .
B . E . E A R . A M E N D
O B S E R V E . M . T O .
R E . G . A N I M A L . M
A A R O N . T . E . . . .
H U R . A S S U R A N C E
```

Puzzle 140

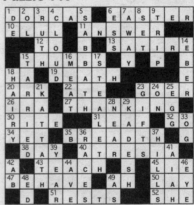

```
D O R C A S . E A S T E R
E L U L . A N S W E R . .
. T O . B . S A T I R E .
T H U M B S . Y . P . B .
H A . D E A T H . . . E .
A R K . A T E . . G O E R
I R A . T H A N K I N G .
R I T E . L E A F . G O .
Y E T . B R E A D T H . G
. D A Y . A T R E S I A .
A . T E A C H . S . L I E
B E H A V E . A H . L A Y
. D . R E S T S . . S H E
```

Puzzle 141

```
S H O E S . A H I S H A R
H E L L . A S . V E R S E
A . D I S P L A Y . . A Z
P P . H O . E S . F M . I
H . K O . J E H O I A D A
A S . R . O P . L L . . .
N H . E L S . G A L L I O
E . P O E . O D E S . B .
C B . H O P E . O R . G A
A N . P H . C R . F E D .
R A I D S . B A A N A . I
. R A . H A M M E R . A .
A Z A R I A H . A M A H .
```

Puzzle 142

```
S H I M S H A I . J O A B
O . O . A S S A U L T . .
L A N C E T . U N I . . Z
I N S . C B A . E V . . A
D G . S H E V A . E B B .
. L O B E . N H A S . U .
D E . E L I A K I M . A D
A . A T L . I . A T O M .
V L F . S W A T H . A R .
I . L B . S H E . . T S E
D . C O S . M U L I S H .
A I R S H I P . . E . U .
A M O N . A D O N I R A M
```

Puzzle 143

	D	A	V	I	D		C	H	I	E	F	
R	E	C	U	R	L		J	E	T	H	R	O
A	C		L	I		S		A	S		I	R
T	E	A		S	M	A	L	L		R	E	P
H	I	N	T		O	L	D		A	N	N	A
S	T		E	E	V		D	A		D	H	
		B	E	T	R	A	Y	E	R			
A	L		T	A		T		N	O		S	S
M	O	T	H		H	I	M		N	O	A	H
A	V	E		N	A	O	M	I		M	M	E
S	E		B	E	N		M	A		U	L	
A	R	R	O	W	S		R	A	C	H	E	L
	S	T	A	T	E		S	M	E	L	L	

Puzzle 144

	M	O	S	E	S		B	R	I	D	E	
D	A	N	I	E	L		R	E	W	A	R	M
A	T		P	L		Z		M	W		M	I
N	U	M		S	H	E	D			T	I	C
D	R	A	W		I	C	E		A	N	N	A
Y	E		R	A		H		A	S		E	H
		Z	E	P	H	A	N	I	A	H		
J	P		N	T		R		D	P		B	F
O	A	R	S		R	I	D		H	E	A	R
N	R	C		G	R	A	C	E		A	L	E
A	I		A	L		H		L	R		S	S
H	A	W	S	E	R		I	S	A	I	A	H
	H	O	S	E	A		N	A	H	U	M	

Puzzle 145

S	C	H	I	S	M		G	R	E	A	S	E
A	H	A	V	A		A		A	R	N	O	N
V	E	R		N	B	A		A	R	T		
A	B	M		V	I	A	L	S		T	R	I
G	A		S	C	H	N	O	O	K		E	R
E	R	S	T		A			N	I	L	E	
		E	U	P	H	R	A	T	E	S		
I	T	E	M		I			E	L	K	S	
N	I		P	L	O	V	E	R	S		I	E
D	G	S		O	P	E	N	S		D	S	C
I	R	E		E	R	G			O	H	O	
G	I	A	N	T			P	I	S	O	N	
O	S	M	I	U	M		D	E	P	E	N	D

Puzzle 146

E	A	G	L	E		P	A	I	N	S	
D	A	N	I	E	L		J	O	S	E	P	H
A	T		G	A		S		N	A		R	E
V	E	N		N	I	C	H	E		L	E	A
I	R	O	N		R	A	M		S	O	A	R
D	Y		O	F		P		A	H		D	D
		S	P	O	K	E	S	M	E	N		
M	E		E	X		G		P	E		E	D
O	L	E	S		C	O	T		P	A	L	E
S	I	N		I	S	A	A	C		P	I	E
E	S		O	T		T		I	D		J	D
S	H	A	V	E	R		S	A	U	N	A	S
	A	D	A	M	S		J	O	N	A	H	

Puzzle 147

W	I	L	D	O	X		C	A	T	T	L	E
E	N	A	C	T		D		C	H	E	E	R
A	D	M		E	R	R		U	A	R		
S	I	P		P	R	O	P	S		T	V	A
E	G		C	H	A	M	O	I	S		E	N
L	O	G	O			E		H	I	N	D	
		A	N	E	C	D	O	T	A	L		
M	O	L	E			A		R	O	T	C	
I	D		Y	E	A	R	E	N	D		E	A
S	D	S		S	W	I	N	E		L	E	M
H	I	M		L	E	D			A	P	E	
A	T	O	N	E		S		L	A	B	E	L
P	Y	G	A	R	G		H	O	R	S	E	S

Puzzle 148

T		B	E	D	S	P	R	E	A	D		P
I	D		N	I	C	A	N	O	R		R	R
M	M		D	R		R		N	M		X	I
O		S	U	E		M		S	O	L		D
N	I	C	E		B	E	D		R	O	B	E
	C	A		A	N	N	A	S		B	A	
P	E	R	K	Y		A		O	C	E	A	N
H	S		W	A	R	S	H	I	P		S	I
I		E	H	E				L	T		C	
L	O	V	E		C	U	E		L	O	C	O
I	R	E					C		P	A	L	
P	E		S	T	A	P	H		N	R	A	
S		P	R	O	C	H	O	R	U	S		S

429

Puzzle 152

Puzzle 153

Puzzle 154

Puzzle 155

	S	O	U	L				L	O	R	D	
G	O		N	E	W		D	I	N	E	R	
H			D	A	I	L	Y	M	E			O
A	A	R	O	N	S		E	N	S	I	G	N
T	H	E			H	A		E	L	S	E	
	A	G	E	D		T	O	W	E	L		
		I	D	A		H	E	U				
	L	O	I	N				T	E	N	T	
P	I	N	T		S	E	A		I	T	A	L
L	E	S			E	N	S		G	O	N	E
A	D		I	B	N	E	I	A	H			A
Y	E		R	E	D		A	R	T	H	U	R
	R	E	E	D				T	H	I	N	

Puzzle 156

W	O	R	D		A	I	D		J	O	B	
A	R	A	R	A	T		O	P	E	N	E	R
S		B	Y	E			O	W	E			A
T	O	B		N	E	E	D	S		W	A	N
	P	I	N	O	N		E	T	H	E	R	
M	E		A	N	D	A	S	S	O		O	N
A	N	E	M		L	I	P		R	O	S	E
N	E		E	N	E	M	I	E	S		E	R
	S	I	D	E	S			S	V	E	N	
A	T	T		E	S	T	E	E	M	E	T	H
C		E	N	D				A	S	E	A	
T		M	U	S	E		M	I	N	T	E	D
S	A	S	S		L	A	Y	S		S	S	

Puzzle 157

	W	I	S	E		S	A	Y	E			
	A	N	O	N		I	B	I	D			
G	A	I	N		D	U	E		I	G	A	L
A	N	T		M	E	R	G	E		E	R	E
B	E		R	E	D	N	E	S	S		A	S
A	R	M	E	D			C	H	A	N	T	
	A	B	D	I		N	A	A	M			
P	A	N	E	L				P	L	A	I	N
A	N		L	E	D		B	E	L		L	E
R	A	P		D	O	M	E	D		S	A	W
T	H	U	S		E	G	G			H	I	S
		P	E	A	R		U	N	D	O		
		S	A	G	S		N	O	S	E		

Puzzle 158

A	B	E		M	I	G	H	T		E	R	E
H	E	R	O	D		O		O	F	T	E	N
E	A	R	N		P	D	Q		L	A	N	D
R	R		I	L	E		U	S	E	S	T	
		N	O		R	I	E	S			S	T
	E	N	O	S		S	O	H	O			H
G	U	R		R	U	S	T	S		D	U	O
A	P		S	E	A			S	O	D		S
L		A		D	O		A	M		M	E	
D	R	I	V	E	R		E	T	A			
S	O	O	N	E	R			G	O	R	E	
H	U	N	T	S			T	A	R	N	S	
Y	R		T	I	R	E	S			S	E	T

Puzzle 159

J	E	S	U	S			J	E	S	U	I	
E	N	T	R	I	E	S		O	P	E	N	S
S	O		I	D	A	H	O	S		E	L	L
S	U	E		E	R	I	T	E	S		I	E
E	G	G	S		E	N		A	S	K	S	
	H		H	A	D		A	V		E		
		T	O	P		L	A	Y				
	S	H	U	T			A	L	G	A	E	
H	E	E	L		H	E	M		E	R	A	N
O	R		D	R	E	A	M	S		N	V	
A	V	A		O	N	R	O	C	K		E	S
R	E	G	E	M		S	N	A	I	L		A
	S	O	L	S			B	R	O	A	D	

Puzzle 160

	G	O	D		S	E	E	
	W	E	R	E		H	A	N	D
	H	A	T	E	D		A	R	D	O	N
L	E	G		B	A	N	D	S		O	I	L
A	R	E	A		N	O	E		O	M	N	I
W	E	S	T				O	N	S	E	T	
			T	A	N		W	E	
K	E	D	A	R		D		D	E	S	R	O	M
E	L	O	I		F	A	R			I	R	A
W	E	T		A	E	N	O	N		S	E	T
A	H	I	R	A		P	E	R	E	S	
D	A	R	T	S		E	R	A	N	
	N	E	S	T		S	O	N	

431

Puzzle 161

Puzzle 162

Puzzle 163

Puzzle 164

Puzzle 165

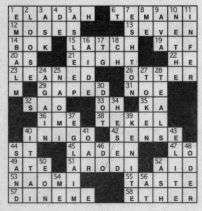

Puzzle 166

432

Puzzle 167

Puzzle 168

Puzzle 169

Puzzle 170

Puzzle 171

Puzzle 172

Puzzle 173

JESUS PREPARE
USES MAACHAH
DAN SAYTO ROT
GUDGODAH COD
MASONS EVENA
ENOS OAR AS
ND PM IS IN
T HE IIM ELSE
SELED INTO E
ILAI LECAHAND
BEL SERAH VOW
REELAIAH META
ITDOWN MOSES

Puzzle 174

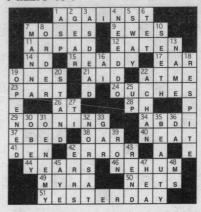

AGAINST
MOSES EWES
ARPAD EATEN
ND READY EAR
ONES AID ATME
PART D OUCHES
E AT PH P
NOONING ABDI
EBED OAR NEAT
DEN ERROR A E
YEARS NEHUM
MYRA NETS
YESTERDAY

Puzzle 175

TWELVE CHRIST
ELOI S ANNA
IRI STEAD NIB
DE PARABLE TO
DAMAGE NAUGHT
O AREA EINE H
IKE S R URI
ENOUGH CA A
MARTYR ITHRAN
ER SEEING BE
NOR SAD MIR
SAIN MELDED
MENTOR ROOTED

Puzzle 176

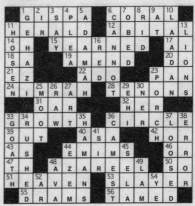

GISPA CORAL
HERALD ABITAL
OH YEARNED AI
SA AMEND DO
EZ ADO PAN
NIMRAH TENONS
OAR HER
GROWTH CIRCLE
OUT ASA HOR
AS EMIMS OR
TH AZAREEL SO
HEAVEN SLAYER
DRAMS TAMED

Puzzle 177

PURGE JABAL
HEREIN ESAIAS
OR INJURED DO
US SORER ER
SIR IIM ATE
ESHEAN YOUTHS
EAR NET
EASTER TELAIM
ARA ASA ISA
TI EVILS HA
ED ELEALEH IT
NAARAN ELASAH
ITEMS RAMAH

Puzzle 178

RUINS DUMAH
RISSAH ESAIAS
ON AVENGED TI
AN YEARS ER
SAP THE ASA
THOMAS EATETH
LAW TIN
MILLET REPORT
IT OWE NEH
CH GOATS LO
AM ENTRIES IR
HASRAH REUBEN
HARTS ERRED

434

Puzzle 179

B E S E T N A H A M
E L D A A H A Z O T U S
T O D R Y S H O D S O
H O S I H O R I R
A D O N E R A N T
M Y R T L E S L I N G S
P O I A R K
S T A Y E D A M A L E K
N A H I P S E L I
A S A M I S S I S
I T H U N T E T H D O
L E B A N A N A A M A N
D E P T H T R I E D

Puzzle 180

Puzzle 181

Puzzle 182

Puzzle 183

Puzzle 184

435

Puzzle 185

S	H	E	A	F		S	M	I	T	E
W	H	E	N	C	E		H	A	T	I	N	G
H	A		D	R	A	W	E	R		E	R
I	R		E	S	H	E	K		M	E
P	O	T		T	O	P		E	Y	E
S	N	A	R	E	S		S	A	I	D	S	T
	B	U	N		U	R	I
S	T	O	N	E	S		C	L	I	F	F	S
H	E	R		A	S	H		Y	E	T
O	R		T	R	O	A	S		N	O
B	E		C	H	A	N	N	E	L		C	O
I	S	H	I	A	H		C	A	U	S	E	D
	H	O	S	T	S		E	L	D	A	D

Puzzle 186

O	U	T	E	R		W	O	M	A	N
H	U	S	H	A	I		I	S	A	I	A	H
A	T		E	S	C	A	P	E	D		P	E
I	R		T	H	R	E	E		K	I
R	U	N		E	A	T		F	I	R
S	N	A	R	E	S		H	A	M	A	N	S
	D	E	W		H	A	I
S	H	A	V	E	H		P	A	N	T	E	D
H	A	B		E	R	E		H	U	R
O	N		F	A	I	R	S		N	O
E	D		C	A	L	A	M	U	S		I	S
S	E	D	U	C	E		I	S	A	A	C	S
	D	O	T	E	D		T	I	T	H	E

Puzzle 187

S	H	A	D	E		S	P	A	I	N
S	H	A	M	I	R		H	A	S	R	A	H
P	E		I	S	R	A	E	L	S		T	O
A	N		H	O	M	A	M		I	S
K	I	R		R	A	T		E	V	E
E	R	I	T	E	S		H	O	L	P	E	N
	V	O	W		N	E	H
C	H	E	W	E	D		C	E	D	A	R	S
O	A	R		E	A	R		I	M
A	R		N	A	H	U	M		S	A
T	H		S	A	L	A	M	I	S		E	R
S	A	L	O	M	E		B	R	E	A	S	T
	S	O	W	E	R		S	E	E	S	T

Puzzle 188

G	I	M	Z	O		A	L	I	A	H
M	A	N	A	E	N		G	A	T	H	E	R
I	S		R	E	W	A	R	D		P	E
C	H		B	A	B	E	S		H	E
A	M	I		R	I	E		L	E	D
H	U	N	T	E	D		D	I	V	E	R	S
	D	E	W		S	O	P
S	W	I	N	E	S		S	A	W	E	S	T
A	H	A		E	P	H		R	A	W
C	O		W	I	S	E	R		T	I
A	R		L	A	Z	A	R	U	S		A	N
R	E	M	O	V	E		A	L	I	E	N	S
	S	E	W	E	D		H	E	A	D	S

Puzzle 189

S	I	A	H	A		C	A	L	A	H
V	I	R	G	I	N		O	P	E	N	E	D
I	S		E	S	C	A	P	E	D		L	O
P	E		S	H	I	P	S		B	E
E	R	R		O	N	E		C	O	R
R	A	I	L	E	R		R	O	M	A	N	S
	N	O	R		W	A	S
R	A	G	G	E	D		M	E	D	E	B	A
A	S	S		I	S	A		S	E	M
H	A		A	V	I	T	H		M	E
A	H		S	H	E	A	R	E	R		O	N
B	E	T	H	E	R		E	L	I	D	A	D
	L	I	E	R	S		D	I	B	O	N

Puzzle 190

Z	E	L	E	K		A	L	I	A	H
D	E	R	I	D	E		S	I	T	N	A	H
I	T		P	A	L	A	C	E	S		N	O
A	H		R	I	T	E	S		A	S
N	A	H		T	E	N		O	N	E
A	R	A	B	I	A		T	H	E	S	I	S
	R	A	N		A	R	E
A	B	U	S	E	D		C	Y	R	E	N	E
L	U	Z		E	P	H		A	T
O	S		B	A	S	E	S		A	H
E	T		P	E	R	A	Z	I	M		M	E
S	E	R	I	A	L		I	Z	E	H	A	R
	D	I	T	T	Y		B	E	T	A	H

436

Puzzle 191

```
 1N  2A  3H  4O  5R      6S  7T  8A  9L 10L
11R   E   M   O   V   E  12T   H   R   O   A 13T
14A   R     15R 16E   P   H   A   I   M  17Y   O
18P   E     19N   A   I   L   S      20E   R
21H   U   L 22 23I   N   K      24P   S   A
25U   S   U   R   E   R 26 27 28S   A   V   E 29T 30H
       31B   A   R      32H   E   R
33S 34H   I   M   R   I 35 36W   A   X   E   T   H 37 38
39T   O   M    40 41N   E   H      42S   U   E
43O   V     44A   S   S   I   R    45T   I 46
47O   E     48A   M   I   T   T   A   I  49O   R 50
51P   R   I   S   E   D    53E   R   R   O   R   S 54
  55S   C   E   N   E    56R   E   I   N   S
```

Puzzle 192

```
 1F  2R  3E  4S  5H      6T  7A  8H  9A 10N
11E   L   I   S   H   A  12A   M   A   S   A 13I
14N   O     15 16T   O   R   C   H   E   S 17A   T
18S   O     19A   D   O   R   N      20M   E
21U   R   I 22 23E   W   E      24J   A   M
25E   S   T   H   E   R 26 27 28A   M   N   O   N   S 29 30
       31H   U   R      32E   A   R
33S 34C   A   L   E   S 35 36A   T   H   A   C   H 37 38
39E   L   I    40 41H   E   B      42H   A   I
43G   O     44H   E   R   D   S    45E   R 46
47U   S     48W   A   R   R   I   O   R  49S   E 50
51B   E   H   O   L   D    53E   L   I   D   A   D 54
  55T   E   N   T   S    56L   E   P   E   R
```

Puzzle 193

```
 1T  2A  3R  4E  5A      6C  7L  8E  9A 10N
11T   H   R   O   N   G  12R   E   P   H   A 13H
14E   R     15 16W   O   R   K   E   D  17H   O
18L   O     19S   E   A   T      20A   S
21A   N   C 22 23E   Y   E      24E   S   T
25H   E   R   A   L   D 26 27 28S   M   I   T   H   S 29 30
       31A   G   O      32A   S   H
33R 34A   G   E   T   H 35 36F   L   A   N   K   S 37 38
39A   S   S    40 41A   H   A      42I   A   L
43H   A     44P   R   I   D   E    45L   A 46
47A   I     48M   I   D      49E   R   Y 50 51M   I
52M   A   N   T   L   E    54T   I   E   P   I   N 55
  56H   O   S   E   N    57H   E   P   T   A
```

Puzzle 194

```
 1T  2E  3A  4T  5S      6S  7W  8E  9P 10T
11S   O   R   R   O   W  12P   I   G   E   O 13N
14H   O     15 16T   O   I   L   I   N   G 17S   O
18A   T     19K   N   O   C   K      20S   A
21P   H   D 22 23E   W   E      24N   E   H
25E   S   A   I   A   S 26 27 28S   T   E   A   D   S 29 30
       31C   I   S      32O   A   K
33L 34A   H   M   A   M 35 36S   U   R   E   L   Y 37 38
39A   H   A    40 41A   S   P      42D   U   E
43K   I     44G   R   E   E   T    45H   A 46
47U   R     48M   A   T   T   E   R   S  49I   R 50
51M   A   H   A   T   H    53C   U   B   I   T   S 54
  55M   E   L   E   A    56H   E   A   T   H
```

Puzzle 195

```
 1L  2O  3O  4S  5E      6G  7O  8L  9A 10N
11P   A   G   I   E   L  12R   U   I   N   E 13D
14H   A     15 16L   E   I   S   U   R   E 17T   O
18E   D     19M   A   I   D   S      20H   E
21B   A   D 22 23B   A   G      24N   E   R
25E   N   E   M   Y   S 26 27 28E   L   D   E   R   S 29 30
       31L   E   E      32O   A   K
33L 34E   A   R   N   T 35 36O   W   N   E   R   S 37 38
39I   T   Y    40 41H   I   P      42B   I   T
43R   H     44H   E   L   P   S    45C   O 46
47A   A     48H   A   R   L   O   T   S  49H   O 50
51N   E   R   V   E    53S   A   I   L   E   D 54
  55E   L   S   E    56E   R   R   O   R
```

Puzzle 196

```
 1C  2E      3G  4O      5S  6S      7A  8M
 9L   A 10T   I   N     11A   C 12C   H   O
13D   O    14H   M    15C   L    16M   A   S 17T
18O   S    19 20Z   A   H   A   M 21 22E   E
23N   E    24D   O   R    25 26Y   E   A   R 27N
28S   T   I   R 30 31 32A   L   A 33T   H   A   T
      34C   O    35H   O   B    36H   A
37D 38E   E   P    39W   E    40A   B   B   A 41 42
43U   S    44 45 46S   I   A 47 48D   E   N 49I   N
50S   A    51B   R   I   N   G 52 53C   D
54T   I    55A   Z    56S   E   L   A 57 58H   R
59A 60H   I   A   H    61G   A   H   A   R 63
64S   O    65N   I    66O   H    67D   I
```

Puzzle 197

Puzzle 198

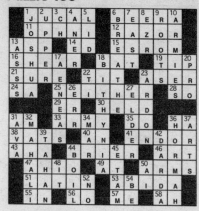

Puzzle 199

Puzzle 200